Software Engineering Risk Analysis and Management

Software Engineering Risk Analysis and Management

Robert N. Charette
ITABHI Corporation

Intertext Publications
McGraw-Hill Book Company

New York St. Louis San Francisco Auckland Bogotá
Hamburg London Madrid Mexico Milan Montreal
New Delhi Panama Paris São Paolo
Singapore Sydney Tokyo Toronto

Library of Congress Catalog Card Number 89-83763

10 9 8 7 6 5 4 3 2 1

ISBN 0-07-010719-X

Intertext Publications/Multiscience Press, Inc.
One Lincoln Plaza
New York, NY 10023

McGraw-Hill Book Company
1221 Avenue of the Americas
New York, NY 10020

Composed by Castle Productions Ltd.

Table of Contents

To Dr. Harold Stone and Mr. Arthur Morin,
two superb teachers and old friends who taught me that:

"If it isn't worth failing at, it isn't worth doing."

Preface

Increasingly, risk analysis and risk management are becoming important ingredients in achieving the successful implementation and application of software systems. Although the concepts of risk analysis and management are standard fare in many fields, they are a recent addition to the software profession. To give an example, the first tentative software risk analysis efforts were undertaken in the U.S. Department of Defense, the largest individual user and developer of software in the world, only in 1969. Since then, however, U.S. government policy has expanded to a degree that software risk analysis and management are now mandated on all new projects having software as a major component.

The increasing emergence of software engineering risk analysis and management can be traced to the realization of a simple truth by corporate senior management. The products and services that provide their competitive edge in today's marketplace are primarily produced or delivered by software-intensive information systems. For many companies, the dependence on these information systems is such that their business operations cease to exist if their information systems cease to operate. Thus, information system risks involving their development, maintenance, operation, and evolution are rapidly becoming the dominant parameters in a company's profit and loss equation. This being the case, senior corporate attention is being refocused on how to reduce these risks.

This book describes the field of risk analysis and management, how it is performed, and provides an identification of the areas of risk in the building of software systems. A primary motivation is to provide a framework from which software engineering risk analysis and management can be conducted in a realistic fashion by practicing software professionals. Thus, we will consider this book as a guide to, rather than a textbook on, the subject of risk.

It should be obvious that the book was written for the computer and management information professional on the firing line, and not necessarily for a person in the computer science academic community. Thus, the book may not, at times, seem serious enough, nor have the proper academic writing tone, for the more rigorous teaching environment at University. I make no apologies. First, the book is not meant to be a traditional textbook, which all too often consists of tremendous amounts of incomprehensible and quickly forgotten theoretical foundations followed by boring exercises. I prefer another style to convey the same information. Second, I believe that the professional and academic each have different goals and approaches to the situations they live with every day, and a traditional textbook approach on these subjects is not useful to most professionals in the computer field. William Rouse articulates the reasons better than I in his article "On Better Mousetraps and Basic Research: Getting the Applied World to the Laboratory Door."[1]

For people such as me, software engineering is a business and not an academic problem to be neatly solved. It is our living, and we must make use of sometimes imperfect theories and hypotheses on how to proceed, especially if more academically sound ones are not made available. Too often the offered models or theories of how computing should be used are shown to be lacking in the academic literature, which is good to know. Unfortunately, few remedies on how to improve them are offered. The professionals in industry need help now, in quantities both large and small. Pragmatically, they really do not have the time to translate from the theoretical into the practical, nor the time (nor in many cases, the experience) to tell the difference between the two. They just need some practical advice using the "best available knowledge" on how to get the job done more easily, or how to get out of a jam without making the situation worse for themselves or for others. The software professional is often like Daniel Boone, who, when asked if he had ever been lost, replied, "Nope, but I was once a mite confused for three days." If these guides help one fare a bit better at developing software systems, then I have achieved a good number of my personal objectives in writing them.

A good guide places one in the right place and in the right frame of mind. This requires a judicious use of background and practical information on a subject, including occasionally quirks and strange stories. Thus, I have tried to base the book upon a few "tenets of guidebook writing for computer professionals," which I will gladly state. These are:

- A guide, for it to be used, must be simple (but not too simple), enjoyable to read, and not take itself or the subject overly seriously (take, for instance, Fred Brooks' *Mythical Man-Month*)[2]

- Most of the ideas must have been used in practice at least once, so people can have some faith that they work (see Barry Boehm's *Software Engineering Economics*)[3]

- A guide must save time by synthesizing the ideas from the various references and texts about a subject (refer to William Rowe's *An Anatomy of Risk*)[4]

- A guide must be easily borrowed from and used by those who are working but who may not have advanced degrees in computer science nor engineering (see Nicholas Rescher's *Risk*)[5]

The last criterion is important, because this group forms the majority of professionals in our field.

I hope others outside the software field, such as those in engineering management, industrial engineering, and business management, will find this guidebook useful as well. The techniques described can be easily translated into their own specialities. Given that needed business decisions are becoming dependent on software systems, it would be advantageous to have a bit of knowledge about where an important ingredient of their business' risk lay. Toward this end, I have included some tutorial-like material in Chapter 1 and later chapters for those not familiar with the concepts, or buzzwords, associated with software and software engineering. Those wanting a more complete explanation can turn to another one of my books, *Software Engineering Environments: Concepts and Techniques*,[6] or any other of the McGraw-Hill series on software engineering.

I haven't totally neglected the academic community, though. Graduate students or seniors in computer science, management information science, or computer systems engineering programs or seminars may also benefit from these books by examining what goes wrong with software engineering theory once it is put into practice in the real world. As one NASA official put it, "Software development is never as the textbooks have told it should be. Let's chase fact, not fiction."[7] The single most important lesson experience has taught me, after managing to get a couple of degrees in computer systems engineering, was that I was faced with dilemmas to manage, not compact textbook technical problems with solutions to resolve. A few professors, in particular Dr. Harold Stone of the University of Massachusetts (now at IBM's Watson Research Center), made this abundantly clear in their classes, but the problems of the outside world of real engineering are not often encountered in university computer science or engineering classes.

Toward helping instill a truer perspective about working in the computing field, I have added a series of questions at the end of each chapter, as well as sprinkled comments about various aspects of the topics covered in the notes. The questions and comments throughout explore some areas not explicitly developed within the text, and should be read for an extended insight. The questions (hopefully) will also stimulate students to think a bit more about what really happens out there, beyond their present horizon of homework assignments and exams. And as a warning, some of the questions do not have standard textbook solutions. Instructors might find the text useful in seminar situations, applying the Socratic method to challenge the "truths" their students have about the concepts they have been taught in other classes. Taking current subjects out of computer science literature and examining them from a risk perspective would help fill out the text.

All books are biased in some way by the experiences of their authors. My experiences, and thus my biases, are founded upon performing risk analysis and management over the past 10 years in software system developments undertaken by government agencies in the United States and the United Kingdom, and by large and small commercial corporations here and overseas. The applications themselves covered the spectrum from large, distributed networked systems to small software engineering development systems, and included both military and commercial software developments. I hope the diversity of experience has tempered my overt biases, although my interests still lean toward investigating the dilemmas of large, complex, distributed systems with geographically distributed development organizations.

This bias shows in how I divided the topics across this book and its follow-on companion, *Software Engineering Risk Analysis and Management—Applications.* I have chosen to subdivide the topic of risk analysis and management into two general groupings: mechanics and application.

This initial book is aimed at investigating the general mechanics of software engineering risk analysis and management. Chapter 1 provides the motivation for the subject. Chapter 2 provides a definition of risk, its history, and an overview of what the components of risk analysis and management are. Chapters 3, 4, and 5 begin our investigation of the subject of risk analysis in depth. The issues of risk identification, estimation, and evaluation are covered, with practical advice given to their application. Chapter 6 examines risk management, covering risk control, aversion, and monitoring. How to make decisions about risk is also covered. Chapter 7 is a wrap up, with a review of "How to perform software engineering risk analysis and management," which is cross-referenced to the most appropriate sections in the book where more detail can be found. The reader, if familiar with some aspects of risk analysis and/or management, can either start with Chapter 7 and work back to specific topics, or start from the beginning and use Chapter 7 as a checklist. In either case, the aim is to provide readers with the fundamentals of risk analysis and management so they can carry it out without too much difficulty.

This book provides us the tools, but tools alone do not make a competent software engineering risk analyst. We need to understand the greater context in which software engineering resides, and the risks and limitations within software engineering itself. Thus, its companion book examines the total software engineering enterprise, its associated risks, and constructive approaches to itsaversion.

Software Engineering Risk Analysis and Management—Applications is divided into two subgroupings. The first logical grouping contains Chapters 1, 2, 3, and 4. Chapter 1 reviews quickly the fundamentals of risk encountered in this book. Chapter 2 provides a systematic view of risk analysis and management, as it applies to the systems engineering and business environments. This helps us identify the sources of risk that originate outside of, and are carried into, the software engineering enterprise. Chapter 3 then examines the software engineering risks that may exist in the software engineering process, i.e., the process models, methods, and automation applied throughout the software enterprise. Chapter 4 investigates the software engineering risks associated with the development of computer applications.

The second logical grouping includes Chapters 5, 6, and 7, and focuses on specialized aspects of risk analysis and management. Chapter 5 investigates the risks associated with software safety, security, and operation. Chapter 6 looks at risk taking as it applies to individual risk reduction programs. Chapter 7 provides a look at future risk issues and provides another step-by-step review. These chapters provide other perspectives on software engineering risk analysis and management that are required to obtain a complete understanding of what is involved when they are actually employed on a project.

Together, these two books should provide a robust foundation from which to guide the application of risk analysis and management within your own unique situation. They should also provide directions to reduce the likelihood of risks negatively impacting your software project's successful development.

In summing up, I would like to point out that these books are a collaboration of effort and ideas from the many individuals I worked with here in the United States, in the United Kingdom, and in Belgium, and those authors who preceded me in this area. It is very hard to describe accurately where one idea came from or to give that person the proper credit, but I have tried hard to give credit where credit is due. If I have missed someone, it's purely unintentional. All the thanks for the good ideas in these books should go to the individuals below, and those who are listed in the chapters' lists of references—I merely synthesized their ideas.

First, thanks go to my friends overseas in the United Kingdom, including Lilian Masterman of the National Health Service; Eryl Thomas of the CCTA; Christine Penn and George Mathieson of the former Department of Health and Social Security; Graeme Ferrero of SEMA Group; Guy Warner of Dowty/CAP; Ken Bayes, Chris Bradley, Bob Gardner, Keith Rayward, and Andy Fawthrop of British TELECOM; Patrick Johnson, Mike Kleinman, and Dave Harris of Computer Sciences Company Ltd.; and Gordon Wasserman of the Home Office. In Belgium, my thanks go to Fred Evans of OSI.

In the United States, my thanks go to Karen Norby of Texas Instruments; Rod Leddy of Mobil Corporation; Tom Conrad and Ron House of the U.S. Naval Underwater Systems Center; Hank Stuebing of the U.S. Naval Air Development Center; Cmdr. Kate Paige of the Aegis Program Office; Andy Ferrentino and Joseph Fox of Software Architecture and Engineering, Inc.; Dr. Check Lao and Mitch Mescher of Unisys; Paul Mauro of Hughes Aircraft Company; Ralph San Antonio of Infotech; Mac Murray of General Dynamics; Jack Devlin of Digital; Agi Seaton, Peter Corte, Robert Converse, and Sam Steppel of Computer Sciences Corporation; Marilyn Stewart of Logicon; and my many instructors on naval warfare and planning at the U.S. Naval War College in Newport, Rhode Island. Each of these individuals contributed in their own way to these books.

Some individuals deserve extra-special thanks, such as Kerry Gentry of Computer Sciences Company, Belgium, with whom discussions on software risk go back to the beginning of my career, and who originally arranged my first assignments to test out our theories on real projects. Other special thanks go to Dr. John Spackman of the DHSS (now with British TELECOM); Harvey Parr, also of British TELECOM; and Dr. Charles McKay of the University of Houston, each of whom let me practice on their organizations and helped turn some raw ideas into practical advice. And finally, thanks go to Alan Rose, my publisher, and Maureen Albrecht, my vice president at ITABHI Corporation, who had to listen to endless, boring discussions about these books. Maureen often tried to help straighten out a convoluted writing style incorporating

French-Canadian, British, and American mannerisms, and mostly succeeded. Without her help and kindness in filling in for my job while I wrote, the time would never have been found to complete them.

Bob Charette
Fairfax, Virginia
May 1989

References

1. William B. Rouse, "On Better Mousetraps and Basic Research: Getting the Applied World to the Laboratory Door," in *IEEE Transactions on Systems, Man, And Cybernetics*, Vol. SMC-15, No. 1, January/February 1985.

2. Fred Brooks, *The Mythical Man-Month*, Addison-Wesley, Reading, MA, 1975.

3. William D. Rowe, *An Anatomy of Risk*, Robert E. Krieger Publishing Co., Malabar, FL, 1988.

4. Barry Boehm, *Software Engineering Economics*, Prentice-Hall, Englewood Cliffs, NJ, 1981.

5. Nicholas Rescher, *Risk*, University Press of America, Lanham, MD, 1983.

6. Robert N. Charette, *Software Engineering Environments: Concepts & Technology*, McGraw-Hill, New York, 1986.

7. James Raney, "Concepts and Expected Use of the Software Support Environment," in *NSIA Conference on "Software Initiatives and Their Impact on the Competitive Edge,"* 10 May 1988.

The Best Possible World

*"If this is the best of all possible
worlds, what then, are the others?"*

VOLTAIRE in *Candide*

1.0 Introduction

Picture this for a moment. It is a hot, windless summer afternoon in New
York City. The smog permeates the air, and after each breath, a slightly
acrid taste is left on your tongue. A man, around the age of thirty-five to
forty, wearily ascends the steps to his house. In his left hand, he is
clutching a briefcase, his suit-coat haphazardly flung across it. The
man's appearance is in keeping with the temperature and time of day—
head slightly bowed, necktie loosened around his unbuttoned collar,
forehead streaked with beads of perspiration. But there is something
more—something a bit odd, and out of character, that a casual observer
would maybe not see, but would definitely sense, if one were able to sense
such things on a hot afternoon in the city. Maybe it is the appearance that
he hasn't slept for the last two evenings, or that each step he takes
transmits a sense of intense trouble, or equally that his face wears a
mask of inner despair.

The man's wife, a pretty woman in her early thirties, but equally worn,
greets him at the door. Scanning his appearance, she, knowing from
experience that he is worried, says in a quiet voice,

"How bad?"

After a seemingly intolerable interval, the man replies, "It's in awful
shape. Profoundly worse than we had thought. After today's review of
the project, it will be hard for them not to cancel it."

The man steps inside, exhibiting a slight shiver as the air-conditioned air hits his body. Following her husband to his chair, the man's wife asks in a soft voice, "What does that mean?"

With the utmost effort, and in almost perceptible pain, the man replies, "It means I'll probably get fired tomorrow."

The man slumps back into his chair, head in hands, while his wife, turning her head away, bites the back of her hand. The man just keeps shaking his head, angrily saying over and over to himself, "If we had only known. If we had only known . . ."

A new cinema verité commercial for a telephone company? A contest entry for worst opening lines to a novel? A bad dream? Unfortunately, it was all too real if you were one of the senior executives at Bank of America who recently lost their high-paying jobs because of a computer system development disaster, or one of the other nonexecutive staff who also received pink slips. It seems that Bank of America abandoned an originally estimated $20 million computer system after spending $60 million trying to make it work.[1] This followed an earlier failed attempt that cost Bank of America an additional $6 million. And, by the way, the second attempt was originally scheduled to be a two-year effort, but was three years late at the time of its cancellation, with no completion date in sight. Needless to say, Bank of America's chairman was not amused, especially since he had very publicly declared that Bank of America's intention was to move to the technological forefront in the information technology business in banking—and this project was to be one of the strategic moves forward in achieving that objective.

An isolated case you say? Hardly. A recent survey of 600 of its largest clients by the big eight accounting firm, Peat Marwick Mitchell & Co., showed that 35 percent admitted computer system developments as having runaway costs.[2] Day after day the story gets repeated, with losses to companies in excess of $80 million common, and up to $250 million not unusual. Business in bailing firms out of computer development trouble is so good that firms like Peat Marwick earn a lucrative $30 million per year doing it. If this is not of any interest, or if you are immune from software failure, then you ought to return this book. It isn't for you.

What we will present are basic guidelines for making your travels in the computing field a wee bit more enjoyable, and definitely less expensive. As a guide, we have tried to provide a judicious mix of theoretical background and practical information, which will allow you to give your project a better than even chance to succeed, or an ability to straighten it out, or to make a little money straightening out others.

Attempting to understand the relationship between software engineering and risk analysis and management is much like taking a long train journey through a foreign land. The understanding of the country is gained not so much in reaching the destination, but through the journey itself. Like any travels in a foreign land, it may take many trips to gain a full appreciation.

To aid in attaining this appreciation, we need to set the right frame of mind for the journey to the land of software engineering risk analysis and management. Thus, in this first chapter we will present a mosaic of images of the interesting, but sometimes confusing, landscape of computing. But be forewarned, it may be a little nasty out there.

1.1 Journey's Beginning

For most software professionals working toward a nearing deadline, going to parties is out of the question. Sleeping and eating are usually out of the question, too. But, if ever again you do find yourself at a party, are feeling really agitated or bored because you cannot get that next tricky design problem out of your head, try this for fun. It might help remove the cobwebs interfering with your thought patterns, and simultaneously provide a bit of lateral thinking. Find someone from outside the computing field who is feeling really relaxed. Ask for the definition of the word "software," and see what type of response you get.[3] Then, assuming you have not by accident asked a professor of computer science at the local university, try to explain it to your unfortunate conversation partner yourself, in terms of the problem you are having difficulty with and at a level that can be understood by a bright high school student. By the time you are done, not only are you likely to get the answer to your design question, but a knowing nod, a brightening of the face, and a response from your partner that typically runs to "Okay, yeah, now I know, it's the stuff that makes computers run." Kind of like petrol, I guess.

Laughter is always good for solving tricky design questions. After you have stopped giggling, go interview a few more party guests (assuming they haven't been warned away from you), and ponder their responses in a bit more detail. An interesting undercurrent in the answers you get will be the range of emotion the word "software" invokes. It is rather amazing, really. Some people seem frightened of the word, like it has some mystical connotation similar to the ancients with their words for god. Say the word "software," and you are forever cursed. Many others exhibit extreme cases of hopelessness, contempt, or even hostility, as they spit out a tale of their incorrect phone bill, or how they had heard on the news that a software failure led a bank's cash dispensing machine to eat one of its customers' ATM cards. I know how hostile I became when one of the things absconded with mine recently. The ATM experience seems, along with the bar-code reader errors at grocery stores, to have touched a nerve in the popular psyche.

For the record, the Institute of Electrical and Electronic Engineers Standard Glossary on Software Engineering Terminology defines software as, "computer programs, procedures, rules, and possibly associated documentation and data pertaining to the operation of a computer system."[4] For most people, this definition leaves them cold, and the definition that it's computer petrol seems more appropriate and useful. As we will see, software has about the same level of importance as petrol for a country's economy.

The reactions of people to the word "software" remind me of one of my old high school teachers lecturing about how one should not be scared of grades. After all, an "F" or an "A" was just a letter, a nonentity. It wasn't going to physically hurt us (he obviously didn't know my father), nor help us in any particular fashion. The word "software" seems to have transcended that particular philosophical argument in people's minds today.

The sharpness of people's emotion for the word software is easy to understand, of course. Everyone has been "bitten" or frustrated by a computer probably at least once in the past month, I would guess. It probably has to do with the fact that everyone has had a bad experience related to the immortal words, "The computer is down." It may be, at least in the Western world, the single most common unpleasant experience shared by people today.

It is a fact of life that computers, for good or evil, are in our society to stay, and are increasingly staking out more of their claims against all facets of our lives. Every now and then, it is instructive to look back at how computing was viewed, before we surrendered ourselves to co-existing with the invasion of personal computersand processing chips, which like a plague of electronic locusts have expanded their territorial grip from our desks at work to our desks at home, automobiles, and lawnmowers.

Return, for instance, just to the year 1973. Then, much more so than now, technologists were frightfully concerned with the social stress of computing,[5] which dutifully received a great amount of press coverage. We have gathered some of the burning issues of that day in Table 1.1.

TABLE 1.1 Burning Issues in Computing, circa 1973

- Will man be replaced by machine?

- Does the computer industry require regulation?

- Can one trust plans made by computers?

- Are databanks threats to individual freedom and liberty?

- Are governmental balances of power being upset by computers?

- Are computers destroying basic value systems?

- Does the world, including third world countries, really need computers?

- Are individuals being alienated because of computers?

- Are there computer applications that should not be undertaken because of moral or ethical reasons?

- Will computers create massive unemployment?

Read them over carefully. One is left wondering how we were all going to adjust. How strange that today, only 15 years later, most of these are "non-issues," as the use of computers to control portions of our lives is generally accepted. The revolution was not televised. Or maybe it was televised, but no one noticed. Given the fact that no permanent social revolution in history has happened as rapidly, this is more than a bit surprising, at least to me. Maybe it was the sense that nothing could be done to change computing's use, or that it was so wrapped up in mystery, and the oncoming pervasiveness so hidden and unknown, that it has leapt up to where it is today in the same fashion as a spring flower after a soaking rain and warm sun. It is interesting also to note, as shown in Table 1.2, that the reasons for using computers have stayed remarkably similar over the same period. The only possible shift has been from a concentration to provide inwardly directed benefits, such as reduction in costs and increased morale, to outward directed benefits. The use of computing today is more concerned with gaining a competitive edge by opening up new markets. So it wasn't a fundamental change in need that caused us to overlook the revolution.

Some may be tempted to argue with the phraseology above, that computers control portions of our lives, but in a very real sense they do. It may not be direct control, but it is control nevertheless. Try hard to

TABLE 1.2 Reasons for Using Computers, circa 1970

Economic Factors:	• Improved productivity
	• Reduction in inventory
	• Reduction in delivery time
	• Reduction in personnel costs
	• Efficient use of capital resources
	• Reduction in capital expenditures
	• Better provision for customer services
Non-Economic Factors:	• Better decision making
	• Improved business image
	• General increase in morale
	• Prevention of competitor malfeasance
	• More accurate measurement of productivity
	• Better understanding of business environment
	• Improved information flow and communications

think of anything we use or buy that doesn't have a computer embedded somewhere in its distribution, billing, or management path. Or take, for instance, the stock market crash in the autumn of 1987. The collapse of the New York stock market helped trigger collapses in the Tokyo and Hong Kong markets, because the traders are now linked via computer networks into a 24-hour market. Moreover, some believe the market collapse was triggered by automatic computer selling.[6]

1.1.1 Warning: Computers in control?

Computers at banks and stock market brokerages are used to keep track of dozens of selected stocks and specific market parameters. The algorithms implemented in the computer software help stock market analysts manage their stock portfolios. These algorithms formulate computerized trading strategies by which investors profit from the difference in price between a group of stocks and their stock index futures or option calls.

Simply put, if the stock market performs in a certain fashion, then a decision to buy is formulated, and the analyst informed. Otherwise, hold or sell orders are suggested. Timing is important, and the rapidity of the buy or sell decision is crucial to analysts making a profit or incurring a loss for their clients. These buy or sell orders themselves, of course, influence the market parameters, which in turn are being used by the algorithms of other computers to calculate individual buy or sell strategies for other analysts. Thus, the analysts, each with their own computerized strategies, are literally competing against other computers. (Or better, programmers are competing against other programmers.)

Now recall the paradox of the stock market: You sell because you think a particular stock will go down, while somebody else buys the exact, same stock because they think it will go up. A bit crazy, one must admit, by any measure of imagination. Anyway, in special circumstances, the market reaches certain conditions whereby the computer algorithms indicate to the analyst a "belief" that everyone else thinks stock prices will fall. Now the analyst is stuck in a bind. Do you or don't you believe in what the algorithms are indicating to you? If stock prices actually do fall, and if you want to keep your job until Friday, you better get out while the getting is good. If you don't believe this will happen, and that the computer is wrong, you might wait a while (as some analysts on Black Monday did), and see what transpires.

The funny thing is, it really does not matter if the analysis is correct or not. If enough other analysts get the same information (the algorithms used are different, but tend to use the same theoretical modeling foundations for determining their equations), it is unimportant what the reality is, because a new reality will take over. If enough analysts start to sell off concurrently, it can trigger sell orders in other computers. The blind leading the blind in a feeding frenzy. Because of the speed and volume of shares that computers can handle, the selling takes on a life of its own, which panics those without computers who don't know what is happening, who in turn sell, etc.

This scenario was pondered in the brokerage houses, but was never really taken seriously, except by a few experienced traders who had watched the upswing in block buying and selling by computers over the previous two years. A few weeks before the crash, many of these traders got out of the market because they felt it was overpriced, and because they saw the scenario becoming a reality.[7]

Although the Securities and Exchange Commission has undertaken steps to help keep this from happening again, the shock of the market collapse was still reverberating over a year later. Although the market has regained much of what it lost, it may take years before small investors regain their confidence (or their lost money). Brokers who did not believe what their computers said, and who lost a great amount of money because of it, might not be so patient next time. The crash also scared many governments, because it highlighted the fact that their power over markets, and their own fiscal policy, is quickly deteriorating.

As one writer on risk and new technology stated, occurrences like Black Monday have "potential consequences which are unprecedently widespread and terrible, and are indifferent to political boundaries."[8] I view it as akin to being part of an experiment, and being the mice.

1.1.2 Computing power as political power

It is still difficult to believe the widespread use of computing, and its pervasiveness, in the industrialized world, as is illustrated in Figure 1.1.[9] Try answering the questions: Where is computing not making a significant impact in industry? Or which industry isn't dependent on computers for its survival? Could any industry shown survive today against its competitors if its computers were suddenly shut down? What would happen, I wonder, if, as in the case of gasoline a number of years back, there was an embargo on software?

In each of the industries shown in Figure 1.1, it is interesting to note that the computer's capacity to do work cheaply, reliably, and more productively is the chief weapon of the industrialized first world to stave off third world businesses, which by sheer use of cheap human labor are trying to take away these same markets—cheap, reliable human labor versus expensive human labor using cheap, reliable machines. Back in 1971, the United Nations conducted a study to understand the spread of computerization throughout the world. They came up with a set of criteria that countries are to be measured against, as shown in Table 1.3. Very few countries were in the top level, and the U.N. thought that the countries would go through a smooth transition from one level to another.

However, the third world countries figured out how, by combining their cheap manpower with the power of cheap machines, they could produce quality high-technology goods at a very competitive price. These low-priced products would be shipped and sold almost exclusively in the largest first world markets, i.e., in the United States and Europe, while any similar products sold in their own markets would be at a higher price to sustain the competitive position abroad. Sacrifice it might be, but, if they gathered enough of a first world's market share, they could then finance their next generation technology with the revenues from the sales of their current technology. This would, in turn, mean their competitors in the United States and Europe could not count on this same source of revenue to fund *their* next generation technology, nor put what was left to as effective a use, since their inherent labor costs were much higher. And with no external market to make up the difference or provide new revenue, over time, the first world businesses would find it

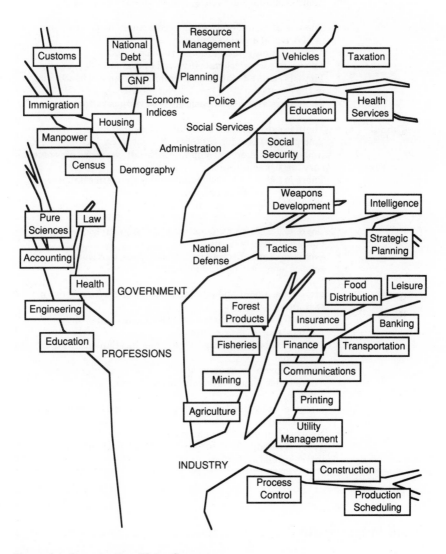

Figure 1.1 Organizations Using Computers

TABLE 1.3 United Nations Specified Levels of Computer Development

Level	Characteristics
Initial	• There are no operational computers in the country. • Few nationals have computer training. • Sources of information are local computer salesmen.
Basic	• There is some understanding of computers in government (and private) decision centers. • A few computer installations are to be found. • There are some nationals involved in computer operations. • There is some education and training in computer technology in the country. • Computers are used in basic government operations.
Operational	• There is extensive understanding of computers in government (and private) decision centers. • Among the numerous computer installations there are some very large machines. • There are centers for education and training in computer technology and some are of excellent quality. • They offer degree programs in computer or information science. • There is design and production of software and some manufacturing of hardware. • Computers are affecting many disciplines, particularly science, engineering, and medicine.
Advanced	• Most government and administrative work is carried out by computers. • There are well-established professional activities and national meetings on computing. • There is a complete range of quality education and training programs. • The number of computers of all sizes is increasing rapidly. • There is design and production of both hardware and software. • Many technologies have been changed or are in the course of being changed. • New applications of computers are found regularly. • There is strong participation in and contribution to international activities.

difficult to regenerate themselves, and they could, since they take a short-term view of business risk and return, be counted on to eliminate themselves from the competition.

By following the steps above, third world countries have leapfrogged second world status directly into the first world, at least economically. This added economic power is now being used to lift them into being true first-class players, where the disparities in the technological and living standard bases are being eradicated altogether. The Economic Tigers of the Far East (Japan, Korea, Taiwan, Hong Kong, and Singapore) are prime examples of how this is happening in practice. Many other countries want to join them. In the age of true world-wide economic competition, low price, high quality, and good business strategy win the largest market share. It is unfortunate that first world businesses don't take the same view.

Anyway, this shift in economic power also impacts world politics. The result of the success of the Economic Tigers is forcing the United States to consider loosening its 300-year political ties with Europe. The U.S. sees the Pacific region as a more important center of power and the source of its future well-being, in any of its attempts to stem its own economic and political power from eroding further.

Economic power is not the only way to view political power, however. Another way to understand political power is to view it as it relates to military power. Here, too, software systems play a large role. An interesting set of figures is shown in Figures 1.2 and 1.3. These figures show the percentage of major U.S. Department of Defense programs that

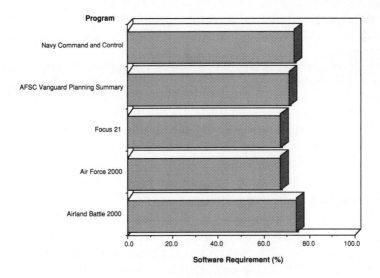

Figure 1.2 Projected Software Use in Selected DoD Programs

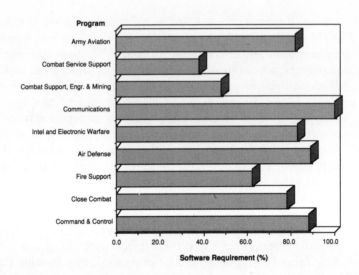

Figure 1.3 Selected Use of Software in Airland Battle 2000

require software. Over 70 percent of the technologies, functions, systems, and actions require software.[10] Some systems literally don't exist without a computer.

The AEGIS cruiser is a prime example of a system that could not operate without computers. It requires computers to help run every one of its major systems, as is illustrated in Table 1.4. Since the AEGIS cruiser is the prime air defense support platform of U.S. Navy carrier forces, its availability is key to U.S. projection of power in trouble spots around the world. If AEGIS were not available, U.S. political policy would be negatively impacted. What is true for AEGIS holds true for most U.S. military weapon platforms today. It is not an exaggeration to say that U.S. defense policy, like the AEGIS, rests almost solely on computing technology, which is also its Achilles heel.[11,12]

1.1.3 The software business

Another way of understanding the pervasive nature of software is by measuring the impact it has on the U.S. economy. The building and maintaining of software is a large growth business in the United States. Although it is difficult to measure exactly (there are no common ways of

TABLE 1.4 AEGIS Cruiser Software-Intensive Systems

AEGIS Weapon System Mk7

- Operational Readiness Test System Mk1
- AN/SPY 1A Radar System
- Weapons Control System Mk1
- Fire Control System Mk99
- Guided Missile Launching System Mk26
- Standard Missile 2
- AEGIS Combat Training System
- Command and Decision Making System Mk1
- AEGIS Display System

Sensor Systems

- Air Search Radar System
- Surface Search Radar System
- Identification System
- Electronic Warfare System
- Underwater Surveillance and Communication System

Communication and Support System

- Navigation System
- Radio
- Logistics Support System
- Combat System Support Equipment
- Underwater Countermeasures System

Weapon Systems

- Seahawk System
- Underwater Weapon System
- Harpoon Weapon System
- Gun Weapon System
- Phalanx Weapon System

measuring software-related expenditures), the best estimates available indicate that software-related expenditures accounted for somewhere around 5 percent of the Gross National Product in 1986.[13] This adds up to about $228 billion being spent per year (includes salaries, training costs, etc.). This is in contrast to the estimated expenditure in 1980 of somewhere around $130 billion.[14]

The asset value of existing software was estimated at $250 billion in 1981, and now could be closer to $350–525 billion, if the growth trends reported are to be believed.[15] Even the market for software tools that aids the construction of software is estimated to be worth $1.5 billion in 1987 and $3 billion for 1990.[16] To get some feeling for the explosive growth in software-related expenditures over a 20-year time frame, from 1963 to 1983, 20 percent of the growth in the U.S. software industry occurred in the first sixteen years, while over 80 percent occurred in the four years between 1979 and 1983,[17] illustrating nicely Toffler's growth curves. If one adds in the presumed growth from 1983 to 1988, the results are even more dramatic.

Other interesting little facts are that in 1950 there were approximately 500 software professionals in the United States, give or take a hundred or two (in 1940 there were none), while in 1980 there were 275,000. According to the latest figures of the American Electronics Association, in June 1988 there were over 450,000 software professionals. And according to one estimate, program code is doubling approximately every 14 months.[18] It probably is a good thing that software code weighs nothing and takes up very little space, or there would be big trouble in storing the stuff. Even so, the residue of software production contains other problems, such as that affecting the toilet paper industry (see reference [7]).

The U.S. government is still the largest single spender on software-related items, topping in at just over $18 billion in Fiscal Year 1988.[19] During that year, for example, the Social Security Department spent approximately $493 million, the Department of Justice $400 million, and the Public Health Service around $278 million. The Department of Defense topped off spending at around $13 billion in expenditures, as is shown in Figure 1.4.[20] However, the U.S. government is now only a minor player in the overall U.S. software market, where less than 15 years ago it was the dominant world player.

1.2 The Middle Journey: What's Wrong With This Scenery?

Given that business is so good, one might get the impression that everything is great in the computer field. The facts that companies are making money, the revenue growth looks continuous, and people are employed are all good news. Unfortunately, there is also some bad news if you happen to be a taxpayer or user of these systems. The numbers above do not give you a good feel for the world-wide expenditure on software-related items, nor who owns the greatest market share. This doesn't mean necessarily who produces the most, but who sells the most.

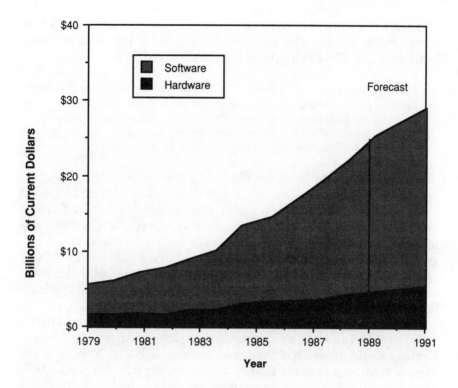

Figure 1.4 Total U.S. Military Computing Expenditures

As we indicated, others are getting into the act. How much of the U.S. (im)balance of trade is accounted for by the purchase of foreign-made software-related goods, or the Economic Tigers' trade surpluses dependent on it? In telecommunications equipment (in which software in embedded computers provides a significant portion of the overall equipment's capability), the Commerce Department reported a trade deficit of $2.6 billion in 1987 with Japan alone, and in electronics equipment as a whole, the United States ran a $15.3 billion deficit. The effects of such large deficits can mean higher inflation, recession, higher taxes, and/or companies out of business.

The second piece of bad news is, you know the money you are spending on computing and software? Much of it is being mismanaged and/or wasted. A prominent U.S. computer industry leader, Howard Yudkin, director of the Software Productivity Consortium, recently remarked at a conference on the "Department of Defense/Government Software Initiatives and Their Impacts on the Competitive Edge":

> My impression after thirty years with the [computer] business is that we are failing over and over again [to produce acceptable software systems, either in cost, schedule, or performance—author]. We are compounding our failures with self-delusion. We are making matters worse by refusing to honestly admit our failures in ways to allow us to change.[21]

Yudkin went on to point out that the software industry's failure to produce acceptable systems is not localized to any particular type of computing system being developed, whether it be a vanilla flavored management information system, a billing system, or a complicated real-time military application. Nor is the failure localized to the programming language being used. Nor is the failure localized to the way systems are being built (fads, as he puts it). Nor is the failure localized to the use of custom-built or off-the-shelf software components. Nor is the failure localized to the type of firm developing the system.

Pretty strong words. One may quickly ask what constitutes his criteria for failure? In Table 1.5, we have tried to summarize them. Most people, I think, would agree that they are reasonable. But is Yudkin really correct in his assessment? Surely it's an exaggeration? A particularly gruesome tale that tends to support his view is told in a Report to

TABLE 1.5 Yudkin's Criteria of Software Failure

Acquisition Status	Failure Criteria
Terminated	- For convenience/nonperformance of contract.
Completed	- System not deployed—users can't/won't use it.
Completed	- System didn't meet originally promised cost.
Completed	- System didn't meet originally promised schedule.
Completed	- System didn't meet originally promised quality.
Completed	- System didn't meet originally promised capability.
Completed	- System can't be evolved in a cost effective manner.

Congress by the Comptroller General.[22] After reviewing an admittedly small number of government projects, some examined precisely because they were in trouble, the Comptroller General found that only about 2 percent of the software contracted for could work on delivery; 3 percent could work after some reworking; over 45 percent was delivered, but never successfully used; 20 percent was used but either extensively reworked or abandoned; and 30 percent was paid for but not delivered, as shown in Figure 1.5.

No general conclusions should be inferred from this one report. But there are enough documented cases, a few of which are listed in Table 1.6, of software failure(s) to make even Pollyanna swallow hard. Again, remember the Peat Marwick Mitchell & Co. report that showed 35 percent of its clients admitted runaway costs, and given human nature, probably another 10 percent had them but wouldn't admit it, and another 5 percent probably didn't know they had them, yet. Consider

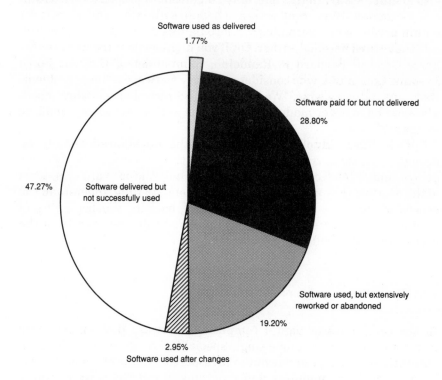

Figure 1.5 Nine Software Development Contracts: Where the Money Went

TABLE 1.6 Cost of Software Failures

System	Minimum Additional Cost*
U.S. Office of Mines	$ 15M
Bank of America	65M
United Airlines Reservation System	145M
NORAD Update	207M
U.S. Navy Automated Financial System	446M
Advanced Logistic System	490M
U.S. Army TACFIRE	525M
United Education and Software Inc.	650M
U.S. Army Sgt. York	1,000M
U.S. Air Force B-1B EW System	1,200M
British Nimrod	2,200M

* 1988 adjusted $

also another study. In this one, only 10 percent of projects were within cost estimates, 15 percent within schedule estimates, and 70 percent within performance estimates.[23] These figures do not include the projects that were cancelled, either. Or, if you like, consider the words of Air Force General Bernard P. Randolph, commander of U.S. Air Force Systems Command, who considers military software a "huge problem" that runs industry wide: "We have a perfect record on software schedules—we have never made one on time yet and we are always making excuses."[24]

But why this litany of failure? To answer that question adequately, we need to understand two things. The first is that cost overruns, schedule delays, and/or inadequate performance are only the outward symptoms of the disease; they are not the causes. Second, to fully understand the causes of the disease, one must venture back to the beginning of computing to understand what is euphemistically referred to in the literature as the "software problem."[25]

1.2.1 The software problem

In the early days of digital computing, software development was primarily aimed at getting a single specialized program to work. Computers then, as now, were meant to save large amounts of manual labor. First generation computers and programs in the 1940s were mainly targeted to the completion of the massive astronomic navigation and ballistic tables used primarily by scientists and the military. In the 1950s, as second generation computers provided more power and flexibility and made it cost effective to use computers, the trend shifted away from the pure scientific and military usage of computers to the processing of business data.

In both the 1940s and 1950s, a program was considered increasingly successful if it (a) executed; (b) executed quickly; (c) gave an acceptable answer. Regardless of the success criteria, the quality of the program was highly dependent on the skill of the programmer. Because of the lack of resources that were currently available on computers, an individual programmer's ingenuity at providing the maximum computation, using the least amount of resources, was highly admired.

New memory technology spawned the third generation of computers. These computers allowed even larger programs to be executed, and many programs to be executed concurrently. This added capability, and accelerated the trend in software development in the late 1950s and early 1960s away from single programs or sets of small programs toward large assemblages of programs linked together to perform a single integrated system function. Large-scale use of software was probably first attempted in the SAGE (Semi-Automatic Ground Environment) air defense system. It contained a computer with 58,000 vacuum tubes, consumed 1.5 megawatts of power, executed a real-time application program of 100,000 instructions, and had a support system of 112 million instructions.[26]

The creators of the SAGE system were the unfortunate first, but by no means the last, to experience the problems surrounding the development of large-scale software systems. Most of the problems they faced are still familiar to those creating software systems today.

For instance, the application program was too large and complex to be created by a small group of programmers, but instead required large teams of programmers. The increased numbers, along with their required logistical support, rapidly escalated the cost of the project (notice the large support system, much larger in fact than the system being built). The problem of scale also appeared. A large program just didn't seem to work all that well.[27] It became clear that as the program size increased, the probability for error increased even faster. Although reliable statistics aren't available, SAGE probably also used most of the programmers then in existence, thus depleting the numbers available for other programming jobs in the commercial sector and driving up labor costs. Finally, a larger program and a more capable computer allowed the programmers to be even more "ingenious" than before.

However, the problems and lessons learned in the encounter with the SAGE system development were to be quickly dismissed, as a period of great fervor and optimism swept the computer field during the mid and late 1960s. Newer, more capable computers and software techniques promised to make any lessons learned obsolete or marginally transferable to new system developments.

It was widely believed, or at least the marketing people claimed, the advent of the fourth generation machines would allow the distribution of programs across networks, forming system magnitudes larger than those ever envisioned by the SAGE designers. Moreover, the costs of the hardware systems were constantly going to be reduced, and what were previously scarce resources (processing speed, memory, etc.) were going to become everyday items. Additionally, to handle the software development of these large systems, it was recognized that some discipline would have to be brought to the software field. But here, too, progress seemed to be making rapid headway.

After all, research efforts were reporting results in the areas of software design disciplines, problem abstraction, and notations for software representations. These would allow a rational approach to software development. Simultaneously, high-level programming languages first developed in the 1950s were finally gaining acceptance by the programming community, as the code generated by the compilers became ever more reliable and efficient. The issues of programmer productivity and software quality, although still not completely solved, were seen as things of the past. The age of functional programming as seen in the 1940s, 1950s, and early 1960s would be replaced by the new age of structured programming.[28] The problems brought out by the development of the SAGE system would soon be solved. However, by the late 1960s this confidence was beginning to wane, as more and more software system developments were being attempted and encountering exactly the same problems as the SAGE system.

The 1970s exacerbated the problems even further. Although more research was being directed at solving the "programming problem," the problem continued to grow and change in form. The mass introduction of minicomputers, microprocessors, and personal computers all happened with incredible speed. These provided more emphasis on computer networks and distributed processing, which meant even larger systems could be built for the same money. Anything seemed possible, if one could afford it. The issue changed from one of building *programs* into one of building *systems*, and no one really knew how to successfully, and repeatably, accomplish that. But that didn't stop people from trying.

The 1980s have seen governmental attempts around the world to gain control of software technology. Private and government sponsored consortia, from Japan to Brazil to Scandinavia, have been created to develop better techniques for building systems in an attempt to develop new technology to capture the information technology market. These efforts have become more critical because of the merging of computers with telecommunications to a degree where the boundaries between the two are blurred. This trend has meant that governmental control of information becomes less potent, with power shifting to corporations. Some corporations, such as General Motors, produce as much wealth as nation states such as Sweden. Some equivalent corporations/nations are shown in Table 1.7.

The research in software engineering environments, which began some 20 years ago, is finally starting to pay off, as practical environments for building systems are appearing.[29] Individual software application systems are growing even larger, with the watchword being "systems integration." Independent software systems are now being interconnected into megasystems. Likewise, software megacontracts now commonly range from $1 billion (e.g., Computer Sciences Corporation's NASA support contract), to over $3.6 billion (IBM's share of the eventual $16 billion FAA air-traffic control contract), and last 10 years or more, to make these interconnected systems a reality.

The underlying characteristics of software systems today are that they are huge, complex, difficult to build, brittle, and costly. To illustrate the size increases, all one has to do is look at how the relative scale to measure size has changed. Figure 1.6a illustrates the size categories for

TABLE 1.7 Comparison of Company Revenues and Selected Countries' Equivalent Gross Domestic Products for 1986

Top Ten World Corporations	Revenue/GDP	Country
General Motors	$112B	Sweden
Royal Dutch/ Shell Group	78B	Belgium
Exxon	76B	Poland
Ford Motor	72B	Austria
IBM	54B	Norway
Mobil	51B	Finland
British Petroleum	45B	Yugoslavia
Toyota Motor	42B	Egypt
IRI	41B	Thailand
General Electric	39B	Columbia

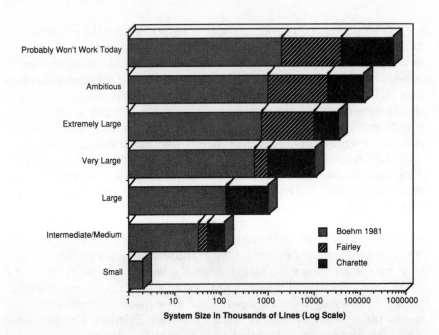

Figure 1.6a Re-Definition of System Sizes

systems from just 1981 to 1986, and the growth in size of some selected systems over the last 35 years.[30,31] The very large program definition has increased by a factor of 20 in a little over five years. Contrast this with operational code sizes of very large systems, which have increased by a factor of 100, and support code by a factor of 300, in 30 years (Figure 1.6b). Operating system sizes themselves increased by a factor of three orders of magnitude in a similar time frame. This should not be surprising, given that at the low end of computing personal computers went from 4 thousand bytes random access memory, to 4 million bytes in less than 10 years. Nor should anyone be amazed that the first billion-line integrated software system project is being currently contemplated to be installed by the mid-1990s.[32]

As a specific example, consider Figure 1.7, which shows the amount of software being used on the NASA manned programs from the Apollo program to the planned Space Station, and their individual total program costs. The Apollo program was totally written in machine assembly language, while the Space Station is being written in the high-level language, Ada. Notice that more software (and functionality) is being

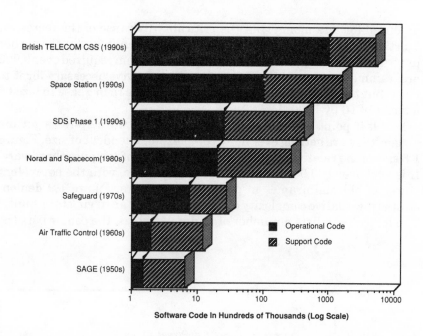

Figure 1.6b Selected Software System Sizes and Growth Trends

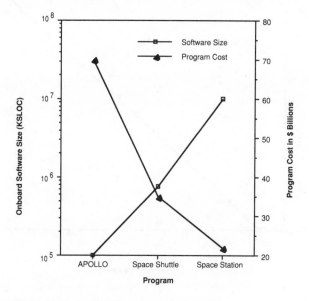

Figure 1.7 NASA Software and its Costs

produced for less money, but the criticality (because of the increased functionality) of the software is even greater than it was in the earlier programs. Similarly, the IBM 360 operating system required over 5,000 programmers to create the one million instructions necessary for it to run,[33] but that the trend is for operating systems to increase in size by a factor of 10 by 1990.[34]

This last point is important. Not only are software systems getting bigger, they are getting ever more complex, independent of size. Figure 1.8 shows the relative increase in the capability of computer hardware. It is well over 100,000 times that of 30 years ago, with the equivalent power of old mainframes in personal computers. Figure 1.9 demonstrates the relative complexity of the systems that are trying to be built.[35] The left column lists a number of minor variables, the center lists the

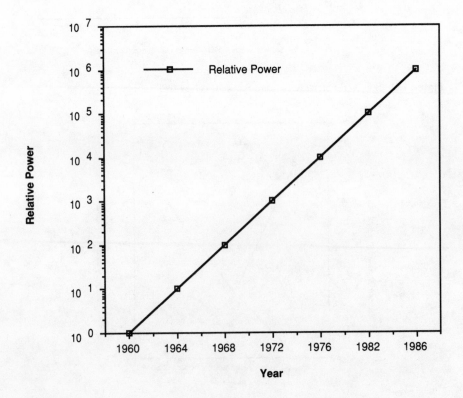

Figure 1.8 Relative Increase in Computing Power Over Last 30 Years

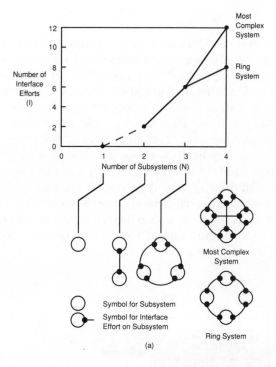

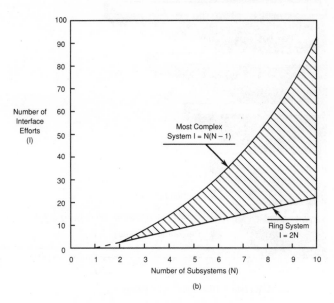

Figure 1.9 System Complexity

number of ways they can interact, and in the right column, the number of different logical functions that can be built with those variables. Even trying to build a small system, which has only eight modules that have to interface with each other, is dominated by an $N(N-1)/2$ relationship, or has 28 communication paths to worry about. What about a system with hundreds of modules? With the aforementioned merging of tele-communications and computing, the problem of system complexity is bound to get worse. Trying to package all this capability into harsh operating environments, like those faced by the military, makes the problem acute. Complexity of software systems has been cited as a primary reason for cost overruns in military systems.[36]

Exacerbating the problem even further is the lack of trained people to build systems. The demand for software programmers is continually rising in the United States. The programmers required versus the

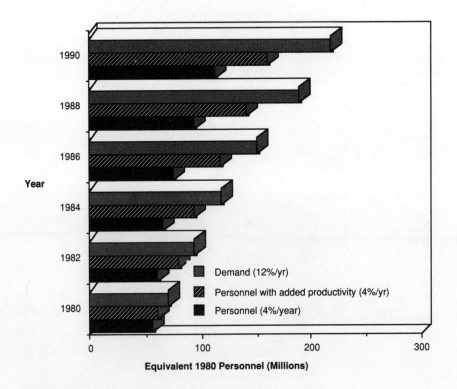

Figure 1.10 Trends in Software Supply and Demand

supply available is large, and seems to be growing larger, as shown in Figure 1.10. Most researchers point to about a 4 percent average increase in programmers available per year, whereas somewhere around 12 percent are required to equalize recognized demand.[37] It is not uncommon for projects to be delayed or abandoned because the personnel were not available to perform the job. Even the largest hardware-independent software company in the world has only 18,000 employees, with no more than a few hundred available to work on any one project at a time. Thus, it is typical for a project to have more than one company working on a software project, which increases the bureaucracy and management problems. Figure 1.11 shows a NASA project that has five contractors working on it. Note the inherent difficulty in trying to separate responsibility and ensure everything is done, especially around the boundaries between contractor responsibilities.

1.3 Journey's End: The High Cost of Failure

As mentioned in earlier sections, most of the money on software systems is being wasted because the systems themselves are failures, either in cost, in meeting schedule, or in performance. Wasted may seem too harsh

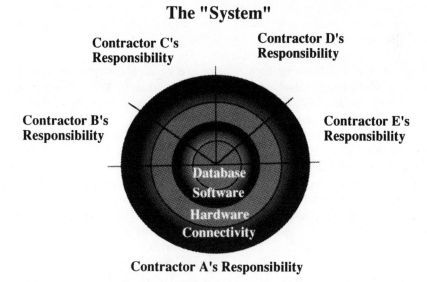

Figure 1.11 NASA Contractor Support

a word, but if you are not getting what you paid for, then it's a waste. The cost of failure is extremely high, in economic, social, and political terms.

1.3.1 Economic costs

The economic costs of software failure are huge. If only 10 percent of software-related expenditures are wasted (using Howard Yudkin's definitions), then this amounts to somewhere close to $22.8 billion per year. A closer guess of the true figure is somewhere around four times that, or close to $90 billion in software-related expenditures that are unproductive. Notice that we do not mean not needed, just unproductive. The value for money is close to being nonexistent in many programs. The Packard Commission on Defense and a Harvard Business School study estimated that close to $6 billion a year could be saved on military systems by control of weapon system complexity.[38] The software is responsible for much of the complexity. Who pays? The taxpayer: in other words, you and I.

Because of the lack of people to build systems, there is an estimated four-year information system development backlog, and a second, hidden backlog of eight years for systems not demanded because of the first backlog.[39] It is difficult to estimate the cost of the backlog, but it could be as much as $1 trillion. The amount of potential employment this represents can be measured in the millions. Who pays? The unemployed and the taxpayer.

Another aspect of the economic costs are related by the level of fraud that can occur via computers. These are at levels unprecedented in history. Volkswagen lost over $259 million due to foreign-exchange contract fraud in 1987. The fraud involved erasure of computer data and tampering with computer programs.[40] Fortunately, this was discovered. How many more frauds are left undiscovered? It is estimated by security specialists that over $3 billion are annually lost by computer fraud. Who pays? The shareholders, ultimately.

Even if fraud isn't at fault, a software failure can cause massive problems. In 1985, the Bank of New York was overdrawn by $32 billion because of software corruption of financial transactions. It took 24 hours to clear the problem. The cost was $5 million in interest to the bank. The mistake caused a panic in the platinum market because rumors were floated that the bank was about to collapse. A description of the problem can be found in reference [41]. Who pays? The bank depositors.

1.3.2 Social costs

As we mentioned above, the cost of the backlog can't be measured only in economic terms, but in social terms such as employment. The unemployment situation could be resolved if people could be trained to perform the proper work.

But there are also other social costs when the software in systems does not work. How does one measure the aggregate cost to society when people get frustrated when their bills are wrong, or their social security check is late, or their reservation at a holiday resort is lost? Take, for instance, the case of the overloaded IRS staff a few years ago. The new computer systems were not installed on time; thus, the IRS was not able to handle the influx of tax returns. This meant tax refunds were delayed, which delayed taxpayers from getting their money to spend. This in turn hurt the economy, because people traditionally spend their tax refunds on paying off old debts, or buying big-ticket items. Another IRS computing snafu sent letters to 100,000 companies threatening to seize their property. In a bit of an understatement, an IRS spokesman later said that these activities "obviously caused some anxiety and they apologized."[42] The cost to society, because people get wary not only of computers, but of all forms of new technology as well, can be staggering.

How does one measure the cost to the parents whose son was choking, but because of a software bug the emergency 911 call-tracing program retrieved the wrong address and sent the rescue team to the incorrect place?[43] What do you tell them? Blame the computer? Or the vacationer, who has saved all year for that one chance to get away, but has to stay in an airport for 36 hours because of air traffic delays due to a faulty program?

How about the executives of businesses who refuse to modernize, or modernize too late, because they are afraid of the computer systems that could help them compete? Or are afraid that, given the many failures of the past systems that were purchased, they are just throwing good money after bad? So, they take their chances in the competitive environment, with information technology introduction hanging over them like the Sword of Damocles. When their businesses start to fail because they can't compete with others who have modernized, cries go up for the government to impose trade barriers.[44] And again the natural reaction is to hide, and not compete, and say it isn't fair.

1.3.3 Political costs

When software systems fail, they rarely cause a major political row. Even wasting tens of billions of dollars on software systems does not seem to create enough political will to do anything about it. The political effects are usually seen only in perspective. Spending $6 billion more than necessary on military systems costs a great amount in terms of political leverage. The $6 billion may only buy one aircraft carrier and its escorts. But, over a 10-year period, that one carrier might be very useful. For example, the lack of a carrier meant that the British had to fight a war over the Falklands.

As another example, the B-1 bomber's electronic countermeasures system "as originally designed, does not have the inherent capacity to process information to handle all current threats. It doesn't have the capacity, the speed, the processing capability or the architecture" to be used to perform certain missions.[45] The B-1 can achieve only 50 percent of its intended capability against Soviet air defenses. It is estimated that it will cost $1 billion to correct the problem. Although the economic costs can be calculated, what does the reduction in capability cost in political terms, when one of the strategic legs of the TRIAD becomes weak? Today's defense against aggression is based upon deterrence: be strong, or at least make the other guy believe you are strong. But if the systems don't work, or aren't available, the deterrence has failed, and you have, at best, only wasted money. At worst, you lose your country.

The record of past software failures makes national initiatives like SDI suspect. The cost of failure may be too high, not only economically, but politically as well. Is it reasonable to expect that something even more sophisticated than any currently developed system, and which can't be tested completely until it is actually needed in a nuclear war, will work? Would we be able to trust it, or have confidence in it not failing? David Parnas, one of the most respected computer scientists in the world, doesn't think so.[46] What if he is right? And even if he's wrong, what is the cost to the economy, the society, and relations among nations proving that he is wrong?

A country's strength depends on its economic power and military power, and the political will to employ them. The political cost of software failures weakens the national defense. It weakens the competitive advantage a country requires to keep its people employed to build and sustain an economy. It saps political will. Why, one may ask, isn't anything being done to combat this problem? Something has, and its been dubbed software engineering.

1.3.4 Software engineering

In 1968 and 1969, at two controversial NATO conferences held in West Germany, new ways were discussed to solve the "software problem" typified by expensive, unreliable, and unmaintainable software. Many problems were recognized with the development practices being used in the specification, design, implementation, test, and evolution of software systems. These development practices could not keep up with the changes in capability that the newer third-generation hardware systems were providing. Some of the deficiencies in software development are listed in Table 1.8. It was felt that many of these deficiencies, especially in achieving efficient use of the hardware, could be overcome if more discipline over the process of developing software could be obtained via utilizing a systems approach (e.g., systems engineering). Thus, the term "software engineering" was coined. Software engineering was defined to mean "the establishment and use of sound engineering principles in order to obtain economically, software that is reliable and works efficiently on real machines."[47]

It took a number of years to get the term accepted and refined, as many practitioners in the late 1960s and early 1970s argued that software development was more an art than a science. However, as the develop-

---

TABLE 1.8 Some Shortcomings of Current Software Development Practices

- Inconsistent, incoherent, incomplete specifications and designs
- Designs fail to provide for change
- Non-reusable software and software designs
- Responsibilities, duties, and accountability poorly defined and controlled
- Developed products hard to operate
- Poor performance of resulting product
- No provision to perform impact analysis in relation to specific parameters
- Completion criteria poorly defined
- Histories unavailable
- No metrics available to test overall system quality
- No effective means to manage complexity
- Ineffective communication/feedback between development and personnel
- "Team" efforts uncoordinated
- Performance assessment done after the fact
- No effective documentation aids
- No assistance available for the resolution of conflicts or issues
- Excessive development costs and schedule
- Unreliable and unmaintainable products

ment of systems, rather than programs, became the rule, the arguments died out. Today the generally accepted meaning of software engineering is the definition, creation, and application of (a) a well-defined methodology that addresses a software life-cycle of planning, development, and evolution; (b) an established set of software artifacts that documents each step in the life-cycle and shows traceability from step to step; and (c) a set of predictable milestones that can be reviewed at regular intervals throughout the software life cycle.[48,49] Concepts and techniques such as software first systems engineering, abstraction, information hiding, top-down design, structured programming, modularity, stepwise refinement, quality assurance, and measurement of efficiency are being embraced as good software engineering practice. The goals or objectives of the software engineering process are shown in Table 1-9.

In short, software engineering defines a life-cycle or a paradigm of the process of software development, from conceptual design to the retirement of the system, as illustrated in Figure 1.12. This provides a uniform framework in which the software developers work. In each phase, explicit prescriptions are given for achieving an activity or set of activities required by the life-cycle model used to develop the software

TABLE 1.9 Objectives of the Software Engineering Process

- To improve the accuracy, performance, and efficiency of the overall product under development
- To apply well-defined methodologies for the resolution of software/system issues
- To provide rational resolution of conflicts, and documentation of differences when resolution is not possible
- To provide for product change in response to new or modified requirements
- To provide an understanding of the role of all stakeholders in the resolution of complex issues and the differing sets of constraints under which they operate
- To provide clear communication among management and the members of the system/software engineering teams
- To improve the understanding of how current systems and the evolution of future products are impacted by present-day decisions
- To provide explicit identification and consideration of all normally implicit trade-offs, assumptions, constraints, and intentions, and recognition of what is, and is not, important for planning and decision-making purposes
- To provide anticipation of contingencies and identification of the impacts of proposed situations
- To document decisions, the rationale behind decisions, and the actions taken; to create and maintain a corporate memory
- To provide explicit descriptions of schedules and milestones, and an understanding of the effects of time upon issues under consideration

product. These prescriptions, or software methods, are the step-by-step rules to building a software product. Sometimes these methods are automated, to help the software developer. If a number of methods are automated, then a software engineering environment is said to exist. These concepts are explored in depth in the companion to this book.

However, there is not yet a totally accepted software engineering life-cycle paradigm, set of methods, nor complete set of automation available. The Department of Defense has defined and mandated a life-cycle paradigm, called DoD-STD-2167A, for use in the development of software for military systems (see Appendix A for a brief description). Few methods and no automation except for language are mandated. There exist at least four different types of software paradigms, and as of yet, no full software engineering environment is commercially available. The Department of Defense plans to spend over $75 million over the next five years in an attempt to procure one.

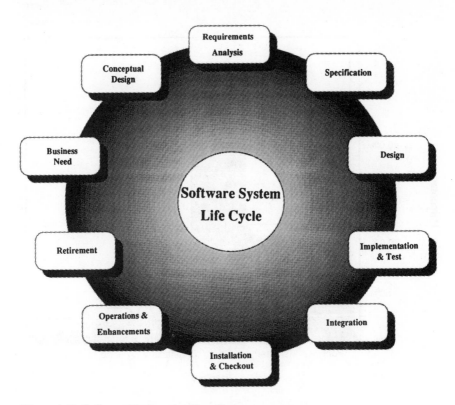

Figure 1.12 Software Engineering Paradigm

Since 1968, the focus of software engineering has shifted from the efficient use of hardware resources to the efficient use of human resources. Furthermore, it has had a positive impact on software quality and the management of software development.[50] However, although some headway in reducing the amount of failures has been made, failures still happen too many times. The basic characteristics of the software problem still remain. Part of the software problem is attitude (many practitioners look at software engineering as a necessary evil), while part of it is the story of the cobbler's children. The state of the software development practice in the United States is charitably characterized as marginal,[51] as shown in Figure 1.13. But more important, a fundamental reason for the terrible performance of the industry can be traced to it not keeping up with the shift in the last decade from coding programs to building systems. Whereas the former is concerned with hardware efficiency, in the latter, human efficiency is more much

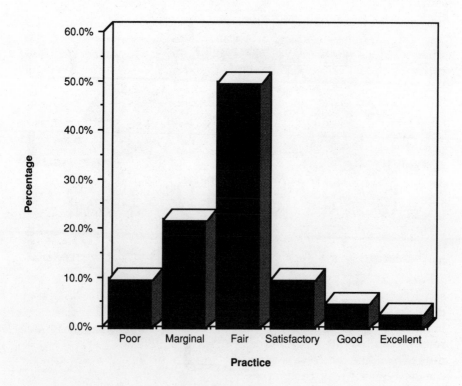

Figure 1.13 State of Software Engineering Practice in the United States

important. This marked a fundamental shift in what software engineering requires to support. As we will see in the companion to this book, this fundamental shift, which is only slowly being recognized, requires the use of a different software paradigm than is commonly used—the current one exacerbates, rather than helps solve, the problems. It also changes the perspective as to what risks should be included in the domain of software engineering analysis and management.

The Defense Science Board (DSB) listed a variety of other reasons why software technology was developing so slowly.[52] One reason is the complete revolution of hardware technology every few years. As we noted earlier, today's hardware offers more than a 10,000-fold increase in price-performance over that of 30 years ago, and one can choose at least a 1000-fold of that gain in either price or performance. With that array of availability and selection in hardware, it is not difficult to see why software technology has had a hard time staying even.

Another reason for the software problem, according to the DSB, was that software is, and always will be, labor intensive. The work and the time should be all centered in development, not in production. Part of the reason is the almost infinite variety of systems that can be built from the wide selection of hardware available at different price/performance ratios; also, most software systems are unique. A banking application for Bank of America isn't used at Citicorp. Each company builds its own, individual system. As a general rule, software systems are not produced en masse.

A third reason for the slowness in the development of software technology is that the essence of software is in the designing of intricate conceptual structures, rigorously and correctly. The labor required to develop these designs will never go away, even though the task of expressing the designs might be made more productive. The design effort is made more difficult because of the necessity for a software product to (a) conform to complex environmental, hardware, and user interfaces; (b) change as the interfaces change; and (c) try to overcome the invisibility of the software product itself.

Fourth, the DSB pointed out that most of the past effort in advancing software technology has been spent on the nonessential, incidental difficulties in the expression of conceptual structures. Three major breakthroughs in software technology each have contributed to the removal of these nonessential difficulties. The first was the awkwardness of machine code and assembly. The advent of high-level language removed this difficulty and increased productivity by a factor of 10. The second was the loss of mental continuity caused by slow turn-around times. Time-sharing and personal computing removed this difficulty, and again two- to five-fold gains in productivity were achieved. The third was the incompatibility of files, formats, and interfaces among software tools required to build systems. Standardization of operating systems, such as UNIX, has helped overcome this problem, has increased productivity by a factor of 2, and will increase it by another factor of 2 or better as open systems become more of a reality.

Finally, the DSB pointed out that no single new technique can be expected to yield 10-fold improvements on productivity, timeliness, or robustness in the next 10 years. However, all the various developments should yield a 10-fold increase in the next decade. The next major advance must concentrate in the conceptual design area itself, if any real progress is to be made, as illustrated in Figure 1.14.

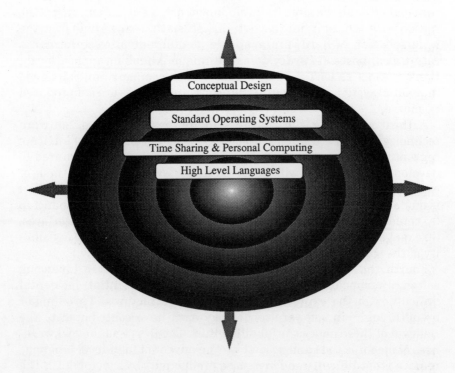

Figure 1.14 Technological Drivers for Expanding Productivity

By now one is probably pretty confused. One is moved to ask, given that things look pretty bleak for successfully developing software, what can be done to increase the probability of success? Since we can't go back, should we just accept it, as one analyst put it, "as the cost of doing business?"[53] I instinctively feel there is something wrong with that attitude. Personally, I would rather let the other person waste their money developing poor software systems. I need money to get an edge, or just to survive. In most other situations, such as skydiving, given what has been presented thus far, one would move to identify the relevant risks and try to limit or reduce the risk of failure. And that is what the major portions of this book, and its companion, are about.

1.4 Summary

Some readers may still feel that I am writing a guidebook for Cassandra: predicting doom with computing as its roots. Quite the opposite. The inherent flexibility of software, the degrees of freedom it allows, is unmatched in any other technology. The benefits to mankind in science, medicine, and engineering are overwhelming.

Some may instead feel that I believe no successful computer system has ever been built, nor ever will. Far from it. The Space Shuttle is a prime example of a successful software system, and serves as an existence proof for such systems.[54] Over 10 million lines of code have been developed, all of it considered a Category I risk (i.e., if it fails, there could be loss of life and/or the vehicle), and only once has there been a delayed launch due to the software. This was only achieved because previous mistakes that occurred in the Apollo and Skylab programs were learned from, and because of 25 missions and over 15 years of hard work. I have been a member of a number of successful projects, managed by tremendously talented and gifted individuals, but I also have been a member of, and led, projects that were nightmares and made me want to dig ditches for a living instead.

In his excellent book, *To Engineer Is Human: The Role of Failure in Successful Design*, Henry Petroski writes that "experience has proven that technology risks are controllable."[55] However, technology is only controllable if we understand the limitations of the technology and have reasonable expectations about its use. Future success is gained by foreseeing current failure. I do get annoyed, angry, and saddened that those who know the problems of software development most do not try more to contain them, or at least explain computing's limitations to those less well-informed. I cringe every time I hear of yet another software failure, because I am part and parcel of the profession that creates these systems.

The primary reason I cringe is not because of the failure (one cannot learn enough from successes to go beyond the state of the art), but from the constant rhetoric on how rosy a system development is, or how easy it will be to develop, or how the risks are minimal, or the self-righteous attitude of many, especially in large, controversial military software programs, that those who do not believe it can be built, should move over and let the *real* (i.e., patriotic) software engineers do it! With complete system failure rates of up to 30–40 percent in the industry, and with budgets exceeded 90 percent of the time? Please! There is no shame in learning from mistakes. There is shame in not learning from them.

Most of the time, the negative rhetoric on a controversial subject is worse than the reality; but, unfortunately, in the case of software engineering today, the reality *is* worse than the positive rhetoric one is constantly subjected too. Healthy skepticism seems to be losing ground in the very programs that require it most. Even if the numbers for failures are exaggerated, how much failure is too much? One-half of what is reported? One-quarter? Pick a number! But at any number you pick, we should be constantly reminded that innocent people entrust their safety and happenings in their daily lives to system and software engineers. We must not abuse that trust. Remember, if pilots landed planes with only 99.9 percent reliability, there would be two unsafe landings every day at Chicago's O'Hare Airport. As Howard Yudkin pointed out, we waste billions of dollars on software every year in systems that have so much impact on our lives, but only invest tens of millions (in a good year) in trying to correct the situation.[56]

As more systems become dependent on software, more failure will spread, more risk will spread to the general population, and more money will be wasted. This is true even where the software is only a small part of the total system cost. The software, because of its nature, is the glue for almost all the systems we interact with today. If the glue shrinks, or never sets, or melts, the system collapses. Even systems that are successful in meeting their original design criteria are usually over budget or late. Again, what are the full implications involved?

The most amazing thing to me is the amount of money being wasted on software, and no one seems to notice it. It's probably because the failures are spread out and don't all happen at once. If $50–100 billion a year (which represents a good chunk of the national yearly deficit) were being wasted by a single organization, the concern would be enormous. Take the savings and loan crisis, for example. Spread it around, however, and it disappears from the landscape of governmental concern.

I suppose the other conclusion one must reluctantly reach about the lack of concern is that the U.S. government and businesses must have money to waste, and that the voices of concern they raise over the trade deficit are a sham. *Some 40–50 percent of money spent on software goes into fixing it.* Could you imagine how long an automobile manufacturer would stay in business if a customer had to spend 2–4 times what it cost originally to keep it repaired? How long would the government or taxpayer put up with that? It isn't surprising that a 1981 technology forecast stated "Already the 1980s have been proclaimed the Software Decade, but the distinction is not an honor. Software is seen as not the biggest contribution, but the biggest obstacle to industry growth."[57]

It's worse today, as the money for new business growth, to maintain the competitive advantage, is being sapped by even more competition from abroad. As a taxpayer and resident of the United States, it worries and concerns me that governmental interest is so low, yet the voices to restrict imports in electronic and other high technology products are so high. Have we really lost our way, and our will, this much?

Hopefully, the vital importance of possessing reliable and affordable computer systems in our lives has come across. There are attempts, like software engineering, to try to reduce the cost of building these systems. But it is not enough. We need more systematic approaches, such as using process-oriented paradigms instead of product-oriented paradigms, where the risks involved in the building of the product, its use, and why it is used, can be more fully understood. We need to do this not only for safety reasons, but because it makes good business sense.

Applying software engineering risk analysis and management techniques to projects can earn 50 percent or more in productivity gains, and better quality systems. Now, if someone else wants to waste their money, let them. If I can apply a technique or method that can save me money, garner me a competitive edge, and at a relatively low investment to boot, then show me how to do it. As Norman Augustine[58] points out in his Law of Counterproductivity, "It costs a lot to build bad products." This book will not change the world, but maybe it can help start the debate on how to change it in an area that is our future, and which others seem on the verge of controlling. I view the appliction of risk analysis to software enginnering as just another (small) step toward making it a true profession.

In conclusion, William Lowrance[59] wrote, "We are adopting innovation for widespread use faster than we can ever hope to learn about their consequences. Let's hope we aren't tragically outsmarting ourselves." Amen to that.

Questions

1 A June 1988 report in *The Wall Street Journal* revealed that 65 percent of the firms surveyed were heavily dependent upon their computers to do business, and 20 percent were completely dependent. Also in 1988, American universities reported declining enrollments in computer science and engineering programs. What are some of the likely outcomes of these two trends, 5 years from now; 10 years from now; and 15 years from now?

2 Review some of the old textbooks on computing, especially those from the late 1960s and early 1970s, concentrating on the future of computing technology. Why do you suppose that the social issues so important in 1973, as illustrated in Table 1-1, are of little concern today? Are issues like stock market automatic trading a danger to the world economies?

3 SAGE probably used most of the programmers then in existence, thus depleting the numbers available for other programming jobs in the commercial sector and driving up labor costs. Do you think that this is true in today's software market? Does the military employment of software engineers hurt the commercial sector and the U.S. competitive position in relation to other nations?

4 Describe the essence of the term "software engineering." How does it relate to a business' profit margin? Is it possible to gain a competitive edge by applying software engineering?

5 It took into the late 1960s for people to realize that schedule and budget overruns were in fact the symptoms of the software problem, and that the causes were related to the software application developed and the means to develop it. What effect does new computing technology have on reducing or increasing the severity and magnitude of these causes?

6 Imagine that you are a Computer Technology Luddite. Discuss at least three reasons why computers should be banned, or why those that build them should be legally responsible for problems caused by their programs.

7 What does the term software engineering risk mean to you? What does it mean as it relates to a firm's basic business objectives? How does one go about reducing it?

8 The SDI is a very controversial program because of the stance taken by Dr. Parnas about its testability and trustworthiness, which are technical issues, not political. Are these issues of significance, and if so, are they enough to cancel the program? What are the risks of building the system, and not building it?

9 Do you personally feel threatened by the fact that computer systems are as prevalent as they are today? On July 18, 1989, the *New York Times* reported that Dean Witter Reynolds Inc. announced it no longer would use computer program trading and criticized other stockbrokers who did. A spokesman for the firm said Dean Witter pulled out of program trading because "it threatened the integrity of the market in customers' minds." Do you believe that systems like the stock market or commodities markets should be kept from doing fully automated trading? Do you think international computer exchanges of information will ever reach the point where networks will be regulated, as some countries are starting to clamor for?

10 Of the last 10 software programs that you were involved in, how many failed, using Dr. Yudkin's measures? Do you consider those failures?

References

1. "B of A's Plans for Computer Don't Add Up," in *The Los Angeles Times*, 7 February 1988.

2. "It's Late, Costly, Incompetent—But Try Firing a Computer System," in *Business Week*, 7 November 1988.

3. We will freely interchange the words "software," "computing," "computer system," "software field," "computing field," etc. in this book. "Information systems" might

also creep in from time to time. It is assumed that the reader will understand when the term is being used in a generic form and when it is being used in a specific context, as in the distinction between "software" and "hardware."

4. *IEEE Glossary of Software Engineering Terminology*, IEEE Std. 729-1983. IEEE, New York.

5. C. C. Gotlieb and A. Borodin, *Social Issues in Computing*, Academic Press, New York, 1973.

6. "How Computers Helped Stampede the Stock Market," in *IEEE Spectrum*, Vol. 24, No. 24, December 1987.

7. In a lucky coincidence, I had a conversation with a senior commodities trader at a New England bank, about computer trading, a few weeks in advance of the crash. He matter of factly, and accurately, forecasted what would happen, and like many other traders, moved in advance to protect his portfolio. A Security and Exchange Commission report later said computerized trading was not the cause of Black Monday, but it did contribute to the panic experienced that day. Another insight given by this trader was that stock futures in companies that manufacture toilet paper might be considered a good investment. It seems that computer paper is recycled into toilet paper, but with the advent of laser printers the paper is not as valuable. Something to do with the difficulties in removing the print from the paper. As he tells it, there may be a scarcity of toilet paper as more laser printers come into use.

8. William W. Lowrance, *Of Acceptable Risk: Science and the Determination of Safety*, William Kaufman, Los Altos, CA, 1976.

9. C. C. Gotlieb and A. Borodin, *Social Issues in Computing*, Academic Press, New York, 1973.

10. Samuel Redwine et al., "DoD Related Software Technology Requirements, Practices, and Prospects for the Future," *IDA Paper P-1788*, 1984.

11. Ronald D. Elliot, "Technological Risk in Automated Systems," in *Signal*, November 1988.

12. "Editorial: Achilles Heel," in *Aviation Week & Space Technology*, McGraw-Hill, 17 October 1988.

13. John E. Hopcroft and Dean B. Kraft, "Toward Better Computer Science," in *IEEE Spectrum*, December 1987.

14. R. Fairley, *Software Engineering Concepts*, McGraw-Hill, New York, 1984.

15. J. Musa, "Software Engineering: The Future of the Profession," in *IEEE Software*, Vol. 2, No. 1, January 1985.

16. "CASE Market Projections," in *CASE Outlook*, Portland, OR, July 1987.

17. Ware Myers, "An Assessment of the Competitiveness of the United States Software Industry," in *IEEE Computer*, Vol. 18, No. 3, March 1985.

18. Norman R. Augustine, *Augustine's Laws*, American Institute of Aeronautics and Astronautics, New York, 1983.

19. "Agency IT Budgets Grow By 3 Percent Again in '89," in *Government Computing News*, Vol. 7, No. 19, 12 September 1988.

20. "Upgrades and Civil Avionics To Counter Budget Squeeze," in *Aviation Week & Space Technology*, McGraw-Hill, 20 March 1989.

21. Howard Yudkin, speech given to National Security Industrial Association Conference on "Software Initiatives and Their Impact on the Competitive Edge," 10 May 1988. Dr. Yudkin recently passed away, and his insightful commentary on the computing industry will be sorely missed.

22. "Contracting for Computer Software Development," General Accounting Office Report, FGMSD-80-4, 9 September 1979.

23. Norman R. Augustine, *Augustine's Laws*, American Institute of Aeronautics and Astronautics, New York, 1983.

24. "Washington Roundup," in *Aviation Week & Space Technology*, McGraw-Hill, 6 February 1989.

25. Extracted from Robert N. Charette, *Software Engineering Environments: Concepts & Technology*, McGraw-Hill, New York, 1986.

26. Norman R. Augustine, *Augustine's Laws*, American Institute of Aeronautics and Astronautics, New York, 1983.

27. Raymond Yeh et al., "Software Requirements: New Directions and Perspectives," in the *Handbook of Software Engineering*, C. Vick and C. Ramamoorthy (Eds.), Van Nostrand Reinhold, New York, 1984.

28. L. Peters, "Special Issue on Software Engineering," in *Proceedings of the IEEE*, Vol. 68, No. 9, September 1980.

29. Robert N. Charette, *Software Engineering Environments: Concepts & Technology*, McGraw-Hill, New York, 1986.

30. Ware Myers, "Software Pivotal to Strategic Defense," in *IEEE Computer*, Vol. 22, No. 1, January 1989.

31. Robert N. Charette, *Software Engineering Environments: Concepts & Technology*, McGraw-Hill, New York, 1986.

32. British TELECOM is currently installing a networked system, which, when completed in late 1990, will consist of 250,000,000 lines of operational and support code. BT expects it to reach a billion lines of code by the mid/late 1990s. From private conversations with Dr. John Spackman, Director, Computer Information Systems, British TELECOM.

33. Fred Brooks, *The Mythical Man-Month*, Addison-Wesley, Reading, MA, 1975.

34. L. Brown et al., "Advanced Operating Systems," in *IEEE Computer*, Vol. 17, No. 10, October 1984.

35. William O. Fleckstein, "Challenges in Software Development," in *IEEE Computer*, Vol. 16, No. 3, March 1983.

36. "Weapon Complexity Cited as Principal Cause of Cost Overruns," in *Aviation Week & Space Technology*, McGraw-Hill, 4 July 1988.

37. J. Musa, "Software Engineering: The Future of the Profession," in *IEEE Software*, Vol. 2, No. 1, January 1985. There is a great debate as to whether there is, or is not, a shortage. The Electronics Industries Association predicts a shortage of one million software professionals for DoD work, while the National Science Foundation predicts a national shortage of "only" 115,000 to 140,000. However, if one examines the number of skilled personnel available per deployed software system in the U.S. Navy and takes into account the increase in productivity due to tools, methodologies, etc., the work capacity per system (number of skilled personnel times the increase in productivity, divided by the number of deployed systems) has been dropping since 1960 (Thomas Conrad and Robert Charette, "Towards Automated Design of Distributed Command and Control Systems," Fifteenth International Conference on Systems Sciences, Honolulu, January 1982). This trend is likely to be true in the commercial sector as well.

38. "U.S. Fraud Probe Rekindles Military Waste Controversy," in *Aviation Week & Space Technology*, McGraw-Hill, 4 July 1988.

39. Itazhak Shemer, "System Analysis: A Systemic Analysis of a Conceptual Model," in *Communications of the ACM*, Vol. 30, No. 6, June 1987.

40. Peter G. Neumann, "Risks To The Public In Computers and Related Systems," in *ACM Software Engineering Notes*, Vol. 12, No. 2, April 1987.

41. John E. Hopcroft and Dean B. Kraft, "Toward Better Computer Science," in *IEEE Spectrum*, December 1987.

42. Norman R. Augustine, *Augustine's Laws*, American Institute of Aeronautics and Astronautics, New York, 1983.

43. Peter G. Neumann, "Risks To The Public In Computers and Related Systems," in *ACM Software Engineering Notes*, Vol. 12, No. 2, April 1987.

44. In the pre-computer age around 1900, staying in business was tough enough. Of the top 25 industrial corporations in the United States, only 2 remain today. One retains its original identity, the other is a merger of seven corporations on the original list. See [42] for further details.

45. "B-1B Defensive Avionics Meet Only Half of Intended Goals," in *Aviation Week & Space Technology*, McGraw-Hill, 1 August 1988.

46. David Parnas, "Software Aspects of Strategic Defense Systems," in *American Scientist* 73:432-40, September–October 1985. His views, which are still hotly debated in the defense community, have recently gathered some support from others previously opposed to them. See John A. Adams, "Star Wars in Transition," in *IEEE Spectrum*, Vol. 26, No. 3, March 1989. Furthermore, on 14 February 1989, U.S. Air Force Lt. Gen. George Monahan, the SDI Director, testified before Congress that the

SDI could never shoot down 100 percent of the incoming missiles, thus admitting the original political goal of a leak-proof nuclear shield was unobtainable. See "Promise of Brilliant Pebbles Casts Doubt on SDI Plan," in *Aviation Week & Space Technology*, McGraw-Hill, 20 March 1988.

47. P. Nauer and B. Randall, Eds., "Software Engineering," NATO Scientific Affairs Division, Brussels, Belgium, 1969.

48. R. Pressman, *Software Engineering: A Practitioner's Approach*, McGraw-Hill, New York, 1982.

49. Robert N. Charette, *Software Engineering Environments: Concepts & Technology*, McGraw-Hill, New York, 1986.

50. Itazhak Shemer, "System Analysis: A Systemic Analysis of a Conceptual Model," in *Communications of the ACM*, Vol. 30, No. 6, June 1987.

51. M. Zelkowitz, "Software Engineering Practices in the U.S. and Japan," in *IEEE Computer*, Vol. 17, No. 6, June 1985.

52. "Report of the Defense Science Board Task Force on Military Software," Office of the Under Secretary of Defense for Acquisition, Washington, DC, September 1987.

53. "Pentagon Anticipates Neutralizing Contracts Tainted by Defense Probe," in *Aviation Week & Space Technology*, McGraw-Hill, 1 August 1988.

54. Ware Myers, "Software Pivotal to Strategic Defense," in *IEEE Computer*, Vol. 22, No. 1, January 1989.

55. Henry Petroski, *To Engineer Is Human: The Role of Failure in Successful Design*, St. Martin's Press, New York, 1982.

56. A higher percentage is spent on the damage caused by lightning. Over $400 million and 200 lives are lost by lightning strikes. About $10 million, or 2.5 percent is spent on lightning research. At the same percentage, the U.S. Government should spend $450 million on software research per year.

57. Itazhak Shemer, "System Analysis: A Systemic Analysis of a Conceptual Model," in *Communications of the ACM*, Vol. 30, No. 6, June 1987.

58. Norman R. Augustine, *Augustine's Laws*, American Institute of Aeronautics and Astronautics, New York, 1983.

59. William W. Lowrance, *Of Acceptable Risk: Science and the Determination of Safety*, William Kaufman, Los Altos, CA, 1976.

A Guidebook Tour of Risk Analysis and Management

"If people don't know what you are doing, then they don't know what you are doing wrong."

Sir Humphrey Appleby's Diary[1]

2.0 Introduction

It was reported recently in local newspapers that the U.S. Navy had abandoned a new computerized accounting system after spending $230 million "to prevent further losses." The Navy judged it to be too costly and unworkable. It had something to do with the fact that new requirements kept getting added on, such that the originally priced $33 million system was now going to cost $480 million, and the life-cycle costs over a 10-year period would have added another $403 million.[2]

The interesting thing about this particular case was that the Government Accounting Office in 1984 had recommended a risk analysis (the Navy had invested at that time $129 million into the system), but it was not performed. Political pressure was the speculated, but not confirmed, reason for the lack of action. A spokesman for the prime contractor, who shall remain nameless, said, "We're disappointed that it didn't work out."

The spokesman went on to say that the firm "has no shame in this matter." Its officers are confident that the customer (i.e., the U.S. Navy) "knew all along that the changes to the system would cost more."

"The Navy is a good customer. I'm not sure what lessons were learned [in this case]," he added.

I guess so. Who wouldn't like customers like that? But to say that one could not figure out any lessons to be learned, or that there weren't any misgivings on the part of his company? A bit cheeky, I think, don't you?

Back in the first chapter, we reviewed the state of software in the United States, of which the above example is just a typical part. The conclusions we reached were pretty grim:

- Software development is the primary obstacle to economic growth.

- Software failure is costing billions, if not tens of billions of dollars in unnecessary expenditures to U.S. businesses.

- Attempts to control costs and create better systems by using software engineering discipline are not making the inroads one would expect.

Recall that the first two issues were only the outward symptoms of having to use a software technology product. Their causes have to do with the lack of personnel available and the increasing demands placed upon the functionality of the systems, with the resultant increases in system size and complexity. The third issue concerns the ill-discipline with which the software systems are themselves created. Therefore, the causes of the software problem are related to *both* the software product and the process by which it is created.

A problem we all must address is, one can't live with software technology, nor without it. Software technology presents us with an added source of risk in our everyday lives, with which we have to cope. This chapter is concerned with the concept of risk, and more important, how one thinks about risk. Chapter 1 touched on this theme a little by concentrating on the overall impacts of computing on society, and indirectly its risk consequences. In this chapter, we wish to provide a more refined view of what exactly is meant when we speak of risk as it is related to software projects. We will begin our journey with an introduction to the meaning of risk, traveling from there to an examination of what risk analysis and management mean in general, finishing by examining what it means in the context of software engineering.

To help place us in the correct frame of mind for our trip, we need to know where we are starting from. For this we turn to William Lowrance, who provides our point of departure.[3] In his book, he considered the general relationship of new technologies to inherent risk, which could just as aptly be applied specifically to software technology:

- Technology, by no means an unmixed blessing, has enriched the human condition and will remain an important aspect of civilization.

- Many problems are technological in origin and will necessarily be technological (as well as political) in their solution.

- Human activity will always and unavoidably involve risk.

- In order to make our world safer, we can only start changing from where things stand today.

One would agree that this point of departure represents a sensible and balanced view between the application of a technology and its risk to a society. It is the last statement, however, "we can only start changing from where we are today," that is a key theme of this book. The situation may not be good at this time in the software industry, but it will be guaranteed to *not* improve if we do not start somewhere.

Every project involves risk, and the competitive world makes it necessary that we take risks that may not be enjoyed. Therefore, trying to completely eliminate risk is a futile endeavor. The essential nature of software makes this doubly true. However, by the application of sensible approaches, these risks might be analyzed and managed better, for everyone's benefit. The remainder of the book's motivation is how to live with software risk and maybe control (but not necessarily eradicate) its negative consequences.

2.1 Risk—What Is It?

We have mentioned the word "risk" many times in the past few pages, but what exactly do we mean when we speak of risk? Risk can be looked at from a number of different perspectives. First, risk concerns future happenings. Today and yesterday are beyond active concern, as we are already reaping what was previously sowed by our past actions. The question is, can we, therefore, by changing our actions today, create an opportunity for a different and hopefully better situation for ourselves tomorrow? This means, second, that risk involves change, such as in changes of the mind, opinion, actions, or places. In a static world, there would not exist a concept of risk. This brings us to the third aspect of risk. Risk involves choice, and all the uncertainty that choice itself entails. Thus, paradoxically, risk, like death and taxes, is one of the few certainties in life.

2.1.1 Risk

The derivation of the word "risk" dates back to at least the seventeenth century and is thought to be Italian in origin.[4] Before that time, the word used generally in everyday writing and conversation was "hazard." "Risk" came to England from France in the mid-seventeenth century as the word "risque," and quickly followed a path to the United States.[5] The Anglicized spelling appeared in 1830, appropriately enough in the records of insurance transactions in London's financial brokerage houses. The two spellings for risk were used interchangeably for about one hundred years, until the twentieth century, when "risque" became the word for a joke that risks offending. Notice that the word "risk" can be used both as a noun (i.e., a risk) and as a verb (i.e., to risk), thus allowing the expression of two ideas: a danger itself, as well as a way of acting that involves taking a chance.

The dictionary definition of risk is "to expose to the chance of injury or loss." Thus, for risk to exist, the chance involved must have some loss associated with it. Some writers have tried to divide risk into two distinct types: speculative (or dynamic) risks and static risks.[6] Speculative risks are those having both profit and loss attached to them, while static risks only have losses associated with them. Gambling, for instance, is considered a speculative risk, whereas for an individual about to go into battle, the risks are primarily static in nature (getting healthier is not usually considered an expected result). For this book, we will consider risks to be of a dynamic nature, since software risks, as we shall see, have aspects of both gain and loss associated with them.

Let's spend a little time clarifying this idea about "potential loss." A potential loss can either (a) make one worse off than the status quo, or (b) have an outcome not as good as some other outcome might have been. The second type of loss is called an "opportunity loss." These may be very difficult to measure because they may not be obvious until after some time has passed, while the first type of loss is easily understood as constituting a true loss.[7] Opportunities gained can change a risky situation into a nonrisky one, and vice versa.

A couple of other points to ponder. One should note that risk in general, and loss in particular, is very dependent upon one's point of view. Obviously, people are concerned most with the consequences of a risk. However, one individual may view a situation in one context, and another may view the exact situation from a completely different one. In other words, risk is not an objective beast. For example, John D. Rockefeller built Standard Oil to minimize his risk and ensure company profitability. Rockefeller did so by systematically destroying the predictability of his competitors' business conditions by creating a monopoly. His gain was a competitor's loss, and vice versa. Figure 2.1 illustrates another example of this point. One should not be misled, however, into thinking that losses are only determined in the form of zero-sum games. Sometimes there are no winners, as all choices bring about some level of loss for all participants. How people react to risk (i.e., whether they are risk favoring or risk adverse) will be looked at in this book's companion.

Another item to observe is that complex systems contain sets of risks, each of which is composed of many contributory risks. It is impossible to find a software project that is not confronted with many different types and kinds of risks. Some of them may be important, some may not. As we will see later, our concern will be with the risks created by the process of creating software-intensive systems and the risks inherent in the type of software application being built.

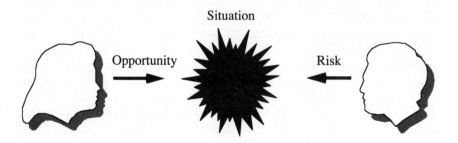

Figure 2.1 Risk Perspectives

2.1.2 Chance

The definition of the word "risk" also makes a very clear statement that there will be a chance of loss associated with it. For instance, a sure loss is not a risk, because it has a certainty of occurrence. In "certainty situations," the gains or benefits can be objectively traded straightforwardly against the losses or costs that exist. Thus, decisions are not influenced by a lack of information about the situation. Swallowing a pill containing 5 grams of cyanide is not a risk, because there is a certainty that the cyanide in that quantity will kill you. The requisite information to make a decision about the situation is known beforehand.

Uncertainty, on the other hand, exists in the absence of information about past, present, or future events, values, or conditions.[8] This means there is a lack of confidence in the correctness of the estimated probability distribution. Uncertainty also exists when each possible outcome can be identified, but the probability of the occurrence can neither be determined nor assessed.[9] There are degrees of uncertainty, meaning that some information about the system may be known, but there is not sufficient knowledge about it to provide certainty. For example, the probability of standing in an open field during a thunderstorm in Kansas, in June, getting struck by lightning, and surviving, is certainly not known exactly, although certainly it is not recommended.

There are three types of uncertainty.[10–12] The first, called *descriptive* or *structural uncertainty*, is concerned with the absence of information relating to the identity of the variables that explicitly define the system under study. This is the information necessary to describe the system in a taxonomic sense, representing the "degrees of freedom" of the system. It consists of a set of variables that, when totally determined, fully describe the system being considered. The variables may include physical as well as nonphysical attributes such as political, legal, or economic. What is included and excluded from consideration of "the system," we will soon see is vital for the later evaluation of the risk consequences.

The second type of uncertainty is *measurement uncertainty*. This is the absence of information relating to the assignment of a value to the variables used to describe the system. This comes from the fact that there exist limits to the observations and/or data available for either their calibration or validation. In situations that involve political issues, for instance, it is often difficult to determine what is a proper measurement scale for evaluating a decision. What does a decision "good for the people" really mean? How good? And for which "people"? If it is good for the people of one county or state, but bad for the populace of the nation as a whole, is it a really sound choice?

The third type of uncertainty is more theoretical in nature and is called *event outcome uncertainty*. It occurs when the predicted outcomes, and therefore their probabilities, cannot be identified. Thus, a person does not know what possible outcomes can occur, given a particular course of action. Some term it belonging to the realm of "chance" or "luck," but in truth it is just a manifestation of random processes.[13] This is termed ignorance and exists when neither the variables nor the measurement of their values for a system exist. Event outcome uncertainty becomes important in risk analysis when predictions about future outcomes, say of using a new technology, or taking a new course of action, have no prior history to draw from.

If we were to take an entropic viewpoint, where zero entropy represents total order, then complete knowledge or certainty would represent zero entropy, while total entropy would represent zero knowledge or total ignorance, as shown in Figure 2.2. The knowledge one often has when beginning a software system lies somewhere to the left of center and proceeds to the right as more knowledge of the system under construction is gained. We will deal with ignorance in the book only implicitly, although on many software developments this state seems to be of more than theoretical importance. It should be noted that some authors (see, for example, reference [14]) try to distinguish among certainty (the absence of risk), risk (the probabilities of alternative, possible outcomes are known), and uncertainty (the frequency distribution of the possible outcomes are unknown), as shown in Figure 2.3. In this book, we will make a distinction only between certainty and risk, believing that uncertainty is only a characteristic of a risk.

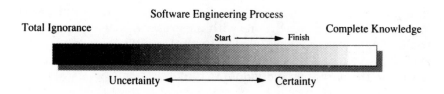

Figure 2.2 Spectrum of Uncertainty

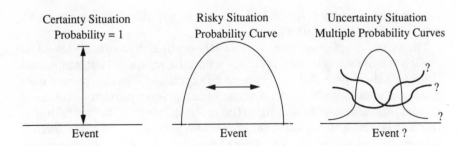

Figure 2.3 Certainty vs. Risk vs. Uncertainty

2.1.3 Choice

The third aspect in the definition of risk, which has already been alluded to, is the fact that a choice is involved. In this book, we will say that being "exposed to the chance" means that a person making a decision can take actions to increase or decrease the chance or magnitude of the loss or gain. Thus, by implication, there also is a probability of not achieving something. Again do not forget, if there is no choice, there is no risk, even though there may be a loss incurred.

This idea of choice is important because a person can incur a risk without explicitly taking it,[15] such as being placed into risk by others. This is illustrated in Figure 2.4, which shows the different ways an individual can be placed into risk. The idea of running a risk without explicitly taking it also means that (a) a person can run a risk without recognizing that it exists, and (b) perceived risks are as important as real risks. In the first case, we will assume that a person involved in a decision is both rational and has some control over his or her actions. In other words, the person, if unsure of the situation, will strive to obtain the information required to make a decision, resulting in benefit. Ideally, this person, if given the greatest flexibility in choices and perfect information, will opt for the one with the greatest benefit or least loss. It also means risks that are wholly circumstantial in nature, i.e., "Acts of God," as in case 3 of Figure 2.4 below, are not considered acts of risk taking on the part of an individual in that situation.

In case (b) above, people have no option but to react the same to real risks or perceived risks, if there is no way to tell the difference. This implies there exist perceived choices, as well as perceived risks. Although we will strive to deal only with real risks and real choices, the

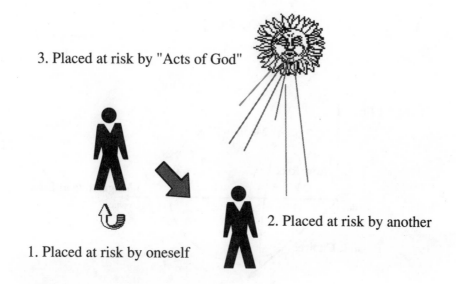

Figure 2.4 Ways of Being Placed into Risk

subjective element must always be recognized as being present. We defer the examination of the psychology of risk and risk taking to the other book.

2.1.4 Risk definition

Summing up, for an event, action, thing, etc., to be considered a risk, there must be:

1. A loss associated with it
2. Uncertainty or chance involved
3. Some choice involved

Remember also, not choosing is considered a choice. In MacCrimmon,[16] the three aspects above are called the magnitude of the loss, the chance of loss, and the exposure to loss. Each is a necessary, but not a sufficient, condition to define risk. Figure 2.5 gives a simple example.

Based upon the foregoing discussion, the general definition of risk we will use in this text is the same as stated in Rowe's book, *An Anatomy of*

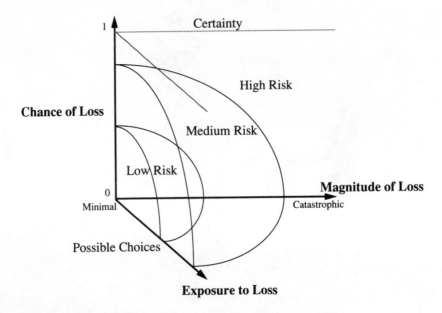

Figure 2.5 Risk Definition

Risk:[17] "Risk is the potential for realization of unwanted, negative consequences of an event." Two things are important to notice about the definition. The first is the magnitude of the loss and the chance can both be measured, but may not necessarily be independent. Dependence can rest very heavily on time, for instance. Coastal hurricane warnings are a prime example of this. A tropical storm on a particular storm track outside the Gulf of Mexico may have a very low probability of reaching the Gulf Coast, and thus residents along the coast may receive only minimal warning from the U.S. Center for Weather Forecasting about possible wind and flooding damage. But if it later gains strength and develops into a hurricane, the damage may be very high, the Gulf may have a higher probability of being directly hit, and thus the risk (and urgency of subsequent warning) is increased.

Second, for simplicity's sake, we do not distinguish among single events, multiple events, or continuous events, nor between single types of loss or multiple types of loss. But it should be obvious that outcomes that depend on only one type of event (e.g., actions of one competitor) are less risky than those that depend on multiple events (e.g., actions of many competitors), or an event that has multiple losses (e.g., political, social, and economic) is more risky than one that has only one (e.g., economic).

2.2 Risk Analysis and Management

Given that if there is risk involved in a decision, it is prudent that the risk be identified, assessed, and controlled in some way. Unless, of course, you like adventures. Questions such as the following need to be addressed:

- What are the risks?

- What is the probability of loss from them?

- How much are the losses likely to cost?

- What might the losses be if the worst happened?

- What alternatives are there?

- How can the losses be reduced or eliminated?

- Will the alternatives produce other risks?

The process of identification, estimation, and evaluation of risk, we will call risk analysis. *The planned controlling of risk and monitoring the success of the control mechanisms, we will term* risk management.[18] The basic goals of risk management are to attempt to find out what may go wrong and to do something positive about it. Figure 2.6 helps illustrate the differences between *risk analysis* and *risk management*.

2.2.1 Risk analysis

Risk analysis is used to identify potential problem areas, quantify risks associated with these problems, and generate alternative choices of actions that can be taken to reduce risk. The first action, *risk identifica-*

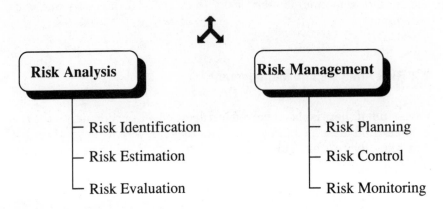

RISK ANALYSIS AND MANAGEMENT

Figure 2.6 Risk Analysis and Management

tion, is conducted in order that there can be a reduction in descriptive uncertainty.[19] In other words, the variables that will be used to describe the degrees of freedom of the system are identified. This is done by surveying the range of potential threats to the system, as well as the threats to required system resources. Threats are defined as the broad range of forces that could produce an adverse result; resources are considered assets that might be affected.[20] Once the risks have been identified, they typically are broken down into different categories for ease of understanding and completeness.

Risk estimation is the reduction of measurement uncertainty.[21] During this phase, three things are accomplished. First, the values of the variables describing the system are determined. This requires some acceptance of a measurement scale on which these values will be weighed. Second, the various consequences of an event occurring are identified. Actions cause reactions, and these must be made known. Third, the magnitude of the risk is determined using the previously selected measurement scale. Also, any modifying factors that tend to increase or reduce the probability of a threat becoming a reality, or the severity of a consequence if it does occur, are considered.[22]

Risk estimation can be categorized as either subjective or objective. Objective risk estimation is linked to situations where a history of precisely the same situation exists; i.e., two people can assemble the facts at hand and reach the same conclusion. Subjective estimation assumes the nonexistence of a base history. Usually both types of estimation are required, because a situation in real life is usually not black and white, nor one of "dejà vu." In software risk analysis in particular, subjective estimation is the rule, as published project histories upon which project planners can draw from are extremely rare. Very little forensic software engineering has been performed and/or published.[23] One reason is that new technology is often used in a project that makes previous project histories of little value. Another is that published "lessons learned" reports on what went wrong on projects are not seen as adding value to a company's self-interest quotient—especially if it is participating in competitive bid work, where it has to have been great and wonderful yesterday in order to get tomorrow's job.

Risk evaluation is the process whereby the response to the risks are anticipated. Insight is sought into the consequences of the various possible decisions confronting the decision maker, with the general acceptability of individually projected outcomes to a decision postulated. Since some risks are more acceptable or more detrimental than others, there may be a prioritization required of the risks involved for later aversion. Evaluation methods may be quantitative or qualitative in nature. Initial approaches to risk aversion, either by reduction, transfer, or elimination (if possible) are identified and are added to the options to be considered during risk management.

Risk identification, estimation, and evaluation are not precisely separated in practice. Each overlap the other in some areas, and the same types of techniques may be used in obtaining information. Figure 2.7 illustrates the overlap. The process is very iterative and can be very complicated. Often the number of risks is reduced to a "top-10 list," or something similar. For instance, the Department of Defense (DoD) primarily groups risks in the following two categories: acquisition risks and decision risks. Events that can occur to increase risks in each of these areas are identified as threats and are then subject to risk management.

2.2.2 Risk management

Risk management is involved with making a decision about the risk(s) after it has been analyzed. It usually consists of *planning*, *controlling*, and *monitoring* phases.

There are two aspects to the planning stage. In the first, the decision makers select a final course of action concerning the situation under

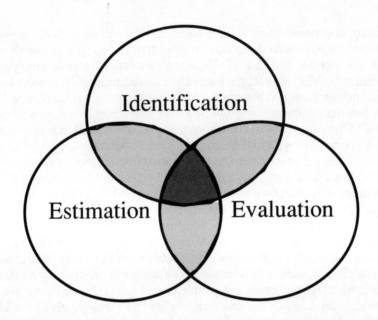

Figure 2.7 Risk Analysis

study. The selected course of action is "signed for," i.e., the risks are acknowledged explicitly and publicly, to ensure that there are no doubts about what is involved. Once a course of action is selected, a plan for carrying out the decision is formulated. Often, this means a second analysis phase is conducted to ensure the plan's feasibility, especially checking that it does not interfere with other decisions made or about to be made. This may seem a bit redundant, or somewhat late, but the principle of late binding applies (wait until the last possible moment before making a decision, to ensure maximum flexibility). Once a decision has been made it becomes a "certainty," and so brings with it more information about future potential risks, as well as the aversion of others. Because of dependency relationships, a decision that was previously acceptable may no longer be feasible. Premature decision making is a deadly vice to be avoided, if possible.

The second aspect of planning concentrates on the selection of the appropriate risk aversion strategies to be employed along with the selected course of action. This is documented in the risk management and aversion plans. During this period, measures are selected for monitoring the risk aversion strategy. Furthermore, any contingency resources that might be required for future risk aversion are identified. Finally, planning is involved with getting a risk aversion strategy back on track if a problem shows up during monitoring.

Risk control involves implementing the plan's control mechanism for the aversion strategies. The plan is realized by providing the required resources to the project. Project plans are changed as required, and new estimates of cost and schedule become the operational imperatives. The key aspect of control is that definitive action is taken.

Risk monitoring occurs after the decision has been implemented, in order to see if the consequences of the decision were the same as envisioned, to identify opportunities for refinement of the action plan, and to help communicate and provide feedback to those making future decisions. Risk monitoring is vital. If a wrong decision has been made, it must be recognized early enough so corrective action can be taken. But it is just as important to recognize when the decision is correct and not to change it prematurely. Constant changing of direction will waste valuable project resources and increase risk tremendously. It is similar to a system controller constantly receiving feedback and never stabilizing. Figure 2.8 shows the interaction of the three elements of risk management.

The process of risk management also should not be viewed as necessarily either sequential or compartmentalized. Different aspects proceed in parallel, and there is constant iteration among the various activities. New options are always being created, and adjustments to decisions are being made.

2.2.3 Risk analysis and management versus "normal" management

A question often asked is, what is the difference between what occurs during regular project management and risk analysis and management? Part of the answer is, in many ways, that theoretically there is none. Risk analysis and management are means to an end, and, as such, must compete with the other means that also serve as instruments to further the objectives of a project. However, there are two key areas where they differ.

The first difference is in risk anlysis and management's perspective or philosophy. We mentioned earlier that Rockefeller, in the creation of Standard Oil, was trying to ensure predictability by eliminating his

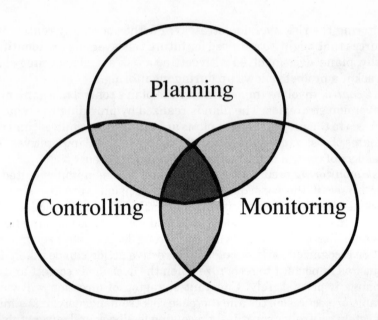

Figure 2.8 Risk Management

risks, but also deliberately increasing risks for others. This was caused, in large part, by the operating environment contained in a free market economy. By understanding and driving toward the implementation of the concept of horizontal and vertical trusts, Rockefeller was able to eliminate any risk that could be decisive. The point is, Rockefeller viewed his world as consisting of threats to be eliminated, if possible, or managed, if not. Risks constrained his ability to operate.

Similarly, viewing the elements involved in the production of a software system (i.e., the process or life-cycle used, if any; the techniques or methods used, if any; the type of application being developed, etc.) as issues increasing or decreasing your risk, and therefore your probability of success, profoundly changes one's perspective. It is this change in mental viewpoint or philosophy of management that is important. You see, risks do not drive one's ability to manage, but set up the boundary conditions under which one operates. This is true in business, which even though dependent on technology, is not driven by it.

The difference can be understood in light of the strategy taken by the Japanese versus United States companies in evolving software systems. The Japanese change a software system primarily in response to the availability of existing software components. The degree of availability influences requirement changes, and thus, the level of new functions of the system that the user can access. Typically, refinements are made to an existing software system, rather than wholesale changes. In the United States, software systems are changed to meet user-requested requirements, whether components are available or not. If new components are needed, then they are built. The difference is, the Japanese approach is risk constrained, or opportunity driven, while the U.S. approach is risk driven, or opportunity constrained. U.S. software systems may have more functional capability, but at greater cost and with suspect reliability. The Japanese approach is software that is less functional but more reliable. The difference, or the view as to which one is a better approach, is a matter of philosophy.

Even if one does not subscribe totally to this viewpoint, the other differences between risk analysis and management and normal management lie in their individual practice. Typical management has what one could call a "success" oriented attitude. Nothing wrong is allowed to cloud the horizon, which, unsurprisingly, is not a new phenomenon:

> Their judgement was based more on wishful thinking than on sound calculation of probabilities; for the usual thing among men is, when they want something, they will, without any reflection, leave that to hope, while they will employ the full force of reasoning in rejecting what they find unpalatable. —Thucylides, approximately 400 B.C.[24]

Software project success is based upon minimizing the *thought* of possible failure ("it cannot happen to me"), or *getting blamed* for failure ("do nothing that might make the project fail on my watch"). Therefore, very little extra is left in the way of contingency in case something does go wrong. This is the ultimate software lesson that we never seem to learn. Contingency planning is scarcely ever done, either. And then there is the assumption that everything will always go right. For some reason, once a schedule is created for a project, people actually believe the project will be completed on the last day indicated! One should always ask, "At what time on that last day will the product be ready? 2 P.M.? 4 P.M.? Not sure?" Then ask, "Why was this particular day picked? Why not the day before, or the day after?" Once the seed of doubt with the estimation accuracy begins to sprout, the belief in the project schedule also begins to crumble; sometimes, anyway. As Francis Bacon wrote: "Man prefers to believe that which he prefers to be true," and no amount of shaking will change it.

This contrast between the two types of management can be seen readily in current project management practice, where an upfront "can do" attitude is rewarded while anything else is regarded with suspicion or doubt. (Who wants to admit that something may go wrong?) When something does go wrong, management becomes very reactive. It quickly precipitates a crisis, which always is a difficult atmosphere in which to make correct decisions.

Risk analysis and management are much more "realistically" oriented. Project success is based upon foreseeing and containing possible failure, much the same way as found in preventive medicine or counterterrorism. Feed-forward, rather than feed-back, techniques are key. Aggression is turned outward, not inward. The author previously called this "Rules for Defensive Management."[25] Management becomes very pro-active, where potential problems are identified and dealt with early. Questions such as the following are asked:

- What can go wrong?

- How and when will I know that it went wrong?

- What am I going to do to prevent it from going wrong?

- What will I do when it does go wrong?

Although these may be seen as a bit paranoic, it is well documented that over 90 percent of commercial product developments fail because of undercapitalization in either funding, time, or personnel resources. Yet, it is almost guaranteed that these same problems will be found in newly founded companies that will turn into bankrupt companies five years from now. If one doesn't believe it, study Figures 2.9a and 2.9b. These are figures from some Air Force projects showing how close the estimates were to the actual projections for software size and schedules. Yet even today, I would wager that there are some Program Officers saying that they are "confident" that their program will meet the estimated schedule or code size, guaranteed in fact, even though none of their predecessors have done it yet![26]

Another way of viewing risk analysis and management practice, as opposed to typical software management, is that they are very much akin to sailing a yacht close-in to shore. Shoals, sandbars, rocks, and other obstructions are marked on the charts, and may or may not come

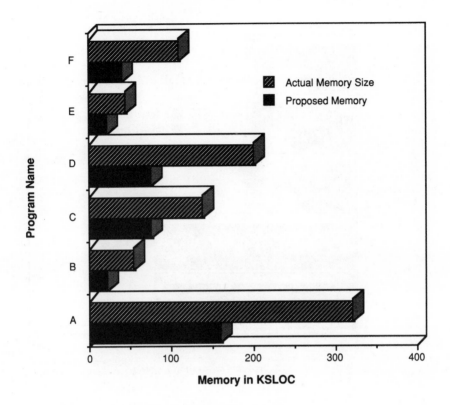

Figure 2.9a Air Force Program Results: Memory Estimates

into play, depending on conditions. The prudent sailor consults the charts and plans ways around them. Ignoring them doesn't make them go away. The process is not clear cut, as the tide may be incoming, outgoing, or there may be an offshore breeze, etc. An alternative might be to sail further out to sea, using more time, but avoiding potential hazards. There is no one way to sail that is the absolute best in every situation. Just as there are many ways to reach a decision on what to do, there are many ways to do risk analysis and management. The key item to remember is, just because a risk is identified does not mean it will occur. We are trying to lower the impact *if* a risk does occur. Thus, risk analysis and management strives to reduce the likelihood, consequences, and magnitudes of the risks encountered.

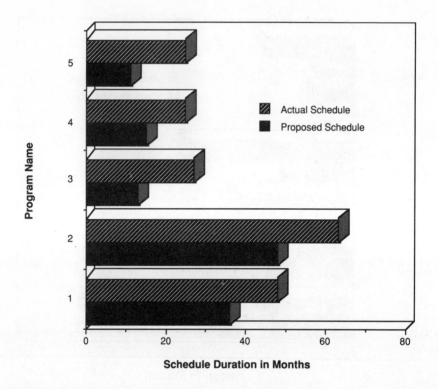

Figure 2.9b Air Force Program Results: Schedule Estimates

2.2.4 Benefits of risk analysis and management

The best way to illustrate why risk analysis and management are different from normal management, and why they are important, is to take a look at their benefits.[27-30] Some of the benefits are:

- Better and more well-defined perceptions of risks, clarification of options, trade-offs, their effects on a project, and their interactions

- Systemization of thought, thereby providing a consistent view of the problem situation

- Confidence that all available information has been accounted for, as well as the explicit identification of project assumptions

- Improved credibility of plans produced, and communication of rationale for actions made, inside and outside the organization

- Better contingency planning, and a better selection of reactions to those risks that do occur

- More flexible assessment of the appropriate mix of ways of dealing with risk impacts, allowing for less reactive management, and more pro-active management

- Better means to identify opportunities, and ways to take advantage of them

- Feedback into the design and planning process in terms of ways of preventing or avoiding risks

- Feed-forward into the construction and operation of projects in ways of mitigating the impacts of risks that do arise, in the form of responsible selection and contingency planning

- Decisions compatible with project policies, goals, and objectives ensured

- Insight, knowledge, and confidence for better decision making, and overall reduction in project exposure to risk.

It is the last point, the reduction in project risk exposure, that provides management with the bottom-line justification for undertaking risk management.[31] Reducing exposure is plain, old, sound business sense.

2.2.5 Costs of risk analysis and management

Nothing in life is free, and so it proves with risk analysis and management. A basic question is whether a risk program is cost justifiable. No simple answer can be given, although as we will see later in situations such as software safety, it may be more easily quantifiable. The problem is, as in a situation involving preventive medicine or counterterrorism, one is confronted with the difficult question, "Did it work?" If a plane isn't hijacked, is it because the counterterrorism procedures worked, or was it because there are no terrorists interested in hijacking planes anymore?

In general, a risk analysis and management program is only justifiable when the risks exceed the cost of conducting it. Another way of looking at it is, how much are you willing to pay to possibly save a project from getting into trouble, or out of trouble once it is in it? But, before dismissing it out of hand, remember it has been stated that not doing risk analysis is one of the highest project risks.[32] Figure 2.10 illustrates some effects of not performing risk analysis. These should be considered parameters in any cost equation.

On medium sized software projects and above, the cost of ignoring a risk can exceed the cost of a risk management program by close to an order of magnitude, giving some general indication of the potential cost/benefit ratio. Other illustrations can be found by referring again to the Peat Marwick & Mitchell and Comptroller General reports described in Chapter 1. Even if one takes a more optimistic view than presented in their reports, there is probably no more than a 40 percent chance that your software project will work on delivery, a 50 percent chance that it will not work on delivery and need (costly) rework, and a 10 percent chance that it will be abandoned with all investment lost. This assumes "normal" software development conditions found in industry hold and no risk analysis is performed. These numbers of course don't indicate anything about whether a project is on time (we assume that virtually nothing is ever delivered early) or on budget (extra time means the associated expenditures would increase overall project cost). If you are a commercial company, and you were faced with these odds, a small investment in the range of 2–5 percent per project might be considered

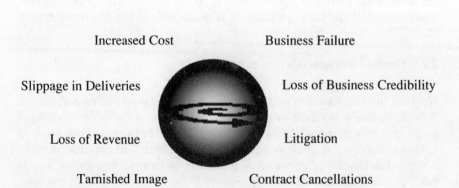

Increased Cost	Business Failure
Slippage in Deliveries	Loss of Business Credibility
Loss of Revenue	Litigation
Tarnished Image	Contract Cancellations

Figure 2.10 Possible Effects of Not Performing Risk Analysis

prudent. How to calculate this number more exactly using expected value calculations will be shown in Chapter 5.

The elements of a risk analysis and management program's cost are the typical ones found in any project. They involve expenditure of funds, time, personnel, and management involvement. Funds are obviously required to perform the risk analysis and risk management duties. The amount of funding will depend upon the degree of analysis performed or required and when it is done. The larger the project, the more the need, and the more expensive the risk analysis will be. Qualitative risk analysis is generally less expensive than quantitative. Risk management requires ongoing monitoring of the project, which on a large project means a permanent staff member should be assigned a job that includes risk management.

Time is another element of cost. If a risk analysis program is not an integral part of an organization, then time must be found for this to be made so. Again, depending on the size, complexity, importance, etc., of the project, the analysis can take from a few days to weeks or even months, as in the case of environmental impact studies. Risk analysis usually takes place in parallel with other planning activities, thereby adding little actual time to the project schedule.

We have already mentioned personnel costs. Someone, usually with a broad background in engineering economics, computer science, and project management, is required to do the risk analysis. Unfortunately, these types of people are also the ones hired to do program and/or project management. Taking an experienced person away from the project may not be feasible or cost effective. Consultants are often used because, not only do they have the requisite background, but they are usually more impartial and have little investment to lose because of corporate politics.

Finally, there is also the cost of management attention. It has been found that for program managers to derive significant benefit from a risk analysis, they must be willing to devote substantial amounts of time and attention to the results of the analysis.[33] They must understand and approve the recommendations, and most important, keep the analysis staff up to date on program changes or new threats to the program, as early as possible. Without this, a project may start out well, but because some risks change magnitude and probability of occurring with time, it may get into trouble by sheer neglect.

In summary, the cost of risk analysis and management must be weighed against the price that will be paid if it isn't done. And in most cases, the price, which includes pride, prestige, reputation, etc., does not necessarily equal the monetary cost.

2.3 Risk Analysis and Management: What They Aren't

Risk analysis and management are not philosophers' stones. They will not change lead into gold. They only form another arrow in the quiver of management techniques that can help a project succeed where it may have missed its target, or utterly failed, in the past. There are a number of limitations to risk analysis and management, which can be considered risks in their own right. The magnitude of the consequences associated with these self-induced risks increases in proportion to the belief that risk analysis and management can solve them.[34,35]

Risk analysis and management do not solve a problem in the engineering sense. Their purpose is to reduce the magnitude of the loss if something untoward does occur. They may help define a better approach to a problem, and may help dig out information to make a problem more tractable, but these are by-products of the process.

Risk analysis and management will not make the operating environment any friendlier, nor turn a bad thing into a good thing. Just because risk analysis and management are being applied, competition won't go away, suppliers won't reduce their prices, or weather won't get better.

Risk analysis and management will not provide hard, concrete data where there is none, nor assure that perceived risks are real risks. That is the job for research and development. They can only use what is available. In the software field, this sometimes isn't too much. Further, the probabilities used to estimate risk may be objective or subjective. If objective, they reflect the actual frequency of the occurrence of an event. Attrition rates in aircraft are an example of this. With a degree of confidence, the U.S. Air Force or Navy can estimate how many aircraft of a certain type will need to be bought every year due to crashes, retirement because of airframe fatigue, etc. Risks that are subjective reflect the assigner's beliefs and may not be based on any statistical data. Military planners for a particular operation are often faced with this problem. In practice, both types of estimates are usually used. However, in certain questions such as safety, this may blur the answer to what is safe and what is not. It is important to recognize the risk technique being used and its inherent limitations.

Risk analysis and management will not assure a successful outcome every time. A risk estimate can assess the overall chance that a threatening event will occur, but it is powerless to predict any specific event.[36] As Damon Runyan said, "The race is not always to the swift and to the strong, but it is the way to bet."

Risk analysis and management also is not *blame* analysis and management. There is plenty of time for that at the end, or after the collapse, of the project. They are not meant to ascertain blame, but to get the facts and provide a mature, rational approach to decision making that will make the project well. The words, "Nam tua res agitur, paries cum proximus ardet," should be memorized by all project participants ("When your neighbor's wall is on fire, it becomes your business"). No project exists in isolation. The goal is to increase a project's chances for success. Only by honest appraisal of the risks involved, and cooperation among all parties, is this likely.

To summarize, risk analysis and management isn't another form of micromanagement, management by walk-about, theory X, Y, or Z management, or worse, management by paralysis. It is supposed to help. If it doesn't, don't use it (but try at *least* once). The worst thing risk analysis and management can do is to plan and contain a failure that doesn't occur.

2.4 Risk Analysis and Management and Software

Risk analysis and management, as it applies to software development, can still be considered in its early maturation stages. Few books or articles touch specifically upon the relationship of risk and software development (see references [37, 38]), and as we have mentioned, no formal forensic science has been developed along the lines seen in other fields. This is somewhat surprising, given that it has been generally known that there are some generic risks in software development, even if they haven't been fully articulated.

NASA and the U.S. Department of Defense have been the main advocates for the use of risk analysis and management in their projects. NASA's risk analysis and management is married to its flight safety procedures, and early risk studies date back to the Mercury and Gemini programs. Today, risk analysis in NASA is guided by NASA Policy Directive (NPD) 1701.1, "Basic Policy on Safety," and is spelled out in detail in an accompanying handbook NHB1700.1 [VI]. This book's companion looks more closely at software safety.

The Department of Defense started to focus specifically on risk in 1969, when the Deputy Secretary of Defense directed the secretaries of the armed services to identify areas of high technical risk, perform formal risk analysis, and include explicit consideration for lowering risks. The reason was that system developments were continually costing more than originally estimated and taking much longer, as well. The time to field a weapon system from conceptual design was starting to reach over 15 years.

In April 1976, the Office of Management and Budget (OMB) issued OMB Circular A-109, "Major Systems Acquisition," requiring consideration of "methods of analyzing and evaluating contractor and government risks" as part of the acquisition process for major systems.

In 1981 the DoD directive was expanded, recommending efforts to quantify the technical risks of systems being developed, and to allocate funds to deal with these risks. In 1985 a software development standard, DoD-STD-2167, was promulgated in which software risks were specifically dealt with (see Appendix A for the revised version of DoD-STD-2167). A unified approach to software development was created; the criticality of software was made visible to the user and developer; increased quality control, configuration management, and test requirements were included; the user had more say in what was to be built; the emphasis was on "working to plan"; and there was a better delineation of requirements versus design.[39]

As an example, in a document called the Software Development Plan (SDP), software risk analysis and management are specifically called for. The document captures the initial cost, schedule, personnel, and equipment estimates, as well as the assumptions about the project. Specific elements of risk analysis and management (i.e., risk analysis and risk management) are seen clearly. As stated in the SDP,[40]

> the contractor shall establish and implement risk management procedures specified in the SDP for controlling risk. The procedures shall include:
>
> a. Identifying the risk areas of the project and the constituent risk factors in each area.
>
> b. Assessing the risk factors identified, including the probability of occurrence and potential damage.
>
> c. Assigning appropriate resources to reduce the risk factors.
>
> d. Identifying and analyzing the alternatives available for reducing the risk factors.
>
> e. Selecting the most promising alternative for each risk factor.

f. Planning implementation of the selected alternative for each risk factor.

g. Obtaining feedback to determine the success of the risk reducing action for each risk factor.

Since 1985, the U.S. Air Force has generated a number of pamphlets to help get better control of software risks. Included are pamphlets on: software management indicators, which provide insights into the "health" of a software project;[41] software quality indicators, which help show the quality, reliability, and maintainability of a software product;[42] software development capability/capacity reviews, which help evaluate a contractor's ability to develop software for defense systems;[43] and one on software risk management for defense systems.[44] The government, through its Federally Financed Research and Development Centers (FFRDC), the Software Engineering Institute (SEI) at Carnegie-Mellon University in Pittsburgh, Pennsylvania, and MITRE Corporation, have developed a method for assessing the software engineering capability of defense contractors, which is similar to the Air Force effort.[45] Each of these will be revisited in later chapters.

2.5 Risks Faced in Software

The categories of risk in software can be divided into those that deal with the process of developing software and with the product itself. The process includes the development process model, the methods, techniques, and/or automation used to develop the product. Some of the issues and concerns with defense development process are illustrated in Figure 2.11, in a still-applicable illustration from 1975.[46]

A few facts of life about software developments are readily apparent.[47] First, software development projects are complex. The elements of the problem are numerous, and the interrelationships among the elements are extremely complicated. No one individual can possibly know and understand everything about a large software project.

Second, relationships between elements of a problem may be highly nonlinear; changes in the elements may not be related by simple proportionality. It is a well documented fact that adding more people to a late project in many circumstances, for instance, will often only make it later.[48]

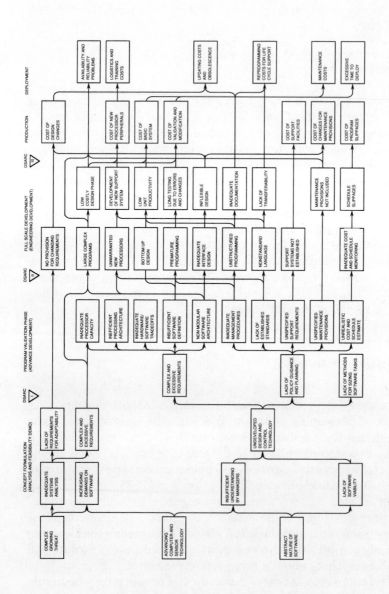

Figure 2.11 Problems in the Software Life Cycle

Third, the elements of the problem are uncertain. Software developers cannot know for sure what is in store for them in terms of budget, labor, etc. The cost of the project and the time to do it may be "fixed," but that is about all.

Fourth, the situation is dynamic. Conditions are changing continuously; thus, equilibrium is rarely encountered. People quit. Suppliers don't deliver. The hardware breaks down. There never is a quiet moment.

Fifth, human value systems are integral essential elements of software development problems. Although managers would like to deal only with economic or technical factors, they are beset with higher level complexities, nonlinearities, uncertainties, and change introduced by conflicting human needs and desires. Software development is a human endeavor, with all the problems that brings.

Then there are risks associated with the application and its use. Some types of applications are more difficult to build and test than others. Further, some applications, because of their intended usage, cross from a risk to a safety issue. In this case, there is a risk to human life (or property) and a value judgement about the magnitude and exposure to the risk. The way a software system is built will influence how safe it is to use. Both categories we will generically call software risks.

There are many types of risk in software systems and many ways of categorizing them. As previously noted, the DoD likes to say there are two types: acquisition risks and decision risks.[49] Acquisition risks are made up of three interrelated risk elements: technical risk (the degree of uncertainty in the engineering process); schedule risk (the degree of uncertainty in meeting desired milestones); and cost risk (the degree of uncertainty in acquisition and/or life cycle budgets). Decision risk has to do with the operational risk (the degree of uncertainty in fielding a system that meets its intended functions) and support risk (the degree of uncertainty in maintaining or enhancing a system within planned resources). Below are just a few reasons for risks existing in these areas.

There are many causes of technical risk. Some of these risks occur when a new technology is introduced into a system, or an old system may be upgraded with newer (albeit not the newest) technology. This is the age old problem of using either the "best" or "latest" technology available.[50] The best technology is a known quantity, allowing for more precise project management commitment. The latest technology has far less practical experience or knowledge but may give added opportunities. Often the government wishes to use the "best" technology, with the ability to use the "latest" as early as possible. This is not always compatible in practice. See, for instance, Figure 2.12. Moreover, the latest technology often means you are the pioneer in it.

Pioneering new technology is risky, because it is like being in a dark room filled with furniture; the first one in will mostly emerge with two black eyes. Whoever follows often carries a match or a torch. For example, parallel processing requires a fundamentally different way of thinking than found in sequential processing. Personnel aren't as experienced in developing software for it, and not every application is suitable. That is why it has taken so long to make effective use of that particular technology. However, one often doesn't realize that until much later.

Cost risks exist because: (a) long-term budgets are rarely fixed; (b) the program may be in competition with others for funds; and (c) in 90 percent of the cases, the cost is underestimated from the beginning.[51] Cost risks may also occur because of contract type. If a contract is fixed price, and if difficulties arise in technical or schedule areas, it becomes a developer's problem. If the difficulties become very large, then it might become the sponsor's problem. When this happens, it becomes a good

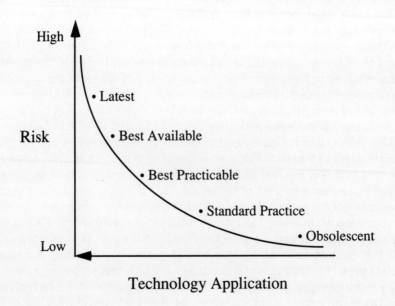

Figure 2.12 Risk vs. Technology

case study on how each risk takes on different levels of magnitude, chance, and exposure to loss, depending on your perspective. It is similar to advice given to small high-technology companies about taking out a loan: if you borrow $100,000 and can't repay, it's your problem; if you take out $10 million and can't repay, then it's the bank's problem.

Schedule risk is directly linked to costs risks. Schedule risk exists because it is difficult to accurately estimate the time it takes to do software developments. A primary issue is the level of productivity assumed. If the personnel are not very experienced in software development or the application area, then productivity may be low until they become trained. Personnel capability is considered the primary productivity driver.[52] In fact, a study of DoD programs led to the conclusion that any project can be completed in only one-third more time than currently estimated. This is known as the Universal Fantasy Factor, and in its truest form, states that no project will ever be completed.[53]

Even after the system is built, there are risks that the system will not meet the users' needs, or that the needs might have changed during the time of the development. One might view this as a risk associated with the acquisition part of the development, but remember that it typically takes 15 years from initial concept to the final fielding of a military system. Then there are the additional 15–30 years that a system is in use to be considered. There is also the risk that maintaining or enhancing the system within planned resources will not be possible, because the original system was less reliable, cost too much money, etc. Notice that both of these risks deal with certainty—what happens after the system is finally built and delivered—if it ever gets that far.

The Department of Defense method of risk categorization is good for their particular types of systems, but may not be as appropriate for everyone doing software development. The DoD doesn't quite have the same pressures as a commercial firm, for instance. It can afford to both do, and not do, risk analysis and management. In the later chapter on software risk identification, we will examine some other ways to categorize risks.

2.6 When are Risk Analysis and Management Done?

A recent GAO report on technical risk assessment in the Department of Defense concluded that, although DoD was concerned with technical risk, it had no clear definition of technical risk; had not developed sufficient training material; in most cases under study, the technical risk assessment was not of a minimal level of quality; nor was essential information on results made available to program managers or reviewers.[54] Recall that conducting risk management is mandated by DoD directives.

A fair question to ask then is when, if ever, are risk analysis and management done? After all, if they are so important, why don't people do it? A number of reasons exist, some of which we have mentioned. Today's management style is success-oriented, where admitting risks up-front may leave the impression that you don't know what you are doing, either to your boss or to your customer. Unfortunately, customers and bosses often aren't sympathetic to this type of aggressive honesty.

Then there is the "crossword puzzle" aspect of contemporary management. Perhaps, if one does the easy parts first, then the hard parts will become easier, or go away. The tendency to postpone difficult problems is a very human tendency.

Usually, people will do risk analysis and management when they have been burned in a similar situation, or the situation looks so bad that no amount of ignoring the facts will help. Pain avoidance is a key incentive.

Pain avoidance is a strong stick, but a carrot is better. People will conduct risk analysis and management if they know how to do it, and do it well. In certain organizations, such as in British TELECOM, risk analysis and management are institutionalized and performed across all internal software projects above a certain size. They are a natural part of the normal management process, and the attitude is, if they aren't done, there had better be a very good reason why. Junior personnel who point out there are risks in a particular project do not face recriminations. Management, after all, is paid big money to resolve hard problems. But management finds this very difficult to do if it doesn't know about them. With over 500 software projects underway at once, it is also crucial to British TELECOM's profitability.

We defer the examination of risk analysis and management organizational practices to the companion of this book.

2.7 Summary

The news recently carried a report of a computer suicide. It seems that a ground controller for one of the Soviet space probes to Mars sent a radio command for a mid-course correction that was off by one character. Upon receiving the message, the computer decided that the earth had ended. Its existence obviously over, and unable to exist alone, it proceeded to turn itself off. Rather a sad story, really.

In this age of glasnost, the controller wasn't secretly fired and given a new job in Siberia. He was publicly fired and given a new job in Siberia. Funny how subtle life is sometimes.

The motivation for this chapter was three-fold: to provide an overview of the concept of risk management; to show why it is important; and to show how risk management relates to software developments. Every software project involves risks of some kind. There is a high probability that we will have less than a full understanding of the requirements of both the software product and process before we begin, and therefore it is likely that it will take longer and cost more than expected. Trying to totally eliminate the risks is a futile effort, whereas managing the risks is something that can and must be done.

Risk analysis and management should be viewed as part of a holistic process or philosophy of management, taking in many different disciplines and understanding how each contributes to the other. It is very much like a jigsaw puzzle, utilizing and coordinating the skills and knowledge from all the personnel involved. Building software systems is also a holistic process, where software is a part of a system that is part of a larger whole, each interacting and influencing the other—an ecosystem, as it were. Risk analysis and management try to keep this delicate ecosystem in balance.

It is appropriate to mention at this time, just before we get into examining in detail risk analysis and management, the great debate swirling around risk analysis. There are two major schools of thought on risk analysis, qualitative and quantitative, which are often at odds with one another.[55] The qualitative school holds, as one strong proponent explained, that "statistics don't count for anything . . . they have no place in engineering anywhere," and that risk is minimized and contained not by statistical test programs, but by paying great attention to detail in a system's design. Risk analysis is seen at best as measuring the difficulty of a project, but should not be used as a basis for whether to implement or cancel and project.

The quantitative school holds that "the real value of probabilistic risk analysis is in understanding the system and its vulnerabilities," and that given the proper data, risk analysis can indicate when a project should not be implemented or stopped. This book's view leans more toward the quantitative approaches, recognizing the limitations that the quality of the input data imposes on the quality of the analysis. When we state, for example, that a software project has a 40 percent chance of success, it is not an absolute measure, but rather a relative one. One may still proceed with the project anyway, and be totally successful at the end. Risks, as we keep saying, are only that—risks, not eventualities. However, if taking another path leads only to a 20 percent chance of success, then one has to weigh carefully which of the two alternatives to take. The biggest obstacle one is confronted with is that it is not known whether a 40 percent chance of success at the beginning of a software project is good enough to make a decision to proceed. At the end of the day, gut engineering based on experience is the final arbitrator.

As one will see in later chapters, both approaches to risk analysis are discussed, and, in many cases, only qualitative risk analysis can be conducted. Furthermore, we view quality and reliability engineering as mandatory means to manage and contain risk, and as part of what should be normal engineering discipline applied to system development. But we believe they are only necessary, but not sufficient, conditions in building software systems. It is the same with software engineering and risk management—they are necessary, but not sufficient, to make the computing field a true profession. We leave it to the reader to determine which risk analysis approach is most applicable to their own situation, but keeping an open mind is strongly advised.

So where are we, and where are we going from here? In Chapters 1 and 2, we have seen the impact of software on society and the economy. We have also seen that there is a set of techniques called risk analysis and management that might help make the process of building software products a bit more manageable and successful. Next, our focus will turn to the mechanics of performing risk analysis and management. We will begin first with risk identification in Chapter 3.

Questions

1 The mid-1970s to mid-1980s was termed by many in the field as the decade of the "software crisis." What do you suppose was meant by this term? Was there really a crisis, or just bad public relations and marketing? What were its causes? What were its symptoms? What, if any, were its cures?

2 Consider the ever decreasing price/performance ratio of computer hardware and the ever increasing ratio of software costs to hardware costs. How much do these two ratios influence buyers', managers', etc., perceptions of how much software should cost, or take to build? How does this influence the risks involved in project planning?

3 Are risks and opportunities co-equal? In other words, does a risk equate to an opportunity exactly, or in some proportion? Give two examples.

4 What are the differences between perceived risks and true risks? Do the differences matter? How do you know?

5 Is all risk subjective, or can risks be objectively viewed? Consider the three types of uncertainty in your response.

6 What is risk management? What is risk aversion? Why are they important?

7 What risks in a company's business environment might influence the risks faced in a software project? In the process of developing software? In the software product itself?

8 Do you think risk analysis and management is a philosophy, methodology, or technique? Why?

9 When should risk analysis and management not be applied? When should it be? Describe attributes of software systems that should be included in the analysis of risk management applicability.

10 Why is an understanding of entropic action in systems important to risk analysis and management? Where does it occur? How is it controlled?

References

1. "Sir Humphrey Appleby K.C.B. Diary," extracted from Jonathan Lynn and Antony Jay, *Yes, Prime Minister*, BBC Books, London, 1987.

2. "Navy wastes $230 million on unwieldy computer system," in *The Washington Times*, 7 February 1989.

3. William W. Lowrance, *Of Acceptable Risk: Science and the Determination of Safety*, William Kaufman, Los Altos, CA, 1976.

4. Kenneth R. MacCrimmon and Donald A. Wehrung, *Taking Risks*, Free Press, New York, 1986.

5. Peter G. Moore, *The Business of Risk*, University Press, Cambridge, England, 1983.

6. Neil Crockford, *An Introduction to Risk Management*, Woodhead-Faulkner, Cambridge, England, 1980.

7. Kenneth R. MacCrimmon and Donald A. Wehrung, *Taking Risks*, Free Press, New York, 1986.

8. William D. Rowe, *An Anatomy of Risk*, Robert E. Krieger Publishing Co., Malabar, FL, 1988.

9. Walter B. Wentz and Gerald I. Eyrich, *Marketing, Theory and Application*, Harcourt, Brace & World, New York, 1970.

10. William D. Rowe, *An Anatomy of Risk*, Robert E. Krieger Publishing Co., Malabar, FL, 1988. Uncertainty is really a measure of the limits of information of a particular knowledge area. One must be concerned with a number of elements of uncertainty in risk analysis, such as tolerance (a measure of the relevance of the information available), statistical confidence (a measure of the accuracy of the sampling), incompleteness/inaccuracy of the information, and ambiguity of the problem domain.

11. Walter B. Wentz and Gerald I. Eyrich, *Marketing, Theory and Application*, Harcourt, Brace & World, New York, 1970.

12. Andrew P. Sage, "Systems Engineering: Fundamental Limits and Future Prospects," in *Proceedings of the IEEE*, Vol. 69, No. 2, February 1981.

13. For the moment ignore the work being done in catastrophe and chaotic theories that might contest this view. These will be revisited in the companion volume.

14. John Canada, *Intermediate Economic Analysis for Management and Engineering*, Prentice-Hall, Englewood Cliffs, NJ, 1971.

15. Nicholas Rescher, *Risk*, University Press of America, Lanham, MD, 1983.

16. Kenneth R. MacCrimmon and Donald A. Wehrung, *Taking Risks*, Free Press, New York, 1986.

17. William D. Rowe, *An Anatomy of Risk*, Robert E. Krieger Publishing Co., Malabar, FL, 1988. This will form our basic operational definition. We also accept with this definition the ideas, as stated by Rowe, that "the assessment of risk is as important as the quantification of risk; and second, that the subjective perception of risk is the basis for risk acceptance regardless of the objective or quantified evaluation." Furthermore, we distinguish a risk from what is sometimes called a hazard, which is an intrinsic property or condition that has the potential to cause an accident. Hazards will be studied more in detail in the chapter on software safety in the companion volume to this book.

18. It should be noted that different authors use different terms or invert the risk analysis with risk estimation (some call that risk assessment), although in all texts

the basic concepts of identifying, analyzing, evaluating, and controlling risks are used throughout. Ours follows generally those stated in Rowe for risk analysis and Boehm for risk control, although we have made some modifications. We would have preferred to have titled the book, *Software Engineering Risk Management*, but it was felt that the title needed to convey more meaning and should not be confused with risk management as it relates to computer security issues. Thus, the reason for the present title.

19. William D. Rowe, *An Anatomy of Risk*, Robert E. Krieger Publishing Co., Malabar, FL, 1988.

20. Neil Crockford, *An Introduction to Risk Management*, Woodhead-Faulkner, Cambridge, England, 1980.

21. William D. Rowe, *An Anatomy of Risk*, Robert E. Krieger Publishing Co., Malabar, FL, 1988.

22. Neil Crockford, *An Introduction to Risk Management*, Woodhead-Faulkner, Cambridge, England, 1980.

23. Some work is being done at a few places, such as the U.S. Air Force Rome Air Development Center and NASA's Goddard Space Flight Center. See, for instance, "Quality Assurance in Future Development Methods," by Joseph Cavano and Frank Lamonica, in *IEEE Software*, September 1987; "Evaluating Software Engineering Technologies," by David Card et al., in *IEEE Transactions on Software Engineering*, Vol. SW-13, No. 7, July 1987; and "Experimentation in Software Engineering," by Victor Basili et al., in *IEEE Transactions on Software Engineering*, Vol. SW-12, No. 7, July 1986.

24. Quoted from Norman R. Augustine, *Augustine's Laws*, American Institute of Aeronautics and Astronautics, New York, 1983, p. 342.

25. Robert N. Charette, *Software Engineering Environments: Concepts & Technology*, McGraw-Hill, New York, 1986.

26. P. S. Babel, presentation given to National Security Industrial Association. Let me be the first to note that the organization (U. S. A. F. Aeronautical Systems Division Software Integrity Program, Wright-Patterson Air Force Base, Ohio) from which these numbers were drawn has instituted a comprehensive risk management approach to try to eliminate this problem.

27. Dale F. Cooper, *Risk Analysis for Large Projects: Models, Methods, and Cases*, John Wiley & Sons, Norwich, England, 1987.

28. "Risk Assessment Techniques," Defense Systems Management College, Fort Belvoir, VA, July 1983.

29. "Technical Risk Assessment: The Current Status of DOD Efforts," Government Accounting Office Report GAO/PEMD-86-5, April 1986.

30. Melvin W. Lifson and Edward F. Shaifer, Jr., *Decision and Risk Management for Construction Management*, John Wiley & Sons, New York, 1982.

31. Dale F. Cooper, *Risk Analysis for Large Projects: Models, Methods, and Cases*, John Wiley & Sons, Norwich, England, 1987.

32. Deputy Secretary of Defense David Parkard memo to U.S. Armed Services, 31 July 1969. "I would, therefore, like each of you to assure that: Areas of high risk are identified and considered; formal risk analysis of each program is made; summaries of these are made part of the backup material for the program."

33. "Risk Assessment Techniques," Defense Systems Management College, Fort Belvoir, VA, July 1983.

34. William D. Rowe, *An Anatomy of Risk*, Robert E. Krieger Publishing Co., Malabar, FL, 1988.

35. Melvin W. Lifson and Edward F. Shaifer, Jr., *Decision and Risk Management for Construction Management*, John Wiley & Sons, New York, 1982.

36. William W. Lowrance, *Of Acceptable Risk: Science and the Determination of Safety*, William Kaufman, Los Altos, CA, 1976.

37. Barry W. Boehm, *Software Engineering Economics*, Prentice-Hall, Englewood Cliffs, NJ, 1981.

38. Nancy G. Leveson, "Software Safety: What, Why, and How," in *ACM Computing Surveys*, Vol. 18, No. 2, June 1986.

39. Joel Glazer, "The Search for a Perfect Solution to an Imperfect Problem: Risks in Software Development," *National Security Industrial Conference on Software Risk Management*, 2 October 1987.

40. "Software Development Plan," DI-MCCR-80030A, DOD-STD-2167A, *Defense System Software Development*, 27 October 1987.

41. "Software Management Indicators," Air Force Systems Command, AFSCP 800-14, 20 January 1987.

42. "Management Quality Indicators," Air Force Systems Command, AFSCP 800-14, 20 January 1987.

43. W. S. Humphrey, W. L. Sweet, et al., "A Method For Assessing Software Engineering Capability of Contractors," Software Engineering Institute, Carnegie-Mellon University, Pittsburgh, PA, February 1987.

44. "Software Risk Management," Air Force System Command, AFSCP 800-45.

45. W. S. Humphrey, W. L. Sweet, et al., "A Method For Assessing Software Engineering Capability of Contractors," Software Engineering Institute, Carnegie-Mellon University, Pittsburgh, PA, February 1987.

46. "Department of Defense Weapons Systems Software Management Study," APL John Hopkins Report APLJHU SR75-3, 1975.

47. These ideas are stated elegantly in Lifson's and Shaifer's book, *Decision and Risk Management for Construction Management*, John Wiley & Sons, New York, 1982. It seems that the construction business mirrors the business of software development.

48. Fred Brooks, *The Mythical Man-Month*, Addison-Wesley, Reading, MA, 1975.

49. "Software Risk Management," Air Force System Command, AFSCP 800-45.

50. Robert N. Converse, "Technological Innovation in Government Contracts," *NSIA Conference on Software Initiatives and Their Impact on the Competitive Edge*, 10 May 1988.

51. Norman R. Augustine, *Augustine's Laws*, American Institute of Aeronautics and Astronautics, New York, 1983.

52. Barry W. Boehm, *Software Engineering Economics*, Prentice-Hall, Englewood Cliffs, NJ, 1981.

53. Norman R. Augustine, *Augustine's Laws*, American Institute of Aeronautics and Astronautics, New York, 1983.

54. "Technical Risk Assessment: The Current Status of DOD Efforts," Government Accounting Office Report GAO/PEMD-86-5, April 1986.

55. "Special Report: Designing and Operating a Minimum-Risk System," in *IEEE Spectrum*, Vol. 26, No. 6, June 1989.

Risk Analysis: Identification

"First reckon, then risk."

VON MOLTKE

3.0 Introduction

In the previous chapter, we covered the following topics: the definition of risk; a descriptive analysis of risk analysis and management, their advantages and disadvantages; and a partial overview of the risks faced in developing software. The operational definition of risk we used was "the potential for the realization of unwanted, negative consequences of an event." A practical illustration of the definition is as follows:

> "Well, my good Comrade from Afghanistan, we have some good news and some bad news. The bad news is that our re-entry computer has failed a second time due to a software error, there are only two days of food and air left, and it will take ground control three days to fix the problem."

> "This is terrible, my Comrade from the glorious Soviet Union who has helped us fight in our cause against Yankee imperialism. What's the good news, then?"

> "I have done a risk analysis, and it shows that the cosmonaut from the Soviet Union, in fact, has four days of food and air left."[1]

Leaving the final outcome of the story to speculation, in this chapter we wish to make the operational definition of risk, which is intrinsically satisfying but difficult to apply, a bit more practical. Thus, we will begin by expanding our knowledge of the basic principles of risk analysis. The subject of risk managment itself is left to be explored in depth in Chapter 6.

3.1 Some Risk Notation

Recalling Chapter 2 for a moment, we saw that our approach to risk involves two interrelated parts, risk analysis and risk management. Risk analysis, we said, identifies potential problem areas, quantifies risks associated with these problems, assesses the effects of these risks, and generates alternative courses of action to reduce risk. Although the exact form that risk analysis will take depends highly on the specific program requirements and organizational concerns, we chose to divide risk analysis into three discrete steps:

- First, comprehensive identification of potential risk items using a structured and consistent method; i.e., what can go wrong?

- Second, estimation of the magnitude of each risk and its consequences, and the creation of options; i.e., what is the likelihood of that happening under the current plan?

- Third, evaluation of the consequences of risk, including prioritization; i.e., if the risk occurs, what is the damage?

The answers reached to the above questions, and illustrated in Figure 3.1, constitute our software engineering risk analysis.[2]

The answers to the questions above can be arranged into a table, as shown in Table 3.1. The first column contains the scenarios of what can go wrong, and can be labeled s_i. The second column contains the generic likelihood, l_i, of the scenarios in column one happening. The third column, x_i, represents a measure of the consequences of the "ith" scenario. This sometimes is called the "damage index." The triplet, $< s_i, l_i, x_i >$ constitutes a particular risk, whereas the set of all such triplets forms the totality of risk to the software development being performed. Thus, the definition

$$\text{Risk} = \{< s_i, l_i, x_i >\}$$

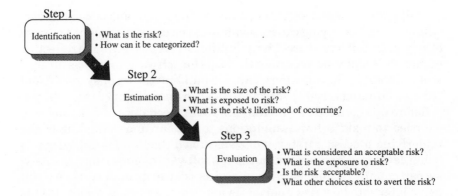

Step 1

Identification • What is the risk?
• How can it be categorized?

Step 2

Estimation • What is the size of the risk?
• What is exposed to risk?
• What is the risk's likelihood of occurring?

Step 3

Evaluation • What is considered an acceptable risk?
• What is the exposure to risk?
• Is the risk acceptable?
• What other choices exist to avert the risk?

Figure 3.1 Risk Analysis

becomes our formal definition of software engineering risk.[3] The remainder of this chapter will be spent on how to determine each of the parameters specified above.

Recalling again Chapter 2, we saw that the application of risk management required a new philosophy of software development. It is a perspective that a software development is a risk-constrained process, where each event that occurs in the construction of the application is viewed as a potential risk. The goal as the development process unfolds, therefore, is the aversion or elimination of risks as a primary source of concern, where each aversion (or optimally, elimination) increases the

TABLE 3.1 Risk Table

Scenario (s_i) (What can go wrong?)	Likelihood (l_i) (What is the likelihood?)	Damage (x_i) (What is the damage?)
s_1	l_1	x_1
s_2	l_2	x_2
s_3	l_3	x_3
s_4	l_4	x_4
.	.	.
.	.	.
.	.	.
.	.	.
s_n	l_n	x_n

overall chance for success. One observes the symptoms of risk, under-stands their underlying causes, evaluates the consequences of a change of action, and effects a cure. The definition of risk above is but a reflection of that philosophy, and becomes the basis for software quality assurance and reliability. The questions, "Are we building the right system?" and "Are we building it right?" become easier to answer under this schema.

Before our detailed examination into the mechanics of risk analysis, we need to make a few assumptions to aid our understanding of the underlying process. First, it will be assumed that a software system is being developed from scratch, although software engineering risk analy-sis can equally be applied when a project is already underway. We will delve later into how risk analysis is applied in a mature project that is in trouble. In this way, the application of the principles of risk manage-ment can be seen from another perspective. Like the defeated, sleepless New Yorker in Chapter 1, this is the perspective from which I suspect most individuals will first begin to apply risk analysis.

Second, we also have assumed at least a draft business/system/ software development plan containing system requirements and speci-fications has been developed and approved at some senior level of management. At the very least, some type of needs or mission statement should have been written justifying the development. Although one of the most effective applications of risk analysis is its use in helping develop a needs statement or system development plan, I have encoun-tered this only infrequently for most large software systems projects. Typically it is completed after the fact to justify the project, or to show why it is in trouble. Where over 60 percent of software development is concerned with evolving a currently existing system, there is likely (we hope) to be some general plan from which to work.

Third, we make an implicit assumption that the software system under consideration is nontrivial and of medium to large size. Smaller systems can benefit from risk analysis, but in all reality, it probably does not leverage well when it comes to cost/benefit ratios.

Finally, we assume that the individuals involved in the risk analysis process are rational people and want to make the best choice for the project. Again, the goal is not to assign blame. Very few individuals go through life intentionally making things messy for other people, even if seems that this is not the case. Thus, we will assume "optimal" decisions are made, given the limitations of information certainty, operating environment, and subjective judgement.[4]

We can now proceed with the first step of the process of risk analysis: identification of risk items using a structured and consistent method.

3.2 Risk Analysis—Getting Started

Before we get started doing risk analysis, we need to take a small step backward. The first question required to be asked is whether risk analysis is necessary in this particular situation. Remember assumption three: There are costs associated with its performance, and it may not be an effective tool in every system development. Therefore, initially, one needs to determine whether or not software significantly contributes to system risk.[5] A number of criteria can be used to answer such a question, such as:

- Are significant amounts of software being developed for the system?

- Do software costs dominate the total system development cost?

- Will software contribute greatly to the operational and/or support costs of the system?

- Is software essential for the successful performance of the system's function?

- Does the software integrate or interface with a number of systems that must inter-operate?

If the answer is "yes" to any one of these questions, then software must be considered a significant contributor to system risk. Thus, risk analysis and management should (really, *must*) be applied. After all, given what we have seen thus far, the probability is high that we have a less than complete understanding of what is required before a project starts, and therefore it will take longer and cost more than expected. If risk analysis is not performed when software is considered a substantial contributor to system risk, then this decision must be viewed as a major risk in itself.

Assuming that it has been determined that indeed a software risk analysis is necessary, the next step is to take our preliminary draft specification or plan, and place it into a form that can be easily analyzed for risks. To accomplish this, we will want our plan to have the format of a Risk Estimate of the Situation.

3.2.1 Risk estimate of the situation

In the second step of risk analysis, we begin by applying to the project specification the techniques found in what we term a Risk Estimate of the Situation (RES). If it sounds military in origin, it is, although it has been tailored a bit. RES is based upon the Navy's traditional Commander's Estimate of the Situation (CES), taught at the U.S. Naval War College.[6]

The basic goal of the software RES is to clearly identify four elements of a project: its *objectives, strategies, tactics,* and *means or assets* to be used in accomplishing the objectives identified. Each of these elements should be clearly spelled out somewhere in the system development plan. Grouping the descriptions of each of these elements together will aid in the determination of the variables of the system under development and the environment, both political and technical, in which it operates. The early termination of false efforts, and the prompt recognition of missing ones, both of which are early progenitors of program slips and cost overruns, are a primary goal of the RES.[7]

Also, assumptions about the product and development process will be explicitly identified. This basic part of planning is often overlooked because of the hurry to move on to the "real work." Assumptions carry risks into the project, because they set up the initial conditions under which we will operate. If we are evolving a system, the reliability, maintainability, management, etc., of the past system will greatly influence the successful achievement of objectives for the next system to be evolved. Since these assumptions are risks, it is useful to acknowledge them up front. This does not necessarily mean there will be any change made to the development plan, but knowing what the initial conditions are helps alleviate much unnecessary analysis later.[8] The companion volume explores the origination of these assumptions in detail.

The objectives are the *measurable* and controllable goals of the project. They are the success criteria for the project as a whole; i.e., they form the unity of effort for the project. Objectives can best be identified by asking the question, "How do I know when I am done?" These success criteria must be explicit, such as within cost, schedule, or a certain performance *envelope.* Since we are not able to yet specify an exact date for delivery, it is pointless to try at this point in time. It is better to state a delivery date of "March," with *both* positive and negative uncertainty (i.e., "January at the earliest, May at the latest"), than to pick a date with zero probability of occurring (e.g., March 15, which is three years hence). If this idea is uncomfortable, pick a specific date, but remember, it is only a target. Writing it down does not mean it is true.

Objectives also should be prioritized in some order of achievement. They must not, if at all possible, be implicitly defined.[9] Implicit objectives lead to too many difficulties because of the uncertainty they inherently carry with them. Not being able to measure whether an objective is reached makes developing strategies or tactics to achieve them very hard, if not impossible. For instance, maintainability of a system is often an implicit objective of many software projects. Unfortunately, this objective won't be able to be evaluated until after the system is completed and is being evolved. The best objectives are binary in nature—either they can be achieved or they cannot be. The major reasons that measurable goals are required are that progress of the project can be measured, trouble can be identified early, trade-offs can be made between objectives, and one can understand when a project will not achieve its objectives—i.e., when it is time to redirect or terminate the project.

Strategy is the collection of broad constraints or rules under which the goals of the project can be met. It is often called "doctrine," i.e., the standard policies, procedures, or methodology that collectively govern a course of action.[10] Strategies are based upon assumptions on the actions of forces outside the project's control, where these actions are predicated on the capabilities (not intentions) of these forces. Imposition of software standards can be considered as reflecting a general strategy.

For instance, the objective in golf is to go around the course in as few strokes as possible, whereas in bowling, knocking down the most pins is the objective. The strategy required in each is different: in golf a minimization strategy is used, while in bowling a maximization strategy is applied. Strategy usually has four components associated with it: *technical* (what are the technologies the strategy is dependent upon?), *operational* (what tactics will be used given a specific situation?), *logistical* (what type and how many assets are to be used?), and *social* (what is the state of political will and social cohesion required to implement the strategy and reach the objectives?). Each of these should be considered when developing a strategy or set of strategies. No one strategy is usually "the best" in achieving every objective, although a rule of thumb is to keep it simple. But bear in mind von Clausewitz, who said, "Strategies are simple. They are not easy."

It is the operational element of strategy, the tactics, that implement a particular strategy. The tactics will determine how the goals or objectives will ultimately be reached on a given occasion. Tactics are the specific actions, the "what," that happens during a particular situation.[11] It is tactics, for instance, that resolve software development bottlenecks. The primary difference between strategy and tactics is: A strategic doctrine holds true as long as the goals remain fixed (time independence), but the tactics may vary according to the situation (time dependence). Other ways of saying it are that strategists plan, tacticians do; or that doctrine is the glue of good tactics; or good tactics overcome the inefficiencies of strategies.[12] Figure 3.2 helps illustrate the concept.

The specific tactics used are the servants of the means or assets available. The assets available constrain the tactics, dictating which are available for use. Again, in golf, the rules state that up to 14 clubs and a ball meeting certain specifications can be used on any round. The rules allow *any* 14, as long as they meet the specifications. So on a course that

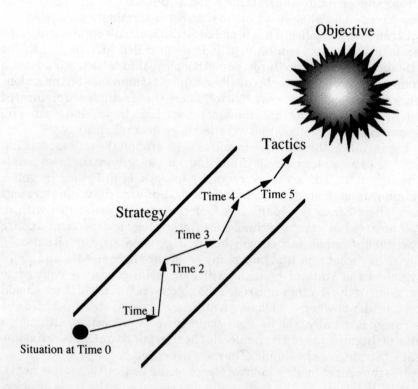

Figure 3.2 Relationship Between Strategy and Tactics

is very long, and if the day is dry and windy, then the general tactic would be to carry clubs that provide extra distance.[13] However, if you can't hit with those clubs very well, then you might decide not to bother. You might just live with the risk of not reaching some greens, and would hope to make up for it by chipping.[14] Thus, you might bring an additional pitching wedge with extra loft for the occasions dictated by the higher probability of landing short most of the time. On another occasion, say when the ground is wet but the wind still, the overall tactics may change once again.[15] Realize, too, that there are strategies for individual holes, which may require a different set of tactics. Thus, to know tactics, one must know the limitations of the means available. But the *overall* strategy and the objective remain the same.

Understanding the role and impact of your assets or means on implementing your tactics, and hence achieving your strategy or objectives, is the key. They set the boundaries for what is and what is not feasible to accomplish. Budget and schedule are two major assets of a software development. Misusing or frittering them away directly impact project success. Remember, present policy depends upon present means.[16]

3.2.2 Why an estimate of the situation?

Do not be put off by the seemingly "military" nature of the technique. The military has had the most practical experience in performing risk analysis, dating some five thousand years plus. Software developers and military commanders face the same types of problems and dilemmas irrespective of the different objectives of their professions. The battle paradigm of the friction and fog of war, i.e., the confusion of battle, the lack of resource, the lack of time, the equipment that often does not work, etc., is analogous to what is found in a typical software development.[17] Better planning and assessment will aid in both situations.

There are a number of other important reasons for using a military paradigm. The primary one is what one would call "hard-nosed." The goal in battle is to reach the objective; other issues are secondary. This viewpoint tends to focus the mind on real, versus peripheral, issues. The objectives are defined, the criteria for success defined, the assumptions used in setting up the plan are explicitly identified, and the delegation of responsibilities is mapped out. The RES should be signed off by the senior manager in corporate who is responsible for the project's success, in order that everyone understands and has the same objectives in mind. Personal commitment helps focus collective energies.

Second, issues such as one's, or another's, "intentions" are dismissed: Only proven capability is really important. Saying that you will have trained personnel to work on such and such a project in a year's time, but don't have any right now, doesn't hack it. As Peter Drucker has said, "Long-range planning does not deal with future decisions, but with the future of present decisions." Thus, there is little room for wishful thinking in achieving the program's objectives.

Third, performing a risk estimate of the situation is a proven, structured, and consistent technique. This is vital to the process of risk analysis, especially in risk identification, where early identification of a risk often can mean the difference between a successful and unsuccessful project. After all, just because a risk hasn't been identified does not mean that it doesn't exist or has gone away.

Finally, using this technique makes it difficult for those who argue against the usefulness or effectiveness of risk analysis. Cries that it is too hard to do, that there are too many variables involved, that it isn't useful, it concentrates on negativism instead of positivism, etc., receive little support.[18] Writing a risk estimate for a naval task force deployment is a difficult task, but is not impossible, and in many cases is done routinely in a matter of days by a small support staff. The British Admiralty staff had to perform such a feat in the Falklands crisis involving dozens of ships and thousands of personnel. If naval planners can do it, one would tend to believe that most software project planners can write and benefit from a software risk estimate of the situation as well.

Some may still wonder why one should go through the work of creating an estimate of the situation, with its emphasis on objectives, strategies, tactics, and means. After all, a software development plan has already been created and approved. It has been my experience, and that of others, that poor goal setting and project planning are the primary causes for software project failure.[19–21] Norman Augustine stated it succinctly when he wrote that current business planning makes astrology look good.[22]

Recall the horror stories from Chapters 1 and 2. The vast majority of software projects fail in some way. But how many times had the developers at the start of the project said, "We know how things are supposed to work out; we know our plan. Now we would like to know what are the possible deviations from that plan."[23] I would challenge 90 percent of current software projects to articulate what their current objectives, strategies, tactics, and means are today, as opposed to the original ones, and to recall exactly when they were changed. I would wager that most projects never sought answers to the question, "We would also like to know when the project is failing and when it should be stopped." I have found that if clear project objectives, and their priorities, cannot be articulated, the project is already in trouble and will probably fail.

For example, take a common occurrence in a software project, where an often stated objective is "low cost." Okay, I will agree that can be done. But first, explain whether the cost sought is lower than the "should cost," or is it the unbiased price of the system?[24] Then, of course, there will be an objective of being "on time." Okay, that can be accomplished too, but is the schedule or the cost the departure point? In other words, was the schedule developed because of the funding available, or was the cost figured out from the time available? And which of the two have the higher priority? Then, inevitably, there comes the objective of "high reliability," whatever that really means. Okay, I will agree to that, too. Just state unambiguously which of the other two objectives you don't want met. There may be an optimal solution to all three, but that usually takes an infinite amount of time and money to obtain. By the way, is it important that the software system being built has to work?

One constantly needs to be skeptical of the free lunch. Human nature being what it is, people want it all. The number of objectives for a software system can often be massive. Figure 3.3 lists just some of the

Correctness	Usability	Flexibility	Interoperability
Acceptability	Operability	Adaptability	Non-complexity
Completeness	User Friendliness	Extensibility	Modularity
Consistency	Accessibility	Structuredness	Communicativeness
Expressability	Convertability	Expandability	Uniformity
Validity	Documentability	Augmentability	Timeliness
Performance	Understandability	Modifiability	Reliability
Clarity	Testability	Availability	Accountability
Accuracy	Inexpensiveness	Robustness	Self-descriptiveness
Maintainability	Portability	Preciseness	Stability
Manageability	Compatibility	Reusability	Integrity
Repairability	Generality	Security	Serviceability

Figure 3.3 Some Typical "Objectives" for Software Systems

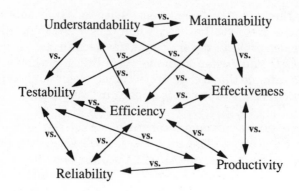

Figure 3.4 Some of the Tradeoffs Among Objectives

"objectives" for systems that have been culled out of the literature. Many require major trade-offs against each other for any one to be achieved. Figure 3.4 shows just some of the trade-offs that can be made; Figure 3.5 illustrates some of the interactions among the software application, environment, and these typical objectives.

A question one must immediately ask is, "Are the objectives stated in the development plan really objectives, or are they in fact strategies, or possibly by-products of the development?" For example, Rockefeller's objective was market stability; his strategy to accomplish this was to

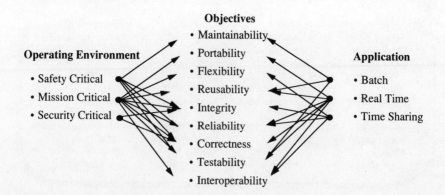

Figure 3.5 Application, Environment, and Objectives Interactions

control the oil from the moment it left the ground to the time it was sold to the consumer. Pepsi's introduction of the 32-ounce cola bottle, on the other hand, was a strategy whose objective was to change the market terrain on which to fight Coca-Cola.

A useful way to clarify one's thinking, and a useful "means test" of a software development plan, is to generate at least two alternative courses of actions to the current way forward. Develop two more strategies and tactics for achieving the same objectives. If it helps, use analogies such as found in the military operations (e.g., siege, trench, mobile) or mountain climbing (e.g., siege, alpine, capsule) to define the alternatives available.[25] One would be surprised how quickly new options appear.

Recall also that the objectives must be measurable wherever possible. Many of those items listed in Figure 3.3, such as robustness, are not measurable by any acceptable standard. One must be very careful to distinguish between objectives that relate to the process of developing a product, and the process itself.[26] If the "ilities" listed in Figure 3.3 are used in the latter way (which is the common way), a case can be made that these are really strategies or tactics used in building a software system, and are not, therefore, objectives of the system development. Reliability, for instance, is built in. On the other hand, if they are attributes of the system, they can be considered objectives. To determine which way a term is applied, use another means test. If one can quantify a particular "ility," then it can be set out as an objective. It is hard, but not impossible.[27] This issue will be returned to later in the book.

Take another example, efficiency. In golf, efficiency can be measured by club head speed, how straight the golfball goes, or how short you can make the course play. However, efficiency is not a basic objective of *the game*. It is a by-product of the strategy to minimize the number of strokes. One can still play and meet the objective of the game without ever being efficient. Profit, similarly, is a by-product of revenue and cost. In software development, efficiency often is equated with productivity. As shown in Jones,[28] using this as an objective is very specious and dangerous. Likewise with the objectives of "low cost" or "on time." Confusion of objectives with strategies is a very common occurrence. Trying to identify a project's risk, without knowing what it is a risk to, makes it very hard to evaluate or minimize. Figure 3.6 outlines what should be in an RES.

For the moment, let's assume that we have reformulated the software development plan into our risk estimate format. Our ultimate goal is to

RISK ESTIMATE OF THE SITUATION

References: (Project plans, budgets, schedules, etc.)

1. PROJECT AND ITS ANALYSIS

    a. Indicate the source of incentive of the project

    b. State project's mission

    c. Study project's mission in relation to overall organizational goals

    d. Study project's mission

        (1) Identify the objective(s)
            (a) Economic
            (b) Non-Economic
        (2) Note contribution to organizational objective(s)
        (3) Note significant elements of the project
            (a) Obvious planning constraints and opportunities
            (b) Assumptions

    e. Note the relationship with other projects or other parties involved in the project

    f. Note general competitive situation

    g. Summarize key points of the analysis

2. CONSIDERATIONS AFFECTING POSSIBLE COURSES OF ACTION

    (For each factor considered, the analyst should draw conclusions as to how it may affect project operations)

    a. The general situation

    b. Characteristics of the project's operations

        (1) General factors
            (a) Political
            (b) Economic
             (c) Organizational
        (2) Fixed factors
            (a) Facilities
            (b) Personnnel
            (c) Other resources

    c. Examine project's requirements

        (1) Compare resources available vs. needs
        (2) Compare quality requirements to project's complexity

Figure 3.6 Risk Estimate of the Situation (RES)—Outline (*Continued on next page*)

(3) Compare organizational capabilities
(4) Compare time and budget factors

d. Assess external forces

(1) Identify deficiencies in information
(2) Tabulate strength and weakness factors
(3) Make initial determination of adequacy of own resources

3. ANALYSIS OF OPPOSING COURSES OF ACTION

a. Factors Opposing Project Success (FOPS)

(1) List and weigh factors which may keep project from achieving
its objectives
(2) Weigh relative probability of factors occurring
(3) Estimate severity of factors if they were to occur

b. Project's Courses of Action (PCA)

(1) List tentative project's courses of action
(2) Consider concept for each course of action
(3) Test for suitability and make preliminary test for feasibility
and acceptability
(4) List retained project's courses of action

c. Analysis of Opposing Courses of Action (OCA)

Commencing with the first OCA and FOPS, each analysis consists of
the following four parts:

(1) Actions which can occur to increase the stated FOPS occurring
(2) Actions which the project must take to implement each stated cours
of action in the face of these occurrences
(3) The interactions resulting from (1) and (2) above
(4) Conclusions as to the probable outcome of the above interactions,
which lead to a basis for judging the feasibility and acceptability of
the stated course of action, and comparing its merits with other
courses of action being tested

4. COMPARISON OF PROJECT'S COURSES OF ACTION

a. List and consider advantages and disadvantages

b. Make final test for suitability, feasibility, and acceptability

c. Weigh relative merits and select the course of action for the project

d. List project's final objectives, strategies, tactics, and means

Figure 3.6 (*Continued*) Risk Estimate of the Situation (RES)—Outline

construct a final RES report with all the risks identified, estimated, and evaluated so that a final software development plan with a selected course of action can be created. The next step in the process is to proceed with risk identification.

3.3 Risk Identification Process

The process of risk identification is associated with the first element of the triplet, s_i. In other words, risk identification involves the discovery and/or recognition of threats to a plan, new relationships among known threats, or a change in the consequences of the threats.[29] In Chapter 2, risk identification was said to be concerned with the reduction in descriptive uncertainty, as well as identifying the degrees of freedom of the system under study. This means the reduction of inclusion uncertainty, or the degree to which a set of risks is collectively exhaustive.[30] More succinctly, we are trying to understand what can possibly go wrong. Our concentration will primarily focus on listing all possible threats to the plan, i.e., the broad range of forces that might adversely affect the accomplishment of the plan.

This process of risk identification and discovery is sometimes difficult, even for experienced personnel, as changes in technology will often change what are considered real risks or perceived risks, including their magnitude. As a project is underway, the development process itself might create new risks, as when engineering changes are introduced that are required to reduce other risks. This increases the importance of risk management, as we shall discover in Chapter 6. Experiences on other programs may have shown a way to avoid risks, or to surface risks that were never encountered before. Thus, threats to a project may involve entirely new risks, previous risks that have changed in magnitude, and/or a change in the perceptions of existing risks.

To fully identify the risks, what must initially be accomplished is the description of the variables of the system under development and the system's relationship to its environment. This means that all the parameters that affect the system development process, as well as the product itself, require identification. Broadly speaking, this includes the political environment, the economic environment, the legal environment, the technological environment, the development environment, and the operational environment in which the system will be used. Typically, these elements are not considered part of the world of the normal software development paradigm, but they are fundamental to accomplishing adequate risk analysis.

3.3.1 The information gathering process

It has been previously said that the risk identification phase of risk analysis is meant to reduce uncertainty and to increase understanding. Given that there exists a plan and its objectives, the strategies, etc., are known, the first item that needs to be addressed is the understanding of the root causes of risk in that plan. This means gathering background information.

The process of information gathering covers past history, current events, etc. Information availability will greatly influence what are considered risks to the plan. Some sources of evidence that should be included in any search are:[31,32]

- Traditional or folk knowledge

- Analogies to well-known cases

- Common-sense assessments

- Results of experiments or tests

- Reviews of inadvertent exposure

- Epidemiological surveys

The first three sources of evidence are generic in nature, whereas the latter three are of a specific nature.

Traditional or *folklore knowledge* is information that "grows up" around a particular topic. It may or may not be based on fact, but is *perceived* as fact by the general user population. This perception is often as "real" as fact, actually. Stereotypical information falls into this category. Unfortunately, in the software field, a great amount of knowledge about building systems is based upon tradition or folklore—a sort of software mythology. An example of such is the statement that adding more people to a late project makes it later, which is better known than Brooks' law.[33] However, detailed studies by Abdel-Hamid indicate that adding more people to a late project always causes it to become more costly, but does not always cause it to be completed later.[34]

Another general source of knowledge is obtained from *analogies to well-known cases*, or other types of activities showing similar traits.[35] The historical data on the development of a particular software system may appear to be very close to another. Lessons-learned or quick-look reports conducted on the previous development may provide invaluable information, which may be applicable because the situation is very similar. Checklists of risks are also a primary source of this type of information. For example, in a new project with new risks, one might seek information from insurance companies. A study of exceptions of liability might give some insight into risks that might be overlooked. Financial and accounting records of previous projects and their original estimates might help as well. Political and legal issues might also provide useful elements to consider. A taxonomy of software ills might be considered a primary source.

A third area of evidence comes from *common sense* or *judgmental assessment*. This may be information based upon other sources of information that are adjusted based upon a personal hunch, or information based upon judgements made after personal observations or experience. This evidence is very important when new technology is being utilized in a project. There may not be any previous evidence to use, thus one's own internal reasoning ability and the degrees of personal belief in the technology, development team capabilities, etc., are the only resources for obtaining information. This is especially true in software engineering risk analysis and management, because the necessity of using a multidisciplinary approach is essential.

Specific sources of evidence include *experiments* and *testing*. Here, uncertainty is reduced by trying to "buy information." This is a very good source of evidence, as long as the experiments and tests match closely with the problems of the specific project. Prototyping is a prime example of this source of evidence. Other examples are mathematical modeling, simulation, or even marketing surveys. Literature searches fall into this category as well. We will look at this in more detail in the next section on risk estimation.

Inadvertent exposure is an interesting source for finding information. This is when a system has been used in ways not thought of or originally intended. An example of this was the use of program compilation techniques to help determine silicon chip layouts, as happens now with silicon compilers. Applying different technology helped surface certain problems not seen before in chip design. Another example is the use of super computers not to design airplane wings, but to simulate the flow of ice cream into molds to produce ice cream bars with no cavities.[36]

The last source of information may be *epidemiological surveys*, or statistical surveys over large populations. These, too, provide valuable information, but there is always the problem of inference, i.e., of relating a cause to an observed effect. Statistical methods cannot establish proof of a causal relationship in an association. They can only indicate that there may be a relationship. This means one must be careful not to think that a symptom is really the disease.

Knowing the value of the information at all times is the key for successful risk analysis. Any information that is used, from any source, should be viewed "cum granis saltis" until it is judged to have an acceptable level of uncertainty. This may sound difficult to accomplish, as what does "acceptable" mean? To help overcome this difficulty, we have listed in Figure 3.7 a number of evaluation criteria for judging the information used in risk identification against its source.[37] Consistency of the association means that the information gained is in agreement with other information from other sources. The strength of the association concerns the degree with which the association actually holds or bonds. The specificity of the association is the degree of peculiarness of the association. The temporal relationship concerns the degree to which time influences the association. The coherence of the association is the degree with which all the factors above, and experience, match or

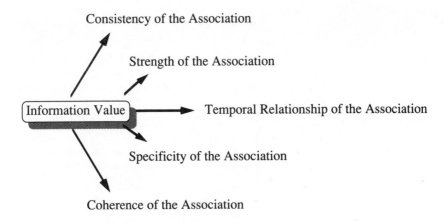

Figure 3.7 Criteria Against Which to Judge an Estimation's Value

calibrate. The greater the level of achieving the criteria, the better the acceptability of the information received.

In each of the above cases, the last point about mistaking symptoms for the disease should be given consideration, although in software engineering, epidemiological surveys are not conducted per se. However, a pathological viewpoint whereby the pathogens of the diseases (e.g., over cost and behind schedule) affecting software developments are identified would be helpful. Forensic software engineering is a requirement for this to occur.

It is difficult to state what the best sources of information are. Information based on past history is probably the best primary source for identifying risks on software projects. For instance, it has been shown time and time again that requirements and design errors account for most later problems found in software systems.[38] The figure lies somewhere around 64 percent. Further, the cost of fixing a requirement or design error can be 1:100 to 1:1000 times greater if found in the stage of development than if it is found in the testing or deployed stage.[39] This would lead one to immediately identify the requirements and design stages of a development as an area of risk, and look at the sources of risk within each stage. For example, Figure 3.8 illustrates the flow of errors that can result from a poor set of requirements or a bad design.

However, because each software development is usually sufficiently unique from any other, one must be careful about drawing the wrong conclusions. This is especially important when new risks are identified.

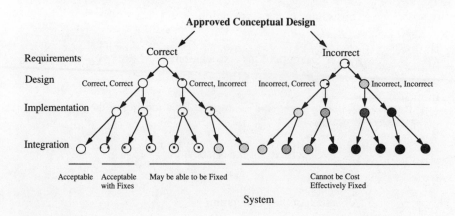

Figure 3.8 Flow of Errors

A new risk may be magnified way out of proportion, or undervalued. Once an impression of a risk is made it is hard to reverse, as we will see in the section on risk estimation.

Also, since the process of developing software flows in some river-like fashion, one would be looking "downstream" for possible risks caused by risk coupling or compounding. These occur when risks are directly or indirectly linked to one another. It may also occur when one risk is substituted for another. Thus, one must be aware that lowering one risk may likely increase the risk someplace else. This is often called the "jello effect," where pushing down one side will cause the other side to go up.

Finally, not only would one look downstream for possible risks, but upstream, prior to when software engineering takes place. The risks that are carried into the software engineering process from the systems engineering and business environments are examined in greater detail in this book's companion volume.

3.3.2 Risk categorization

After having identified the risks using our six sources of evidence, the next step is to attempt to categorize them in some fashion. Because one is often confronted with a mosaic of risks, usually what is required is a number of risk categorization schemes. No single categorization method is best, but a simple way, very effective in practice, is to create trial categories of *known risks*, *predictable risks*, and *unpredictable risks*. These categories are based upon the frequency of the risks encountered and their timing,[40] as is illustrated in Figure 3.9.

Known risks are those that a thorough, critical, and honest analysis of the project plan would illuminate as frequently occurring and with a high probability of currently existing. Typical known risks in software developments that fall into this category are the lack of system requirements, overly-optimistic productivity rates, short schedules, etc. These will be identified from sources of information that include traditions, analogies to well-known cases, or statistical surveys.

Predictable risks are those that experience dictates one may encounter with a high probability. Risks that fall into this category include lack of timely client approval, reviews, personnel turnover, labor problems, and late deliveries by subcontractors. For example, late deliveries by subcontractors are estimated to constitute 40–50 percent of the late deliveries experienced by prime contractors of U.S. defense systems.

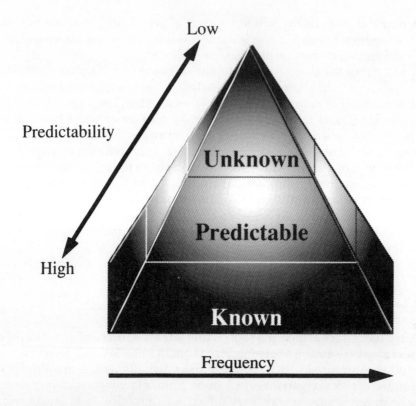

Figure 3.9 Likelihood and Frequency of Different Risk Types

Unpredictable risks are those that could happen, but the likelihood or timing of these events occurring cannot be projected very far in advance. These unpredictable risks are also called unknown or unidentified risks. They can stem from new risks, unobserved risks, or risks that have delayed manifestations. These typically are a result of external influences such as acceptability to the client of growth in schedule, cost, or scope; funding availability; poor management; acquisition strategy change; political redirections; inflation rates; contractor motivation; or erroneous inputs to the decision process. Unpredictable risks usually expose themselves in the guise of "fire drills" or in "crisis management," which typically cause more confusion than actual workable solutions.

TABLE 3.2 Possible Categorization of Risks

Risk Sources	Known	Predictable	Unpredictable
Lack of Information	•	•	•
Lack of Control	•	•	•
Lack of Time	•	•	•

Once the identified risks have been categorized, a second subcategorization along another axis is done. One excellent method is shown in Table 3.2, where risks are subcategorized along the lines of the three primary causes of risk:[41] the lack of information, the lack of control, and the lack of time. For instance, a known risk such as a schedule risk may be caused by a lack of information about productivity rates, a lack of control over the types of development staff available, and/or the lack of time because the system is needed six months earlier than expected. Taking each risk and placing it in the proper group will make the process of its later aversion easier to handle.

Further subcategorization of each risk may or may not be effective. For instance, each cause of risk can be grouped as either being strategic or operational. If they are strategic variables, then they are outside the direct control of the project. Known risks, which are strategic in character, often are the assumptions of the project and therefore must be accepted. Operational risks are those that are within the control of the project. These are also called indirect risks and direct risks, respectively.

Another way to categorize risk is by perspective. As with the buying and selling of stock, one person's risk is another person's opportunity; the perspective of the risk is important. The perspective can focus on either the process of developing the product or on the product itself; the user or developer; or in the case of government contracts, the sponsor, the user, or the developer. Failure to recognize from which perspective risks are viewed, makes their later aversion difficult. As a general rule, all perspectives should be considered initially and then reduced to a working set.

A third way is to categorize the risks as the Department of Defense does, along the lines of acquisition risks and decision risks, with the former being further subdivided into technical, schedule, and cost risks,

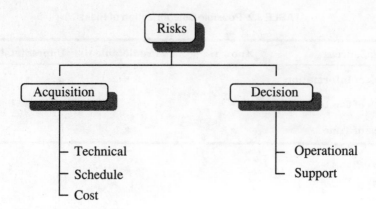

Figure 3.10 DoD Division of Risks

and the latter into operational and support risks. This is illustrated in Figure 3.10. Chapter 2 delved into these in greater detail.

There are virtually an infinite number of categories that can be used. For some, political, economic, or social categories of risk might be added. It really just depends on the project and the view of the analyst. For the purposes of this book, we will assume the categorization as shown in Table 3.3.

3.4 Identification Summary

The process of risk identification involves the discovery and/or recognition of threats to a plan, new relationships among known threats, or a change in the consequences of the threats. In other words, risk identification is the reduction of inclusion uncertainty, or the degree to which a set of risks is collectively exhaustive, to form the definition of the scenarios s_i. More succinctly, we are trying to understand what can possibly go wrong. Risk identification is a two-step process.

The first step is to formulate a Risk Estimate of the Situation, which will force a reexamination of the project plans from another perspective. By clarifying the objectives, strategies, tactics, and means available, risks that might not have been observed will become clear. Hidden assumptions, and their risks, will also surface.

TABLE 3.3 Basic Risk Categorization Chart

Risk Sources	Known	Predictable	Unpredictable
Lack of Information			
Cost			
Schedule			
Technical			
Operational			
Support			
Lack of Control			
Cost			
Schedule			
Technical			
Operational			
Support			
Lack of Time			
Cost			
Schedule			
Technical			
Operational			
Support			

Second, risks will be identified by using various sources of evidence of possible risk. From this information, we will categorize the risks using a taxonomy. One basic approach is to search for the effects of the three basic sources of risk caused by the lack of information, the lack of control, or the lack of time. The other is to search for opportunities to avert risks, the inverse of which will be possible risks themselves. Whatever categorization approach is used, it should be consistent and helpful in the later management of risk.

The next stage is to estimate the size of the risk and its possible consequences. This is termed risk estimation, and will be the subject of Chapter 4.

Questions

1 Explain the difference between objective and subjective. Why isn't risk analysis considered an objective approach?

2 Illustrate the use of the risk set, $< s_i, l_i, x_i >$, in relation to playing a round of golf, or bowling a frame of tenpins, or some other game you are familiar with. Then take a small software development and do the same. How are they alike, and how are they different? When and where do analogies differ?

3 Why should an RES be completed before the risk analysis, and not after? Should business considerations, such as project profit and loss considerations, be part of the RES? Why or why not?

4 How much will assumptions about the development process influence the risks to the project?

5 What is wrong with project objectives being implicitly defined? Can all objectives be explicitly defined? Which ones in Figure 3.3 are objectives, and which are strategies or tactics?

6 Why do project tactics and means constrain the objectives and strategies of the project? Of the four, which is the most important? Justify your answer.

7 Of what importance is the consideration of the political, social environment, etc., for identifying risks to the software projects?

8 What are some other sources of evidence in the software engineering literature that illustrate folklore, inadvertent, and epidemiological information? Which type do you find dominates? How useful is the information that you found in identifying, estimating, or evaluating software risks?

9 Describe two other risk categorization schemes. What are their strengths and weaknesses?

10 What does estimation mean? What does it mean in relationship to risk?

References

1. That story courtesy of Jack Devlin of DEC.

2. "Post-Challenger Evaluation of Space Shuttle Risk Assessment and Management," National Academy Press, January 1988.

3. Two items to note. First, the outer brackets represent the notion that we are talking about the set of all risk triplets that are present in a software development. Second, software risk includes both the risk inherent in the process of software development *and* the product itself.

4. Rational decision makers are related to the idea of the "Economic Man" of Edwards (W. Edwards, "The Theory of Decision Making," in *Psychological Bulletin*, Vol. 51, July 1954), an idealized person who knows no uncertainty. An economic man has the following attributes:
   1. Economic man is completely informed. In other words, he knows all courses of action open to him, and also knows which state will occur and what the outcome of each will be.
   2. Economic man is infinitely sensitive. In other words, he is capable of distinguishing among alternatives which may have only infinitesimally small differences.
   3. Economic man is rational. In other words, he possesses consistent preferences for the outcomes of selected courses of action, and he chooses the best alternatives available to him.

5. "Software Risk Management," Air Force System Command, AFSCP 800-45.

6. U.S. Naval War College, Newport, RI. Taught in the Employment of Naval Forces course "The Military Planning Process."

7. Theodore C. Taylor, "Perspectives On Some Problems of Concept Selection, Management and Complexity In Military System Development," in *Naval War College Review*, Vol. XXXIV, No. 5/Sequence 287, September/October 1981.

8. Ideally, assumptive risks are normally risks that have well-known consequences, and therefore are accepted. In other words, they should form certainty situations as described in Chapter 2.

9. In software engineering these are often termed nonfunctional requirements, while measurable requirements are termed functional. See Robert N. Charette, *Software Engineering Environments: Concepts & Technology*, McGraw-Hill, New York, 1986.

10. The way risk analysis is being performed in this book can be considered a doctrine, for example.

11. The tactics will help formulate our scenarios, or the s_i's in our risk triplet.

12. Wayne P. Hughes, Jr., *Fleet Tactics: Theory and Practice*, Naval Institute Press, Annapolis, MD, 1986.

13. Note that the particular situation will be used to formulate another aspect of our triplet, the l_i, or likelihood of the situation. We still need to quantify how often this particular situation would occur, however.

14. This is part of our damage index—i.e., the consequence of our tactics, or the x_i.

15. Thus, we would have a new risk triplet $< s_i, l_i, x_i >$ for this situation.

16. Wayne P. Hughes, Jr., *Fleet Tactics: Theory and Practice*, Naval Institute Press, Annapolis, MD, 1986.

17. The analogy of software development to a war has been noted by others, such as J. J. Jordan, in "The Neo-classical Napoleonic Method of Project Management," in *ACM Software Engineering Notes*, Vol. 11, No. 3, July 1986.

18. "Technical Risk Assessment: The Current Status of DoD Efforts," Government Accounting Office Report GAO/PEMD-86-5, April 1986.

19. "Post-Challenger Evaluation of Space Shuttle Risk Assessment and Management," National Academy Press, January 1988.

20. Norman R. Augustine, *Augustine's Laws*, American Institute of Aeronautics and Astronautics, New York, 1983.

21. "Technical Risk Assessment: The Current Status of DoD Efforts," Government Accounting Office Report GAO/PEMD-86-5, April 1986.

22. Norman R. Augustine, *Augustine's Laws*, American Institute of Aeronautics and Astronautics, New York, 1983.

23. "Post-Challenger Evaluation of Space Shuttle Risk Assessment and Management," National Academy Press, January 1988.

24. One wonders how many "over-budget" software projects are actually over budget. How many are really deliberate under-budget estimations?

25. The use of the mountain climbing analogy to systems development, and the strategies that can be employed, are found in Peter Salenieks' paper, "Software Development: Advice by Analogy," in *ACM Software Engineering Notes*, Vol. 14, No. 1, January 1989.

26. Michael Deutsch and Ronald R. Willis, *Software Quality Engineering*, Prentice-Hall, Englewood Cliffs, NJ, 1988.

27. T. Gilb and S. Finzi, *Principles of Software Engineering Management*, Addison-Wesley, Reading, MA, 1988.

28. Capers Jones, *Programming Productivity*, McGraw-Hill, New York, 1986.

29. William D. Rowe, *An Anatomy of Risk*, Robert E. Krieger Publishing Co., Malabar, FL, 1988.

30. ——, *An Anatomy of Risk*, Robert E. Krieger Publishing Co., Malabar, FL, 1988.

31. William W. Lowrance, *Of Acceptable Risk: Science and the Determination of Safety*, William Kaufman, Los Altos, CA, 1976.

32. Neil Crockford, *An Introduction to Risk Management*, Woodhead-Faulkner, Cambridge, England, 1980.

33. Fred Brooks, *The Mythical Man-Month*, Addison-Wesley, Reading, MA, 1975.

34. T. K. Abel-Hamid, "The Dynamics of Software Project Staffing: A System Dynamics Based Simulation Approach," in *IEEE Transactions on Software Engineering*, Vol. 15, No. 2, February 1989.

35. Peter Salenieks, "Software Development: Advice by Analogy," in *ACM Software Engineering Notes*, Vol. 14, No. 1, January 1989.

36. "Federal Bytes," in *Federal Computer Week*, 27 March 1989. Use of supercomputers for these commercial and "mundane" types of applications are reported to represent the fastest growing segment of the supercomputer market.

37. William W. Lowrance, *Of Acceptable Risk: Science and the Determination of Safety*, William Kaufman, Los Altos, CA, 1976.

38. Robert N. Charette, *Software Engineering Environments: Concepts & Technology*, McGraw-Hill, New York, 1986.

39. One must be careful how one uses such numbers. What is meant by this is that if we knew what we were doing in the requirements or design stage, then the cost of fixing an error because of an incorrect requirement or design would be significantly less. See Jones [28] for a further explanation.

40. Nicholas Rescher, *Risk*, University Press of America, Lanham, MD, 1983.

41. Kenneth R. MacCrimmon and Donald A. Wehrung, *Taking Risks*, Free Press, New York, 1986.

Risk Analysis: Estimation

"The Titanic is unsinkable."

CAPT. EDWARD J. SMITH

4.0 Introduction

At this point in time, all the possible risks, s_i, to our software development plan have been identified (we hope), and placed into trial categories. It is now time to attempt to rate the risks as to their likelihood, l_i, and consequence, x_i. This requires an estimation of:

- the chance of potential loss; i.e., the values of the risk variables in the previous section are identified; and

- the exposure to potential loss; i.e., the consequences, or magnitude, of the risks are identified.

Notice that we use the word "estimate" above. An estimate can mean, on one extreme, a careful computation of something for which the exact magnitude cannot be determined, or on the other extreme just an offhand approximation that is no better than a guess.[1] Recalling from Chapter 2, risk estimation is concerned with the reduction in measurement uncertainty. Measurement uncertainty is the degree to which the descriptions of the risk or the possible outcomes are mutually exclusive, and the degree to which the relationship among events is known.[2] Risk estimation may also include the reduction of inclusion uncertainty, as it pertains to risk consequences.

Additionally, we have stated all risks have a subjective or personal element associated with them. This means there will always, to some extent, be some error attached to the estimate. Therefore, the best we can ever hope to accomplish is to estimate a risk value to some known level of uncertainty, and to keep the value and uncertainty level consistent across different risks. This will not usually be the case, as the risks identified will come from sources of evidence having different degrees of uncertainty attached. This valuation difference also begins to some degree, albeit crudely, the moment a risk is placed into some specific category.

During risk estimation, four items are accomplished. First, the values of the variables describing the system are determined. This requires determination of a measurement scale against which these values will be estimated and later evaluated. Second, the various consequences of an event occurring are identified. Actions cause reactions, and these must be made known. Third, the magnitude of the risk is determined using the previously selected measurement scale. Also, any modifying factors that tend to increase or reduce the probability of a threat becoming a reality, or the severity of a consequence if it does occur, are considered.

A fourth objective we wish to accomplish during risk estimation is "surprise elimination." We do not want to be saying afterwards, like our New York friend, that we did not know how bad an individual risk really was. Managers are not fond of surprises, and if they are not properly informed of any qualification to the accuracy of the estimate, there could be trouble later on. Therefore, understanding the true accuracy of the risk estimate is vital.

The basic difficulty in estimating software engineering risks is that most prospective project risk estimates being made are unique—i.e., substantially similar projects have not been undertaken in the past, under conditions that are the same as expected in the future.[3] This is true even though the generic risks involved may be identical in the current and a past project.

4.1 Measurement

A good place to start the discussion of risk estimation, then, is with the question, "What does measurement mean?" Broadly speaking, the purpose of measuring is to produce numbers or an ordering of elements.

More formally, measurement is "an assignment of numbers to objects or events according to a rule—any rule."[4] Because the risks identified previously are likely to be of many diverse types, and their ordering may not be clear, a short digression on the differences in measurement scales might make it easier.[5,6]

The simplest scale that can be used is the *nominal scale* (also termed the identity-taxonomy scale). This scale is used to name objects or events. Using this scale, risks are distinguished by one or more properties. These properties are used for identification purposes only, and have no quantitative implications associated with them. The categorization of risk in the previous chapter used this type of scale. This scale is used when one does not fully understand all the implications of a risk, or how it is associated with other, better known, risks.

The next scale in complexity is the *ordinal scale* (or order-risk scale). An ordering or ranking of items is performed by the degree they obtain some criterion. Risks can be distinguished from one another, and we can tell when one risk is greater than, equal to, or smaller than another. (Note: we cannot tell *how much* one risk is greater than, less than, etc., another, just that they are.) The criterion used can be subjective or objective, although the latter is generally preferred. For example, the risk classification scheme of known, predictable, and unpredictable risks in the previous section uses this scale.

Moving up a bit more, the third scale available is the *cardinal scale* (or interval scale). Using the cardinal scale, risks can be distinguished from one another, ranked, and the differences between the risks defined. This scale is used when the differences between properties are required; i.e., the differences between measurement criterion are known. A cardinal scale is continuous between two end-points, neither of which is necessarily fixed. A thermometer is an example of a cardinal scale.

The final scale that can be used is the *ratio scale* (or zero reference scale). Using this scale, risks can be distinguished from one another, ranked, the differences between the risks measured, and there exists a unique origin from which to begin measurement. This is a cardinal scale with one end-point fixed by reference to an absolute physical end-point, from which are developed other cardinal scales, all of which are related by simple ratios.

Different types of risks will often be measured using different types of measurement scales, either singly or together. For instance, political risks may need to be classified into categories using an ordinal scale such as politically suicidal, politically neutral, or politically advantageous. It is not important to measure much more than degree of accuracy. Cost, schedule, or performance risks, on the other hand, might make the most sense when being measured using a ratio scale. See Table 4.1 for some other examples.

4.1.1 Estimation approach

Knowing which scale one uses is of more than passing interest. The more complex the measurement scale used, the more one understands a risk and its implications. We also need to know the proper scale to use because of the way information about the risk may be presented. Typically, information about risks will be presented in one of three forms: *narrative, qualitative,* or *quantitative*.[7]

Narrative information describes potential risks that may preclude something from happening, or indicates the source of a risk (and possibly its control). An example of narrative information is called for in the DoD STD-2167A Software Development Plan, which was shown in Chapter 2. Use of a nominal scale or an ordinal scale might be the best we can do to estimate the risk likelihood or consequence.

Qualitative information is usually expressed using some sort of ordinal rating system. Examples are a scale that categorizes risks as being high or low, or in-between ratings, using some color coded method, such as red for high, yellow for medium, and green for low, for example. Figure 4.1

TABLE 4.1 Measurement Scales

Scale	Empirical Observation	Statistical Measure	Examples
Nominal	Ascertainment of equality	Mode	- Car license no.s - Soc. Sec. no.s
Ordinal	Ascertainment of Greater or Less Than	Median	- Street no.s - Ordering by weight, height - Material hardness
Cardinal	Ascertainment of Equality	Expected Value	- Temperature - Clock time
Ratio	Ascertainment of Equality of Ratios	Geometric Mean	- Length - Profit - Loss

shows another way of creating a qualitative risk rating system, this time for a navy command and control system. Here, the assignment of a ranking to a risk is based upon modes that the particular navy platform operates in, and the subsequent possible consequences of that risk.

The difficulty with measuring risk using a qualitative scale, and which keeps us from using a cardinal or ratio scale, is that the words used to describe the risk are imprecise. Words such as:

• high	• low
• probable	• expected
• not certain	• doubtful
• likely	• quite certain
• maybe	• unlikely
• little chance that	• hoped
• we believe that	• possible
• improbable	• not unreasonable that

have different meanings to different people. This was shown graphically in a study conducted at the London School of Business.[8] When 250

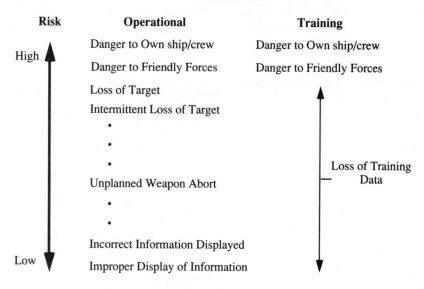

Figure 4.1 Navy Risk Taxonomy Using Operational Modes

executives were asked to rank 10 words or phrases similar to those listed above in decreasing order of certainty, only three people actually listed them in the same order. More interesting, a study conducted a few months later had people changing their original ordering! Not surprisingly, this problem of the inexact meaning of words has led to situations where decisions were made under false assumptions.

Quantitative measurements use either a cardinal or ratio scale, where the risk is expressed using a fraction representing the likelihood (or probability) of something occurring. In other words, a number is used with some zero point attached as a reference point. However, note that the probability of something happening is still only a *belief* that something will occur. Using a scale that has numbers attached doesn't necessarily, nor automatically, increase the accuracy of the estimation (remember—garbage in, garbage out). It is easy to fall into this trap. Numbers can be misleading. One should not forget that statistics are often the last refuge of a scoundrel. Take, for example, the case of a half-horse/half-rabbit stew—one horse and one rabbit.

There are some good reasons for using numbers, however. Quantitative risk measurements, if one is careful, are less imprecise and ambiguous than qualitative ones. They tend to permit more objective assessment of the information and data on identified risks. Also, by assigning numbers we can manipulate them, as opposed to narrative descriptions or qualitative measures. More important, we can tell how much difference exists between one risk and another—an important factor for doing

Risk Rating	Probability of Failure	Interpretation
Extremely High	.99 - .81	Beyond state of art. Technical problems assured.
Very High	.80 - .61	Beyond state of art. Technical problems very likely.
High	.60 - .50	Latest technology, not fully developed. Technical problems likely.
Moderate	.49 - .25	Best technology. Minimal technical problems expected.
Low	.24 - .10	Practical technology. No technical problems expected.
Very Low	.09 - .01	System in use.

Figure 4.2 Quantitative Risk Ratings

intelligent evaluation of a risk. Figure 4.2 provides an example of a quantitative risk rating.

Beware of the problem of mixing different scales, or of mixing ratings of different risk types, however. One does not often encounter the situation where risks of different types can easily be traded against one another. Cost, schedule, and quality may be intuitively tied together in a software development, but a change in one may affect the others in terms of magnitude and severity in nonlinear ways. This can be understood better in the context of the determinants of the magnitude of a potential loss related to a risk.[9]

Three components play a role in determining the overall magnitude of a loss: its *character*, its *extent*, and its *timing*. The character of the loss is concerned with its qualitative nature—is the loss physical, political, economic, etc., or some combination? It is "the varied spectrum of available unpleasantness," as Rescher nicely puts it.[10] The extent of the loss has two parameters: the severity and its distribution. The severity is the amount of loss—how much physical pain, political retribution, money, etc.? Is the loss severe, modest, or trivial in nature? The distribution concerns the loss coverage—is it an individual, group of people, nation, or is it the world? The timing component has to do with the chronology of the loss. Will the loss be immediately felt, or is it spread out over time, or is it felt all at once, but at some later point in time? How these three components interact form potentially enormous variation.

Rescher also points out that the different components of the magnitude of potential risks are not necessarily commensurable. Thus, one is not able to formulate an exchange rate among what on the surface appear as identical consequences—the loss of a husband and wife in a car accident that leaves three young children orphaned, for, say, the loss of three single pilots involved in a mid-air collision. Trying to formulate a single number to describe the loss in both situations is an oversimplification of the problem at best, and wrong at worst.

This being the case, there is no single best type of measurement scale. Which one will be used in a risk analysis will often depend upon many factors, ranging from the criticality of the software, to the project's success criteria, to the funding available for the risk analysis. Narrative information has an advantage of providing contextual information, but does not allow the level or magnitude of the risk to be measured. Qualitative and quantitative scales do indicate levels or ratings but lack the information content. The narrative approach is easiest and least costly to produce, followed closely by qualitative, whereas quantitative is most difficult, costly, and time consuming. Most programs that do risk analysis tend to use qualitative measurements, as a result. A combination of a qualitative or quantitative assessment with a narrative approach is considered ideal, as shown in Figure 4.3.

4.1.2 Uncertainty and availability

Estimates, by their very nature, are appraisals of incomplete information indicating what the future may hold. Thus, in performing risk estimation, there are two major obstacles to overcome. The first, as we

Rating and Term

High (red)

Solvable with changes in schedule or performance schedules

Beyond the state of the art

Probable failure

Major problem

Test plan not yet devised

Current state of the art

Moderate (yellow)

Some development success but still uncertain

Solvable with no changes in schedule or specifications

Test plan devised but testing not yet completed

Solvable

Low (green)

Proven technology and no problems

Test plan devised and tests completed

Solvable with no major schedule changes

Figure 4.3 Combination of Narrative and Qualitative/Quantitative Risk Ratings

have implied above, is that in applying each measurement scale there is a form of subjective judgement involved. Therefore, there exists some uncertainty attached to the estimate of the magnitude of risk we have identified, as shown in Figure 4.4.

All measurement has some level of uncertainty associated with it, as has been shown by the Heisenberg Uncertainty Principle.[11] The level of uncertainty in the variables that are used to describe a system depends on the precision of the measurement system used, as well as on the accuracy of the measurement. This means in practice, there is a difference between accuracy and uncertainty in our measurement of risk, just as there is a difference between faulty and missing information. A measurement might be considered precise; i.e., there is a lack of uncertainty with a particular measurement, but it may be inaccurate because of the use an incorrect measurement scale.

An illustration might help clarify this. In Figure 4.5 we have four sport shooting targets. On target one, we have a spread of bullet holes that is inaccurate and imprecise. On target two, we have a spread of bullet holes that is accurate but imprecise. On target three, the spread is inaccurate but precise. On target four, the spread is accurate and precise.[12] Accu-

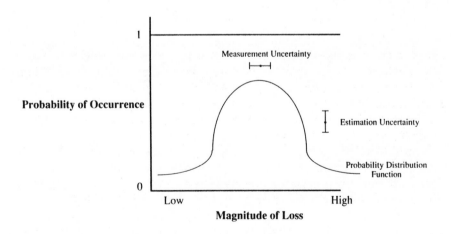

Figure 4.4 Uncertainty Sources

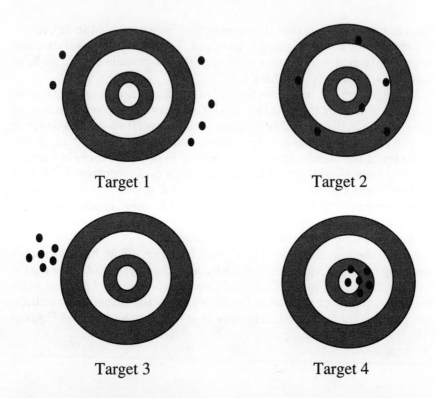

Target 1   Target 2

Target 3   Target 4

Figure 4.5 Precision and Accuracy

racy is the quality of being free from error, whereas precision is the exactness by which a quantity is stated. These distinctions were lost on the Indiana General Assembly, when in 1897 it passed a bill declaring that the value of π was 4, instead of its usual 3.141. . . . This minor difference ensured that a large proportion of the mathematical and engineering calculations in the state would be wrong.[13]

One is faced with similar situations all the time in our daily endeavors. For example, Figure 4.6 illustrates the problem of trying to sort out the accurate from the precise for various daily events. Generally, the greater the number used in a measurement, the greater the need for precision and accuracy in the measurement device. One thing can be certain, though: If one says that the risk will occur some "X" percentage of the time, then, as Norman Augustine aptly puts it, "the last digit will be right 10 percent of the time."[14]

Event	Number of Significant Digits Required For Description	
Number of mothers an individual has = 1	1	Low
Average temperature in Washington, DC in May = 75° F	2	
Exchange rate £ to $ in United Kingdom as of 1 May 1989 = 1.67	3	
Calories in a 2-lb. jar of peanut butter = 5510	4	
Population of St. Pierre, 1978 = 23, 567	5	
Taxpayer share of Savings & Loan bailout = $1,532.17	6	High

Level of Uncertainty

Figure 4.6 Accuracy of Daily Events

4.1.3 Estimation bias

The second obstacle one is faced with in estimating risks is the availability of information from which to make judgements.[15,16] We have already mentioned the sources of information that can be used to identify risks, but this information rarely includes the magnitude, severity, or frequency of such risks. Furthermore, when the information is disseminated, individuals often misinterpret or misunderstand its meaning. This is termed "information availability bias." Availability bias is related to the fact that if an event's occurrence is easily recalled, for instance a plane crash caused by a terrorist bombing over Christmas, then an individual will tend to assign a higher magnitude of loss to it. It has been shown that individuals commonly overestimate the frequency of well-publicized events, while the frequency of less-publicized events is commonly underestimated.

Individuals tend to have selective or biased perception, which creates another problem. In other words, anticipation of expected information will color one's thinking. Often, this happens to the degree that information that meets the individual's bias is received, while any contrary information is filtered out. This is sometimes called "management bias" or "expert bias." Management bias occurs when an individual views an uncertain parameter, say the cost of a software development, as a goal, rather than an uncertainty. It is typified by individuals wanting to reduce cost, rather than trying to figure out whether a given cost is correct or not. Expert bias occurs when the individual thinks they must be an "expert," and therefore must be sure of things. "Experts" are assumed not to be uncertain in their judgements, correct?

An example of this happened in early 1914. At that time, Germany was feeling threatened by the mobilization of the Russian armies in the East, created by the political tensions over the assassinations of the Austrian Archduke and his wife by a Serbian national, and resultant war-posturing of Axis and Allied powers.[17] A German war plan, named the Schlieffen Plan, after Graf von A. Schlieffen, had been developed and refined over a 15-year time frame by the German general staff and delineated the cornerstone to German military thinking. Key character-istics of the plan were that it was massive, scenario driven, highly inflexible, and total. Once one part of the plan was implemented, all of it had to be implemented. The plan could not be compartmentalized. And it was engraved on every German staff officer's mind as the only way to proceed.

When the mobilization of the Russian army began in the East, the only military option the plan called for was a preemptive strike to the West. When the Kaiser asked the Chief of Staff of the German army, Helmuth von Moltke, if there was no other possible alternative to the invasion of France, the answer was "No." The Kaiser answered, "Your uncle would have had a different answer," referring to von Moltke's uncle, Field Marshal Helmuth von Moltke, his predecessor, who was not biased by the Schlieffen Plan mindset. The results of the Plan's implementation turned out to be disastrous. As a result of this experience, the German staff's outlook after the war changed to one of ultimate questioning of superiors' thoughts and ideas (it was a duty, in fact), with the result that new ideas, such as blitzkrieg, came into being.

Another aspect of the selected perception phenomena is that people tend to rely solely on either qualitative or quantitative information, to the exclusion of the other. To overcome these biases, a single basis of assessment, preferably quantitative, should be used in order that all evidence can be used on a common scale.

A number of other cognitive biases should also be remembered when performing risk estimates.[18] First, individuals tend to believe they are more certain than they really are. In other words, estimations of risk will tend to be either skewed in a positive direction (less risk) or a negative direction (more risk). A balanced view is what everyone thinks they possess, but this is not proven in practice.

Second, individuals commonly demonstrate an inability to revise, accurately and consistently, initial estimates in the light of new information. People tend to hold on for a long period of time to their initial impressions. This is especially true when new risks are identified. Since they are rarely quantified when first identified, they will take on qualities that may have high degrees of bias (positive or negative) attached, which can prove to be difficult to dispel later.

Third, individuals seem to be insensitive to sample sizes. This means that the notion of probability does not exist intuitively in most people's way of thinking. Further, most people's intuitive combining of probabilities is not usually compatible with the mathematics of probability. For example, whether the likelihood of a risk takes on a normal or Poisson distribution, or a combination of some others, is not high on most people's list of things they are knowledgeable about.

Fourth, individuals will anchor, or use a particular point of departure, in making their initial judgements, and revise all future judgements based on that initial condition. The initial condition can markedly affect any prediction made. Thus, one should be careful not to add "fudge factors" without thinking about their later effects.

Fifth, individuals will often make predictions by a simple matching rule—the estimation of possible outcomes is the same as the intuitive impression of the distribution. In other words, if an individual thinks that a technical risk is low, he will say that its contribution to cost risk is also low.

The factors above have some rather significant implications to the planning process. It turns out that project plans are usually made up of events where a sequence or series of subevents must each occur (called conjunctive events) before the project can be successfully completed. Unfortunately, any tendency to overestimate the probability of conjunctive events can lead to an unwarranted optimism that the project will be completed. And this is the tendency shown in individuals.

On the other hand, in risk situations, one must usually consider events where at least one of the subevents must occur (called disjunctive events). In complex systems, the system will fail if any one of its critical elements fail. Even though the likelihood of failure in any one element may be small, the overall probability of failure may be high if many elements are involved. Individuals in these cases often tend to underweigh the distributional information.

Because of the phenomena above, assessors tend to underestimate the overall probability of failure in complex systems, while simultaneously overestimating the probability of completing it on time. Thus, remember the two trends: Those events that are chain-like structures of conjunction can lead to overestimation, while tree-like structures of disjunction can lead to underestimation.

Being aware of the above tendencies will help estimators make better judgements (e.g., by recognizing a conjunctive event, an estimator will be aware of the inherent bias), and helps explain why software development schedules are often in reality underestimated and software product quality overestimated. Also, a primary reason for using the RES approach is to help overcome these inherent tendencies found in typical planning documents.

4.1.4 Uncertainty reduction

Given that one is faced with these estimation uncertainties, what can be done to overcome them, other than recognizing that they exist?

The simplest approach is to recognize that the precision and accuracy of an individual risk's estimate is determined by the processes in which the risk belongs. All risks can be considered belonging to one of the three following processes: *behavioral, natural,* or *random.*[19]

Behavioral processes are those that involve the "rational" behavior of an intelligent opponent (refer to reference [4] in Chapter 3). We say "rational" behavior, because a person does not always act rationally. Thus, a risk may arise because of the actions of others, or ourselves. A key element of behavioral processes is that they have a large amount of uncertainty associated with them.

Natural processes are those that may be ascribed to empirical, natural laws, such as physical laws. Natural processes are "repeatable," or "deterministic," and thus can be predicted with some amount of confidence. That the underlying causes and effects produced by natural laws can be "discovered" and understood, which implies that their certainty theoretically can be reduced to zero, is an elemental characteristic of natural processes.

Another type of natural process is a *random process.* This means that given a particular set of risks, any one will have an equal likelihood of occurring. In this case, the key aspect is the dependency upon statistical means for the understanding of the uncertainty involved. Table 4.2

TABLE 4.2 Uncertainty Limits

Process	Descriptive Uncertainty Reduction	Measurement Uncertainty Reduction
Behavioral	Limited by ability to define parameters of human behavior	Limited by rational human behavior
Natural	Theoretically unlimited, but limited in practice	Limited by precision of measuring system
Random	Theoretically unlimited, but limited in practice	Cannot be reduced

illustrates the uncertainty limits for describing a risk (i.e., identifying a risk), and estimating the likelihood and/or magnitude of a risk (i.e., measuring a risk), for each of the three process categories.

A more structured way is to apply a group consensus approach called the *Delphi* technique.[20] This technique originated at the Rand Corporation as a means of predicting future consequences of then-current policy decisions. Basically, a group of experts are gathered and are asked, by a group coordinator, their opinion about a topic, say, in our case, an estimate of the likelihood of a specific risk and its possible consequences. Each expert writes down his opinion anonymously. They cannot discuss their opinion with any of the other experts, although they may ask the coordinator questions about the risk. In this way, detrimental face-to-face confrontation is avoided. The coordinator then prepares a summary of the experts' responses, circulates the summaries, and asks for another estimate—but reconsidered in the light of new data, estimates from the experts—and the rationale for their new opinion or a defense of their previous one. This goes on iteratively until a group consensus is reached or until the coordinator feels it is appropriate to stop (i.e., it is of questionable value to continue). During the entire process, the experts should not talk to one another.

The aim of the Delphi technique is to reach a group consensus and increase the accuracy of the estimate by surfacing and examining as many relevant issues as possible. The technique works if the participants do not hold too tight a bias, and if crucial information is not left out. Unfortunately, as we mentioned previously, experts often do not want to be seen as not certain, even in anonymous circumstances.

A similar but different technique that can be used is called *probability encoding.*[21] Instead of a group getting together as in the Delphi approach, a team of questioners conducts interviews with individuals about a subject. The subject is some topic where a measurement is required in relation to some parameter called a variable. The team has been trained to spot individual biases and to point them out to the interviewee, in hopes of overcoming their biases.

Probability encoding consists of a seven-step process, which includes:

1. Motivation (identifying and understanding the individual's motivation and biases)
2. Structuring (providing a definition of the variable to be assessed and identifying any assumptions about it)
3. Conditioning (does the variable pass the "clairvoyance test"—i.e., could a clairvoyant give an unequivocal value to the variable?)
4. Encoding (the quantification of the uncertainty of the individual's estimate of the variable's value)
5. Verifying (does the individual really believe in the estimate?)
6. Aggregation (making use of additional information from other individuals about the same variable to calibrate the results)
7. Discretizing (allowing an infinite number of possibilities to be reduced to a finite number)

In specific circumstances, probability encoding is very good at overcoming individual or group estimation bias.

A fourth approach is to ascertain the certainty of the risk estimate and attempt to "buy" information about the risk itself. Typical techniques include building prototypes, doing simulations, performing surveys, conducting benchmark tests, or creating analytical models. However, before we spend money on buying information, we need to see if it is worth our while. We will investigate this issue in more depth in a few moments.

To fully understand the implications of uncertainty, we need a mechanism to quantify what is meant by the terms "likelihood," "possibility," or "statistical means."[22] To accomplish this, we need to divert our attention for a few moments to the calculus of probability theory. The following is just a refresher for those who have forgotten their probability theory. Those who do not require a refresher can skip to the next sections. For those who do, we have limited ourselves to the very basic requirements: Those wishing to delve deeper or who have no background should turn to the standard texts on probability and statistical theory.

4.2 Probability Theory

A probability is a measure of chance.[23,24] This measure has been defined
as a ratio scale starting at the number zero and going to the number 1.
An event A having a zero probability, is said to be impossible or
nonexistent, while event A with a probability of 1, is said to be a surety,
i.e., a certainty. A probability cannot be greater than 1 nor less than zero.
By convention, we denote the "probability of A" by $P(A)$, and by definition:

$$0 \leq P(A) \leq 1 \qquad (4.1)$$

Thus, the probability of event A happening is represented by some
number, and the probability of its not happening (called its complement)
is $1 - P(A)$. The probability of event A and its complement must sum up
to 1.

We can represent probabilities by Venn diagrams such as the ones that
were used in Chapter 2. In Venn diagrams, probabilities are represented

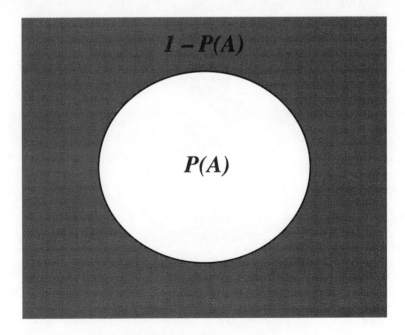

Figure 4.7 Venn Diagram of Probability of Event A

by areas. In Figure 4.7, the probability of event A is shown by the area inside the circle, whereas the area outside the circle is the probability that event A does not occur.

Basic rules are used to calculate probabilities of more than one event. The easiest to understand is the joint occurrence of both event A and event B, which is denoted by the symbols $P(A \cap B)$. This is represented by the cross-hatching in Figure 4.8. Let us assume the probability of event A occurring is 50 percent (or .5), and the probability of event B occurring is 70 percent (or .7). In a Venn diagram, the probability of event A would be represented by the smaller circle, while the probability of event B would be represented by the larger circle.

The occurrence of event A or B is denoted by the symbols $P(A \cup B)$. It represents the total area enclosed by both circles. This can be written as:

$$P(A \cup B) = P(A) + P(B) - P(A \cap B) \qquad (4.2)$$

This is easily seen from the diagram where $P(A \cup B)$ is represented by the area in the two circles, minus the area of the cross-hatching (this is to prevent a double counting of the cross-hatched area). From our example, the probability of event $A \cap B$ occurring must be at least 20

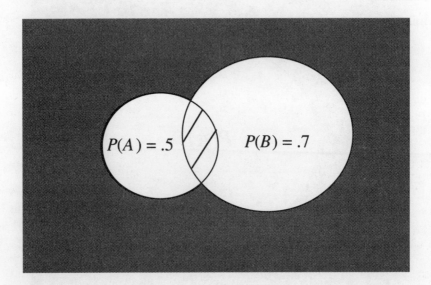

Figure 4.8 Venn Diagram of $P(A)$ and $P(B)$

percent, or it could be as high as 50 percent, but more information is required to proceed further. If, for example, we knew that $P(A \cap B) = 30$ percent, then $P(A \cup B) = 90$ percent.

Now, let's assume that events A, B, and C are mutually exclusive (i.e., the events cannot happen simultaneously), and that the $P(A) = 35$ percent, $P(B) = 40$ percent, and $P(C) = 25$ percent. Then we can say that the probability of either A or B occurring is the sum of both probabilities, as denoted by $P(A + B) = P(A) + P(B)$, or 75 percent. In general, in the case of mutually exclusive events,

$$P(A + B + \cdots) = P(A) + P(B) + \cdots \qquad (4.3)$$

We can also look at events that are conditional on other events occurring. If in Figure 4.8 we know that event B has occurred, then the $P(B) = 1$. If we wish to know the $P(A)$ given that B has occurred, then the cross-hatched area represents this probability. The $P(A)$ is then a fraction of the circle B. We denote this as $P(A \mid B)$, and it is read as the probability of event A given that event B has occurred. The conditional probability is computed as follows:

$$P(A \mid B) = P(A \cap B)/P(B) \text{ if } P(B) \; 0 \qquad (4.4)$$

and similarly,

$$P(B \mid A) = P(A \cap B)/P(A) \text{ if } P(B) \; 0 \qquad (4.5)$$

Now, if events A and B are probabilistically independent, in other words, the probability of event A is not affected by event B, then the $P(A \cap B)$ is just equal to $P(A)$ times $P(B)$, or:

$$P(A \cap B) = P(A)\,P(B) \qquad (4.6)$$

Similarly,

$$P(A \cap B \cap C \cap \cdots) = P(A)\,P(B)\,P(C) \cdots \qquad (4.7)$$

This says that for mutually exclusive events, the conditional probabilities $P(A \mid B)$ and $P(B \mid A)$ can be reduced to:

$$P(A \mid B) = P(A) \text{ and } P(B \mid A) = P(B) \qquad (4.8)$$

The second to last piece of knowledge required for the moment is the recalculation of initial probabilities given that new information is available. We can accomplish this by using Bayes' theorem. Let A_1, A_2, . . ., A_n etc., be mutually exclusive events and the only such events possible (i.e., their union makes up the full sample space). Let E be an arbitrary event of the sample space such that an event $P(E)$ 0. Then the probability:

$$P(A_1 \mid E) = \frac{P(A_1 \cap E)}{P(A_1 \cap E) + P(A_2 \cap E) + \cdots + P(A_N \cap E)} \qquad (4.9)$$

The same holds true for events A_2, A_3, etc. Bayes' theorem allows one to calculate the conditional probabilities based upon some event in the sample space occurring. This is important because as a software development unfolds, new information will come to light that will influence our beliefs and, thus, the estimates of the likelihood of what may occur. One would like to be able to explicitly modify the probabilities, so that a consistency of revised beliefs with new information and with prior beliefs can be validated; this is what Bayes' theorem provides.

Another way of stating Bayes' theorem is:

$$P(E) = P(A_1) \, P(E/A_1) + P(A_2) \, P(E/A_2) + \cdots + P(A_N) \, P(E/A_N) \qquad (4.10)$$

where $P(E)$ is called the total probability.

The last equation we require is that of the expected value or arithmetic mean of an event occurring. This is the probability of the "average" event, as opposed to the probability of a single event. If a course of action can result in r different outcomes with values v_1, v_2, . . . , v_r having probabilities P_1, P_2, . . . , P_r respectively (the sum of P_1 through P_r equals 1), then the expected value of the action is:

$$E_v = v_1 P_1 + v_2 P_2 + \cdots + v_r P_r \qquad (4.11)$$

One can think of the expected value as what one would expect to occur most often, if a particular risk were to happen time and time again. We will use expected value computation as a "standard" in our risk estimations and evaluations.

One may want to ask why the use of expected values over something else? The use of expected values for our standard has a number of advantages. It has the means of providing a procedure for the comparison of risks independent of the particular scaling factors used in our selected measurement scale. In other words, the relative size of a risk's expected value is independent of scale. Expected values also allow one to aggregate or disaggregate outcomes without disturbing comparisons among different risk alternatives. For example, if we have:

$$E_v = v_1 P_1 + v_2 P_2 + v_3 P_3 \qquad (4.12)$$

we can write it as:

$$E_v = v_1 P_1 + v' P' \qquad (4.13)$$

where
$$P' = 1 - P_1 = P_2 + P_3$$

and
$$v' = \left(\frac{P_2}{P_2 + P_3} \bullet v_2 \right) + \left(\frac{P_3}{P_2 + P_3} \bullet v_3 \right).$$

Finally, the use of expected values also allows one to perform uniform evaluations of real losses or mere losses of opportunity. It does not matter what sort of gain/loss perspective a risk is viewed in, the same exact comparative results will emerge.

With this information in our possession, we can now return to the problem of reducing uncertainty of our risk information.

4.3 Value of Estimation Information

In a previous section we asked the question, "Is it worthwhile to try to gather a better risk estimate?"[25] With the bit of mathematics above, we are now in a better position to formulate an answer.[26-30]

Suppose, for instance, that you are the senior systems engineer taking over a new phase of a large, integrated voice and data telecommunication network being built for your company's most important client. The last senior engineer decided to quit because of the pressure. Reading the papers he thoughtfully left for you just before he quit, you learn that he had just discovered a possible major risk to the project. The newly installed computer for testing the newly designed communications protocol might have a technical fault in it. The new computer is a special type, which supposedly will save the project $200K in testing time over any available on the market now, and is the item the company is counting on to show profit on this job. You see, the contract is a fixed priced one, and because of previous problems, the profit margin has been eaten away.

You suspect there is a problem in the computer also, not only because the weekly computer rags have rumored such for a few weeks now, but because numerous calls to the manufacturer have only produced strongly resented denials. They have asked if you have actually discovered and proven that a fault exists in the machine, which you have admitted not to be the case, yet. None of your friends in the industry that you called have run into a fault, either. One friend, however, told you of this highly reputable computer diagnostic and repair company that was familiar with the new computer, and could, if there were indeed any faults, find them quickly and at a reasonable price. The project being under tight cost and time schedule constraints, any problems that caused money to be spent unwisely will be magnified severely in your bonus and possibly your career. What to do?

After thinking about it for a while, you have concluded that getting a replacement computer at this stage is impossible. The approval process, even if the current computer were to stop working altogether, would take too long.[31] Therefore, you have worked out two alternative courses of action. One alternative, which you call A_1, assumes the new written protocol programs executing on the suspect computer will not show any errors because no fault exists, and thus everything will be okay. If, after proceeding down this path, the computer does indeed have a fault, then the project will be slowed down tremendously as normal software errors caused by the testing will require to be sorted out from the hardware-induced error(s). Major management panic will ensue, and you better pack your bags.

The other outcome, which you, being clever, have called A_2, assumes there is a fault in the computer, programs will start to show errors immediately, and therefore the computer should be tested rigorously by that outside firm right away. There may be some delay and cost, but the sooner the program management knows about it, the better. They will not like it, but if your arguments are sound, they may keep you around for another year.

Let us assume that, after some rough figuring and telephoning around, the cost to the project if a fault is found after the computer is in use will be $350K. On the other hand, if we decide to call in the computer repair company, the cost will be $125K. Given this information, we can compute a value for each alternative.

If nature is good to us, then net value to the project of A_1 will cost $200K, as everything will proceed on track, you can breathe a sigh of relief, and buy your son the birthday present that he has been hinting at. If nature is not kind, the cost to the project will be $150K loss (we lose the savings the new computer bought the project and go $150K more into the red), and, have a very angry five-year-old on your hands. For A_2, the net value will be $75K regardless of the state of nature (the $200K minus the $125K), and possibly a placated child.

We can write out a payoff or decision matrix showing our choices, as shown in Table 4.3. For each alternative and state of nature, our payoff is indicated. Let's assume that we now have to make a decision. What can we do?

4.3.1 Decision under complete uncertainty

Since we do not know the likelihood of either alternative occurring, we are in a situation of trying to make a decision under complete uncertainty. There are three basic strategies that we can use, if we find ourselves in this situation: the *maximin rule*, the *maximax rule*, and the *Laplace rule* (also called the equal-probability or median rule).

The *maximin rule* states that one should determine the minimum payoff for each option, then choose the option that maximizes the minimum payoff. This is obviously a conservative, safe strategy. It hinges on what happens if "worse comes to worst." In Table 4.3, A_1 has the minimum payoff of -150, while option A_2 has a minimum payoff of 75. The alternative to choose using this strategy is A_2—call in the computer repair company.

The *maximax rule* states that one should determine the maximum payoff for each option, then choose the option that maximizes the

TABLE 4.3 Payoff Matrix with Two Alternatives

| | State of Nature | |
	Favorable	Unfavorable
Alternative 1	200K	–150K
Alternative 2	75K	75K

maximum payoff. Using Table 4.3, this would mean choosing A_1—gut it out. This strategy might be summed up as an optimistic approach, where "nothing ventured, nothing gained."

The third strategy is to start considering the likelihood of each alternative actually occurring. The *Laplace rule* states that nature is equally kind and unkind; i.e., there exists equal probability that a fault may or may not exist. Thus, determine the expected value for each option, and choose the option with the maximum expected value.

Using equation 4.11 found in the section on probability theory, the expected value of A_1 can be calculated as follows:

$$E_v = A_1 \bullet P_{[\text{Nature is kind}]} + A_1 \bullet P_{[\text{Nature is unkind}]}$$

$$= (200) \bullet (.5) + (-150) \bullet (.5)$$

$$= 100 - 75$$

$$= 25$$

For A_2, the expected value is:

$$E_v = A_2 \bullet P_{[\text{Nature is kind}]} + A_2 \bullet P_{[\text{Nature is unkind}]}$$

$$= (75) \bullet (.5) + (75) \bullet (.5)$$

$$= 32.5 + 32.5$$

$$= 75$$

Using the Laplace rule, the strategy to select is A_2.

The Laplace rule is a good rule, if the likelihoods of each situation really are equal. However, a little simple math will show what happens as the probabilities take on a range of probability factors.

Let the probability of nature being kind be x, while the probability of nature not being kind is $(1 - x)$. Thus, the expected value now becomes:

$$E_v = A_1 \bullet P_{[\text{Nature is kind}]} + A_1 \bullet P_{[\text{Nature is unkind}]}$$

$$= (200 \bullet x) + (-150 \bullet (1 - x))$$

$$= 200x - 150 + 150x$$

$$= 350x - 150$$

Similarly for A_2, the expected value is:

$$E_v = 75x + 75 - 75x$$

$$= 75$$

The result, as the probability changes, is a spectrum of expected values from which to choose, as is illustrated in Figure 4.9. Examining the chart, one can see that when the probability equates to zero, then we correspond to the maximin rule; whereas if the probability is equal to one, we have the maximax rule. The crossover point of the two lines is called the break-even point. This is the point where, if the probability of nature is to the right of the point (in our case, if one feels that 64.3 percent of the time there will not be a fault in the new computer), then one should choose alternative A_1. If one feels that there is more than a 35.7 percent

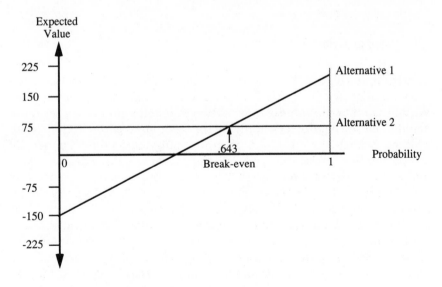

Figure 4.9 Break-even Diagram

chance that there will be a fault, then go with option A_2, which is the decision to the right of the break-even point. The Laplace rule equates to the mid-point,

$$P_{[\text{Nature is kind/unkind}]} = .5$$

or the 50 percent point.

A few items should be noted. In the situation described above, we are examining the payoffs that are dependent on the likelihood of two sets of alternatives occurring. There is nothing magic about two alternatives, however. We could increase the number of alternatives to three, five, etc., without changing the way we would have computed the expected value. Note, though, that we were given known estimates of the outcomes, but not of the likelihoods of their occurrence. In practice, we are likely not to know either very well, thus forcing us to use some type of method such as Delphi, probability encoding, modeling, etc., to obtain them. Changing the estimate of the costs might then change dramatically the choice we might make. For example, if the computer repair costs were more in the range of $175K instead of $125K, the choice might not be so obvious.

4.3.2 Value of perfect information

This brings us back full circle to the value of information. Of what value is it to us to know exactly the estimate of a risk's likelihood or magnitude? We will say that the value of information that helps qualify the estimate about a risk, be it gained by applying the techniques of the Delphi group process, probability encoding, or prototyping, etc., is determined by comparing the difference between the expected value of a decision with and without perfect information. This will become clear in a moment.

Let's assume that, for the example above, you are going to give yourself a third option. You really do not want to call in an outside group yet. Their cost is a bit high, and you are skeptical about the results. Luckily, one of the new hires on the project is a first-class engineer who was trained to diagnose and separate hardware errors from software errors. She happens to have worked with almost exactly the same type of computer in the military. The only difference is, it was the militarized version, which is one revision removed from the current computer your company now possesses. Excitedly, you call her in and sketch out the problem. She assures you that she could recreate a diagnostic program, which she had developed in the service, to test out 100 percent of that particular computer's circuitry. If, after running the diagnostics, errors are found, she would recommend calling in the computer repair company, as in option A_2. On the other hand, if no errors are found, you could then choose option A_1 with confidence.

She goes on to say that it will take about a week to create the test suite, and another three days to ring out the machine, with the total cost being approximately $35K. You say thanks, you will get back to her later that afternoon with your answer.

Given these extra bits of news, you set off to compute the expected value of this new alternative, A_3. The new payoff matrix will have as its entries $165K if the test program shows no errors ($200K – $35K), and $40K if an error shows up ($200K – $35K – $125K), as shown in Table 4.4. Again, using equation 4.11, we get the following:

$$E_v = A_3 \cdot P_{[\text{Nature is kind}]} + A_3 \cdot P_{[\text{Nature is unkind}]}$$

$$= 165 \cdot P_{[\text{Nature is kind}]} + 40 \cdot P_{[\text{Nature is unkind}]}$$

$$= 165 \cdot x + 40 \cdot (1 - x) = 125x + 40$$

This line is shown in Figure 4.10.

If we knew, for certain, that the probabilities of nature were .5, then the expected value of alternative A_3 would be 102.5. Option A_3, to say the least, now seems very attractive.

The Expected Value of the Sample of Information (EVSI) gained, by investing $35K in a test suite, over another option, is the difference between the expected value of the test suite and the expected value of not

TABLE 4.4 Payoff Matrix with Three Alternatives

	State of Nature	
	Favorable	Unfavorable
Alternative 1	200K	–150K
Alternative 2	75K	75K
Alternative 3	165K	40K

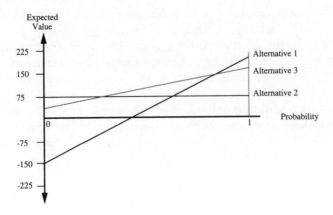

Figure 4.10 New Payoff Options

having the information (at the same likelihood of occurrence). Thus, the expected value of the information gained by the test suite over calling in the computer repair company right away is $102.5K – $75K, or $27.5K, and is $77.5K over gutting it out. In fact, this means we could have invested another $27K in the test program and still come out ahead of calling the computer company right away. (Remember, this is still our best choice, if we do not decide to build a test suite, and if the likelihood remains at .5.) Thus, we could say, in this case, that the Expected Value of having Perfect Information (EVPI) is $62.5K. Interpreted another way, the expected value of perfect information is the maximum expected value of the sample of information.

4.3.3 Utility

It appears that the decision to go with developing a test suite is now a foregone conclusion. The "utility" of it seems proven, as we can reduce the uncertainty about our situation at a cost that we could not have achieved previously. However, before we proceed further, a moment's digression to discuss the concept of utility would be fruitful.[32–33] The reason is that the ideas of the value of something and its utility (or function) are often used interchangeably (as we did above), but in fact represent subtly different ideas.

John von Neumann and Oskar Morgenstern[34] investigated the modeling of value systems and the rational dealing with risk. They formulated a set of assumptions about an individual's preferences when making a decision, and from these assumptions showed the following:

1. A cardinal scale for measuring an individual's preferences (called a utility scale) exists.
2. The utility scale is so defined that, if the individual chooses the alternative with the highest expected utility, the individual's choice will be consistent with the expressed preferences that were used in defining the scale.

The purposes of this definition of utility are twofold. One is descriptive; i.e., it is a tool for predicting decisions people will make. Second, it is prescriptive; i.e., it establishes how people ought to make decisions. Of course, these two purposes depend highly on whether the individual accepts the underlying assumptions about the utility scale.

Thus, in general, utility is the degree of worth that a person attaches to something when a need is filled to some level of satisfaction. For example, food has a certain monetary cost associated with it. For "x" dollars, one can buy "y" amount of food. But food also takes on more importance than a pure monetary element if we are poor and have a starving family to support. Food means survival. As we increase the availability of food (i.e., increase the amount of food by measured increments) from providing a subsistence level, to a level of plenty, to a level where there is more food than the family can possibly eat, the utility of the food to the family at first increases, then peaks, and then either levels off or decreases, as shown in Figure 4.11. The degree of worth the family attaches to the food changes with the satisfaction of their need to survive. Its utility may also change with respect to its worth in other social contexts. In seventeenth and eighteenth century England, for instance, the amount of food one possessed indicated social status—those with food must be rich. Exactly where something such as food changes from a necessity to a luxury is dependent on an individual's preference.

The idea of utility is also important in software systems. For instance, in testing a computer program, it is usually impossible to test every possible program path. Generally, one can generate more code than can ever be completely tested. Thus, past a certain threshold, no matter how much more we test, the degree of worth to us of the extra effort diminishes. The reader is probably aware of the concept as the law of diminishing returns. Where this threshold lies is usually a great matter of debate, especially in safety-critical systems. The same concept holds

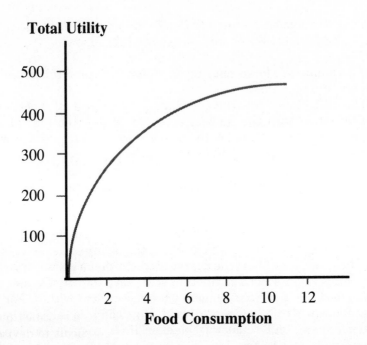

Figure 4.11 Utility of Food

true when new requirements are added to an existing system to get that "one extra feature." This is sometimes referred to as "gold-plating."

Another example of utility was shown in Chapter 1. Recall that some studies indicate that only 10 percent of software projects finish within budget, 15 percent finish on schedule, and 70 percent finish with the desired performance. These figures indicate that performance for most developers is of a higher utility than either cost or schedule.

Now, also recall our assumption in the beginning of this chapter about rational people and economic man: The concept of value (as opposed to utility) is not constrained to the concept of rationality. It includes all the intangible elements of emotions, morality, ethics, and aesthetics used to satisfy an individual's needs and wants. Utility, on the other hand, is defined purely in rational, economic terms. In other words, an incremental change in the economic value of an item will engender a change in perception of utility of that item.

Thus, utility is a special subset of value. In other words, utility denotes the rational behavior of people in terms of satisfying their needs and

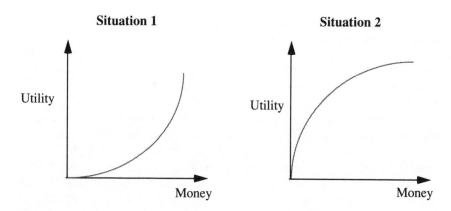

Figure 4.12 Utility Comparison

wants. It has been shown that utility can be quantified, but always in terms of rational *economic* behavior. However, the perception of value and utility makes sense only for a specific individual at a specific time. The utility of something for a group is extremely difficult to devise, unless all members of the group perceive "identical" needs and wants. This does not occur very often, as the value of something, and its utility, will change with respect to time for each individual as their specific circumstances change. "All for one, and one for all" makes for good literature but lousy utility theory.

The idea of perception can be shown by Figure 4.12, which illustrates in two different situations the marginal utility of money to a gambler.[35] In Situation 1, the marginal utility is increasing, but the money is decreasing. This indicates a gamble unfavorable in monetary terms might be favorable when compared to its utility. In other words, although the monetary gain itself might be small, the gain in some other dimension, such as the pleasure derived from taking a risk itself, might be high. (The example of the utility of system performance might also fit this type of curve.) Individuals in this situation might be considered risk-favoring.

In Situation 2, one sees a reversed curve. Individuals might now tend to be risk-adverse, even though the money available is increasing. For example, if one wins too much money in one night playing blackjack at the casinos in Vegas, he will be banned from coming in the next evening. It is better to get less money on any one night and to keep coming back. Another situation might be when you are gambling on your ability to call a coin heads or tails, starting at $50, and continuing the bet as "double or nothing." If you have won five times in a row, even though the chances are 50–50 that you will be right, the amount of money you may lose may not make it worthwhile for you to continue. Company decision-makers tend to follow this pattern of behavior.

The conclusion that should be reached is, although expected value computations are valuable, they are not sufficient for making a decision. We need to compute the utility of each decision as well. The problem, of course, is that we need to determine the utility function of each alternative, and these, as was shown in Figure 4.12, are not often linear. The subject is a bit trickier than implied above, because it is rare that an individual or group will have only one function to consider. Multi-attribute utility theory, deals with two or more preference decisions. It is beyond this book to show how one should go about developing utility curves or computing the associated error, although the general information-gathering techniques are similar to those described earlier on estimation. The reader can refer to notes [36–38] for more information about accomplishing this task.

Returning to our example of the poor senior engineer, we have constructed a hypothetical utility curve showing utility versus the payoff for each of the available courses of action, illustrated in Figure 4.13. The expected utility of each is computed the same way as the expected value. Table 4.5 shows each alternative's expected value and expected utility for a probability of (.5). Notice that A_1 has a negative expected utility, whereas the utility of A_2 and A_3 is positive. Given this data we would still go with A_3 as a choice on how to proceed.

As a general rule, expected utilities will be the preferred way over that of expected values for making a decision, if there is a choice available. As with expected value computation, the more positive the expected utility, the more preferable the choice. In fact, negative expected utilities, even

TABLE 4.5 Expected Value/Utility Payoff Matrix

	Favorable Payoff/Utility	Unfavorable Payoff/Utility	Expected Value	Expected Utility
Alternative 1	200K/10	–150K/–18	25.0	–4
Alternative 2	75K/3	75K/3	75.0	3
Alternative 3	165K/8	40K/51	102.5	3

where there exist positive expected values, will make an alternative unattractive. The reason is, decision makers tend to be risk-adverse rather than risk-favoring. They are more adverse to losses than for the opportunity to gain. The key ideas to remember at all times are: We are dealing with individual perceptions and subjective probabilities, and these will always color what we can do in risk analysis and management.

4.3.4 Value of imperfect information

For about five minutes, you are feeling pleased with yourself. You have decided to go ahead with the test suite development. You are just about to call and tell the engineer to go ahead, when she rings you instead. She has been doing some analysis of the new computer. She says that because of the enhancements to it, she feels that she could tailor her test program coverage to include most, but not all, possible faults.

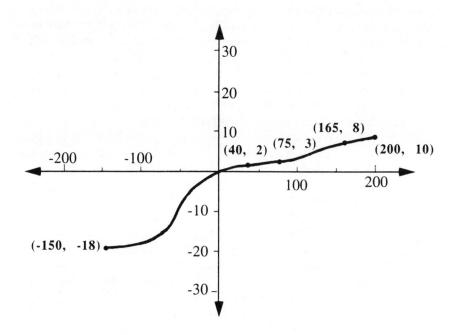

Figure 4.13 Example Utility Curve

Getting butterflies in your stomach, you ask about her use of the term "most." She points out that since the enhancements effected approximately a 10 percent change to the type of computer she had worked on previously, there may be some areas she can't guarantee would be checked. Even with the tailoring of her test suite, about 1–2 percent of the machine would go unchecked. This area might be where the faults lie, because this is where the new features were added. But usually, new features are also the ones that would have received the greatest amount of testing by the manufacturer. In her opinion, if errors were present, they would occur in the interplay of the new features with the old, and therefore most likely show up while programs were executing on the unchanged bits of the computer. Now you are really uneasy, especially about the extensive use of the term, "most likely." What do you do now?

In general, one cannot obtain perfect information about how nature will treat us by developing test suites, applying the Delphi method, creating simulations, etc. We will always have some imperfection in any path we take.[39] In the above situation, for example, there are two sources of imperfection with which we must live.

The first is the probability that the execution of the test suite will lead you to not call the computer repair company, when, in fact, there was a fault present. In other words, because of imperfections in the test suite, a fault actually present was not detected. This means that you would run the test suite, find no faults, and choose to go on with alternative A_1. One can state the situation as a probability, using the notation $P(A_1 \mid F)$, which is read as the probability of choosing A_1 given that a fault F exists. From the problem, the probability that no repair is required, when, in fact, one is needed, can be estimated to be at least .02, i.e., 2 percent.

The second source of imperfect knowledge is a little harder to see. Here, the execution of the test suite would lead us not to call the computer repair company, when, in fact, there wasn't any need to anyway, because a fault never existed. Thus, we "wasted" our money looking for a nonexistent fault. This situation can be written as $P(A_1 \mid NF)$, where NF means "no fault exists."

Now the $P(A_1 \mid NF)$ will not always be 1.0, because again there may be errors in the test suite. In contrast to the first source of imperfection, there is some probability that the test suite might find errors that did not exist, forcing us to call in the computer repair company when it wasn't required. After talking to the test engineer, she says there is a 5 percent chance that her test might detect something that is not really present, or a 95 percent chance that our test result showing no fault really is correct. Thus, $P(A_1 \mid NF)$ equals .95.

It is important to see that the two cases of imperfection are not necessarily symmetrical, nor should we necessarily want them to be. After all, detecting a "fault" that may not exist may be "easier" than detecting one that may exist. It may also be of more importance—it is of greater worth to think a fault is there and show that it is not than to skip over one that actually is there.

For this example, to make life easier, we will assume that utility equals value. What you need to calculate, then, is the expected value of using the test suite to determine whether to gut it out, i.e., option A_1, or to call the computer repair company, i.e., option A_2. Let's assume that nature is still equally kind and unkind; i.e., the probability of a fault equals the probability of no fault, or $P(F) = P(NF)$. The expected value is calculated as before, by multiplying each potential payoff by the probability of its occurrence, with the addition that now there is a conditional probability involved, as follows:

$$E_v = P(A_1) \text{ (payoff if using } A_1) + P(A_2) \text{ (payoff if using } A_2)$$

$$= P(A_1) \{P(NF \mid A_1) (\$200K) + P(F \mid A_1) (-\$150K)\} + P(A_2)(\$75K)$$

$$= P(A_1) \{P(NF \mid A_1) (\$200K) + P(F \mid A_1) (-\$150K)\} + P(A_2)(\$75K)$$

We know some of the probabilities in this equation, such as:

$$P(F) = P(NF) = .5 \quad P(A_1 \mid NF) = .95 \quad P(A_1 \mid F) = .02$$

To determine the other probabilities, one only need turn to Bayes' theorem, as shown in equations 4.9 and 4.10. With a little algebraic manipulation,

$$P(A_1) = P(A_1 \mid NF) P(NF) + (A_1 \mid F) P(F) \text{ thus } P(A_2) = 1 - P(A_1)$$

Similarly, we need to compute the probability that there was no fault, given we were going to take option A_1. This is expressed as:

$$(NF \mid A_1) = P(A_1 \mid NF) P(NF) / P(A_1)$$

thus $\qquad\qquad P(F \mid A_1) = 1 - P(NF \mid A_1)$

We now have all the equations we require. Substituting,

$$P(A_1) = (.95)(.5) + (.02)(.5) \qquad\qquad P(A_2) = 1 - .485$$
$$= .485 \qquad\qquad\qquad\qquad\qquad = .515$$

$$P(NF \mid A_1) = (.95)(.5)/(.485) \qquad P(F \mid A_1) = 1 - .979$$
$$= .979 \qquad\qquad\qquad\qquad\qquad\qquad = .021$$

Thus, substituting into the original equation,

$$E_v = P(A_1)\{P(NF \mid A_1)(\$200K) + P(F \mid A_1)(-\$150K)\} + P(A_2)(\$75K)$$

$$= (.485)\{(.979)(\$200K) + (.021)(-\$150K)\} + (.515)(\$75K)$$

$$= \$132.1K$$

Since the largest expected value we could obtain without running the test suite was $75K using option A_2, then the expected value of the imperfect information provided by the test suite is $57.1K. This is less than the $62.5K having perfect information, but then it is still worth more than the $35K spent developing the test suite. The moral of the story is, we should proceed with the test suite, even if there are flaws in it at the levels we have predicted.

One other approach that might be considered at this point is whether we indeed need to spend $35K on the test suite. Could we instead use a less tailored approach, which could mean more error might be possible, but one that could save us more money? Table 4.6 illustrates what might

TABLE 4.6 Expected Values

$Cost	Estimated $P(A_1 \mid F)$	Estimated $P(A_1 \mid NF)$	Expected Value	(EVOI) Expected Value of Information	(ENVSI) Expected Net Value of Test Suite
0K	–	–	75.0K	0.0K	–
10K	.10	.80	87.9K	12.9K	2.9K
20K	.05	.90	125.6K	50.6K	30.6K
35K	.02	.95	132.1K	57.1K	22.1K
50K	.01	.98	135.2K	60.2K	10.2K
62.5K	0.00	1.00	137.5K	62.5K	0.0K

happen if one were to spend less on the test suite. The probabilities shown are the new estimates for $P(A_1 \mid NF)$ and $P(A_1 \mid F)$, at the different test suite costs, given that $P(F) = P(NF) = .5$. If one were to plot these results as in Figure 4.14, one would see that if, and that is a big if, the probabilities were as shown, a test suite could be built for \$20K that would give us better results than the one for \$35K. The Expected Net Value of Sample Information (ENVSI) is computed as the expected value of the sample information, minus the cost of the sample information—in this case the test suite. This is an example of where spending too much money can be as bad as not spending enough.

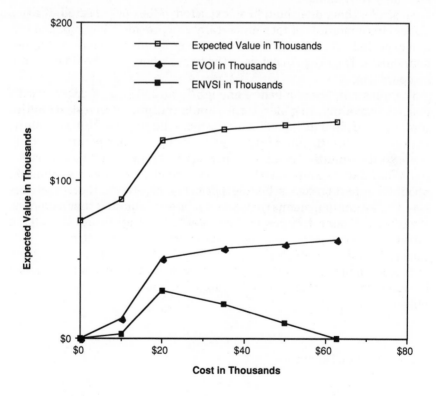

Figure 4.14 Graphs of EV, EVOI, and ENVSI

4.3.5 What price uncertainty reduction?

Of course, it is important to keep remembering that the above computations are based upon estimates of the likelihood of certain occurrences. If these estimates are off, then the computations are misleading at best and meaningless at worst. The expected value of information is best used when either the likelihood or magnitude of the risk is known. Having both unknown requires doing this type of calculation for each independently, and then trying to do them together. For example, if in the example above one could have run another set of computations about how certain the accuracies were for the estimates $P(A_1 \mid NF)$, $P(A_1 \mid F)$, $P(F)$, or $P(NF)$. This could go on to every variable affecting a risk. There is a point where one must draw the line and state that one cannot know for sure what is true and what is not, and that the best we can hope for is to show boundary conditions.

As a rule, then, one should use expected values or expected utilities under circumstances of total uncertainty to provide a lower boundary, and expected values or utilities under perfect information to give upper boundaries. The range in between the two is where one should expect to be operating.

The question, "How much is enough?" can never be answered with absolute certainty. In general, one should continue to invest in studies until the marginal utility of investing more diminishes. Unfortunately, in practice, it is difficult to estimate the utility function of further study because it is multiattributed. We want to know about both a risk's likelihood and its consequences—and in the next section on evaluation about its impact on cost, schedule, performance, etc. Further, resources spent on estimation means they may not be available for other purposes. If we feel that our estimates are "acceptable," taking into account all the pitfalls concerning the issues of measurement scales, estimator bias, estimation uncertainty, etc., then a hard look should be taken at putting any more money into refining the estimates. It may turn out that it can be wiser spent in either the risk evaluation phase or risk management phase.

4.4 Estimation Summary

Earlier in this chapter, we asked the question, "Given that one is faced with these estimation uncertainties, what can be done to overcome them, other than recognizing that they exist?" A number of different ways were listed, the first being to understand to which process an identified risk belongs. All risks, it was said, can be considered belonging to one of the three following processes: behavioral, natural, or random. Table 4.2 also pointed out the limits under which one operated in making estimations by trying to reduce their uncertainty. Looking at the table once again, it should now be clear that reducing the uncertainty of risk does not, in and by itself, reduce a risk.[40] Furthermore, there is a limit to what price should be paid for reducing uncertainty. Thus, overall, we will say the true value of the information can only be measured against the degree of control it provides over subsequent actions. Toward this end, and to avoid any possible misunderstanding, all risk estimates should have their uncertainty explicitly shown. This uncertainty should be explicitly acknowledged by senior management so they will not be surprised later.

In Chapter 5, we will explore the mechanics of how the estimates developed in this chapter can be used to increase the degree of available control over a software engineering risk.

Questions

1   Can risks be objectively estimated, or must they always be subjective?

2   Of the four objectives of estimation, which are the most important? Why?

3   Why is the type of measurement scale applied important to risk estimation? Do you think anyone notices the differences? How do you use the words *probable*, *most likely*, and *expected*?

4   What is the quantitative difference between the words above in your vocabulary? How sure are you? When do they mean the same thing, and when do they differ? What are some other synonyms?

5   What does measurement uncertainty mean? How is it related to precision and accuracy?

6 How do human estimation biases interface with measurement accuracy and precision? Name three software and/or programmatic software systems where human estimation biases can cause technical risks.

7 Name four ways to do uncertainty reduction. Which, in your opinion, is best? Justify your answer.

8 What does utility mean? How are value and utility different? When are they the same?

9 Why is the true value of information measured against the degree of control it provides subsequent actions?

10 Find the general formula for the expected value of perfect information. Next, find the general formula for the expected value of no information. Then find the general formula for the expected value of imperfect information. When is expected value of information misleading?

References

1. John Canada, *Intermediate Economic Analysis for Management and Engineering*, Prentice-Hall, Inc., Englewood Cliffs, NJ, 1971.

2. William D. Rowe, *An Anatomy of Risk*, Robert E. Krieger Publishing Co., Malabar, FL, 1988.

3. John Canada, *Intermediate Economic Analysis for Management and Engineering*, Prentice-Hall, Inc., Englewood Cliffs, NJ, 1971.

4. S. S. Stevens, "Measurement, Psychophysics, and Utility," in C. W. Churchman and P. Ratoosh, Eds., *Measurement: Definitions and Theories*, Wiley, New York, 1959.

5. Kenneth R. MacCrimmon and Donald A. Wehrung, *Taking Risks*, Free Press, New York, 1986.

6. Melvin W. Lifson and Edward F. Shaifer, Jr., *Decision and Risk Management for Construction Management*, John Wiley & Sons, New York, 1982.

7. "Technical Risk Assessment: The Current Status of DOD Efforts," Government Accounting Office Report GAO/PEMD-86-5, April 1986.

8. Peter G. Moore, *The Business of Risk*, University Press, Cambridge, England, 1983.

9. Nicholas Rescher, *Risk*, University Press of America, Lanham, MD, 1983.

10. ——, *Risk*, University Press of America, Lanham, MD, 1983.

11. The very act of measuring something changes the measurement of what it is we are measuring; therefore no measurement can ever be exact. (If we knew the exact measurement, we wouldn't have to measure it, would we?)

12. L. Oxelheim and C. Wihlborg, *Macroeconomic Uncertainty—International Risks and Opportunities for the Corporation*, John Wiley and Sons, Chichester, England, 1987.

13. Stephen Pile, *The Book of Heroic Failures*, Routledge & Kegan Paul Ltd., England, 1979.

14. Norman R. Augustine, *Augustine's Laws*, American Institute of Aeronautics and Astronautics, New York, 1983.

15. Peter G. Moore, *The Business of Risk*, University Press, Cambridge, England, 1983.

16. Miley W. Merkhofer, "Quantifying Judgmental Uncertainty: Methodology, Experiences, and Insights," in *IEEE Transactions on Man, Systems, and Cybernetics*, Vol. SMC-17, No. 5, September/October 1987.

17. Scott A. Hastings, "A Maritime Strategy for 2038," *The Naval Institute Proceedings*, Vol. 114, No. 7, July 1988.

18. Over twenty specific cognitive biases have been associated with human decision making. We will examine these in more depth in the companion volume on individual risk taking. Refer to Andrew Sage's excellent article, "Behavioral and Organizational Considerations in the Design of Information Systems and Processes for Planning and Decision Support," in *IEEE Transactions on Systems, Man, and Cybernetics*, Vol. SMC-11, No. 9, September 1981.

19. William D. Rowe, *An Anatomy of Risk*, Robert E. Krieger Publishing Co., Malabar, FL, 1988. Sometimes, one will see risks as also being modeled only along the lines of probabilistic or deterministic processess. In other words, probabilistic or deterministic exposure, and probabilistic or deterministic effects. For this book, we feel the behavioral process is of sufficient significance to have its own category.

20. O. Helmer, *Social Technology*, Basic Books, New York, 1966.

21. Miley W. Merkhofer, "Quantifying Judgmental Uncertainty: Methodology, Experiences, and Insights," in *IEEE Transactions on Man, Systems, and Cybernetics*, Vol. SMC-17, No. 5, September/October 1987.

22. In this text, we will concentrate our efforts primarily on probability theory, which deduces from a mathematical model the properties of a physical process, whereas statistical inference infers the properties of the model from observed data. The reader should refer to a book on statistical methods for the other perspective.

23. Nicholas Rescher, *Risk*, University Press of America, Lanham, MD, 1983.

24. F. Mosteller et al., *Probability With Statistical Applications*, Addison-Wesley Publishing Company, Reading, MA, 1970.

25. We will include, for discussion's sake, all elements of our risk triplet {< s_i, l_i, x_i >}. It should be realized that buying information may include any combination of the elements such as the likelihood of the risk and/or its magnitude. This only complicates matters slightly mathematically. More typically, information buying is not done to qualify the estimate of a risk, but to determine if a risk is missed. This is more cost effective and is more in line with putting a valuation on the risk process as a whole. This is accomplished either at the risk estimate stage or at the risk identification stage of the risk analysis process.

26. Nicholas Rescher, *Risk*, University Press of America, Lanham, MD, 1983.

27. William D. Rowe, *An Anatomy of Risk*, Robert E. Krieger Publishing Co., Malabar, FL, 1988.

28. Melvin W. Lifson and Edward F. Shaifer, Jr., *Decision and Risk Management for Construction Management*, John Wiley & Sons, New York, 1982.

29. Barry Boehm, *Software Engineering Economics*, Prentice-Hall, Inc., Englewood Cliffs, NJ, 1981.

30. Realistically, this option should also be included in the analysis, but as we will see in the next section on evaluation of risks, we will dismiss extremely unlikely circumstances.

31. Richard S. Eckaus, *Basic Economics*, Little, Brown and Company, Boston, 1972.

32. Nicholas Rescher, *Risk*, University Press of America, Lanham, MD, 1983.

33. William D. Rowe, *An Anatomy of Risk*, Robert E. Krieger Publishing Co., Malabar, FL, 1988.

34. John von Neumann and Oskar Morgenstern, *Theory of Games and Economic Behavior*, Princeton University Press, 3rd edition, 1953 (First edition 1944).

35. Nicholas Rescher, *Risk*, University Press of America, Lanham, MD, 1983.

36. Richard S. Eckaus, *Basic Economics*, Little, Brown and Company, Boston, 1972.

37. W. Edwards, "The Theory of Decision Making," in *Psychological Bulletin*, Vol. 51, July 1954.

38. Harry Rarig and Yacov Haimes, "Risk/Dispersion Index," in *IEEE Transactions on Systems, Man, and Cybernetics*, Vol. SMC-13, No. 3, May/June 1983.

39. A good survey discussing how imperfect information is handled using various approaches can be found in H. Stephanou and A. Sage, "Perspectives on Imperfect Information Processing," in *IEEE Transactions on Systems, Man, and Cybernetics*, Vol. SMC-17, No. 5, September/October 1987.

40. William D. Rowe, *An Anatomy of Risk*, Robert E. Krieger Publishing Co., Malabar, FL, 1988.

Risk Analysis: Evaluation

"Be wary then; best safety lies in fear."

Hamlet I, iii, 43

5.0 Introduction

So far, in Chapters 3 and 4, we have investigated the means to identify a risk to our project and estimated the likelihood and consequences of such a risk. But, in so doing, we have limited our view to a solitary risk and the individual components that make up its risk triplet,

$$< s_i, l_i, x_i >.$$

It is now time to turn our attention to the larger set of risks confronting a software project and investigating their interactions with one another, as given by the risk set,

$$\{< s_i, l_i, x_i >\}.$$

As a reminder, s_i concerns the scenarios of what can go wrong; l_i concerns the generic likelihood of the s_i's happening; and x_i represents a measure of the consequences of the "ith" scenario, or the "damage index."

The purpose of performing risk evaluation is threefold. The first is a "final" quantification of the likelihood and consequences of the risks identified in the previous two sections. By final quantification, one wants to reduce any nagging uncertainty there may be in the estimates of the likelihood and consequences at this time. It is likely to be necessary to reanalyze a risk's likelihood and possible consequences as the situation changes later on, however.

The second purpose is to provide some mechanism of prioritizing the risks within the classes or categorizations defined in the risk identification phase. By prioritization, we mean a risk can be evaluated against another and ultimately be placed into some order. Figure 5.1 illustrates two risk evaluations along the axes of uncertainty and magnitude. This ordering is required as input to the next phase on risk management, which will be discussed in its own right in Chapter 6.

The third purpose is to seek preliminary ways of averting risk by considering alternative outcomes. The initial elements of contingency planning are also begun for each alternative. This does not mean that risk management will be performed now, however. What is sought is an anticipated response to a risk, in order to provide to the decision maker all the necessary information required to make a well-informed and rational decision.

The reader might be a little confused at this point. Wasn't there some risk evaluation in the previous chapter on estimation? Well, yes and no. We did use some techniques, such as expected value computation, to evaluate whether one should spend more time and effort on obtaining

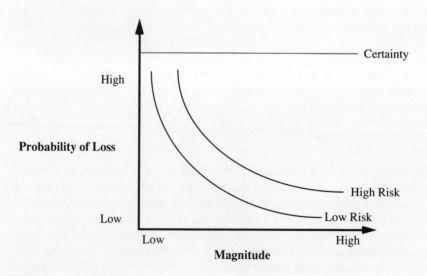

Figure 5.1 Risk Evaluations

better estimates of an individual risk's likelihood and/or consequences. However, we did not evaluate the risk itself in conjunction with other risks in the context of the project objectives, which is the purpose of the evaluation process. One cannot look at a risk in isolation. Therefore, one must understand all the threats or range of forces that could produce adverse effects; all the resources or assets that could be affected by the threats; all the modifying factors, those particular features, internal and external to the resources, such as risk coupling, that tend to increase or reduce the likelihood of the threats becoming a reality; and all the consequences of the risk, the manner in which or the extent to which the threat manifests its effects upon the resources.[1] This understanding is of double importance when new risks are being evaluated.

As will be seen, the techniques used in the estimation process are often the same type that will be used in the evaluation process. Remember from Chapter 2 that there is a significant overlap among identification, estimation, and evaluation, and it is often difficult to distinguish where one starts and the other ends. It will also be seen that, when one does risk management, the elements of risk analysis will be constantly applied in an iterative fashion, as risks change in their likelihood and consequences, and, unfortunately, as new risks appear.

The evaluation process consists of three general steps.[2] The first is the establishment of what is called a risk referent level. This is simply an established level of "acceptable" risk, either absolute or relative, for each category of risk consequence. It is important that this level be established independently of a particular type of risk, and that one finds a level balanced between "good enough" and "perfect." However, a single base referent level for all risk categories might prove necessary.

The second step is to determine the level of risk associated in total with the project or system under study, called the system risk referent. This means trying to understand how, why, where, when, etc., all the various risks interact. Ideally, the system risk referent is an aggregation of all the individual risks, which can provide a single reference point for the project. It instead may be, due to circumstances, one or more individual risks that as a group make up the most severe risks to the project's success.

The third step is to compare the calculated project risk with the system referent level, within acceptable error limits of the estimates and the referent. Simply put, this means trying to determine whether one should stop the project now, regroup and try a different approach, or press on, since the project's risks all seem to be within acceptable limits.

Once these steps are undertaken, risk management actions are next.

5.1 Evaluation Criteria

One of the first necessities in performing risk evaluation is determination of the evaluation criteria the individual risk consequences are going to be measured against. As was mentioned, there may also be a requirement for project base referent risk criteria to be established.

If one has done the Risk Estimate of the Situation (RES) as called for in the beginning of Chapter 3, then the general criteria for success should be established. If this has not been done, then some thought must be given to accomplishing this now. Success criteria are founded upon the idea of successfully obtaining one or more of the objectives set out for the project. These objectives may be stated in rather broad terms, such as:

- maximize profit
- minimize cost

- minimize risk of loss
- maximize sales

- minimize cyclic fluctuations
- create a favorable image

- maximize quality of service
- maximize growth rate

- maximize employee satisfaction
- maximize firm's prestige

- minimize loss of life
- minimize loss of property

Most of these objectives are measurable to some degree. For example, take the objective "maximize sales." A target level of some monetary value or number of products sold can be set, against which a particular course of action can be measured. On the other hand, maximizing a firm's prestige might be harder. One might need to set up the number of favorable references in a particular journal or set of newspapers as a referent level against which to measure. A risk and its consequences might then be measured against this background.[3]

As was stated in earlier chapters, it is often the case for computer systems that the project's objectives are ill-defined (such as the system must be maintainable), or that they are, in fact, strategies in disguise. Recall the list in Figure 3.3. It is crucial that the risk referent level be measurable, but just as important is the fact that the referent level have an actual go/no-go decision or referent point.[4] This is the point, often called the break-point, where the choices are equi-acceptable. To make the evaluation process worth the trouble, it is imperative that the point against which the project will be stopped, or that an individual risk is too difficult to overcome and thus replanning must be accomplished, *be determined.*

For example, in software projects, the three typical referent levels are defined by a predetermined project cost, schedule, and performance. Given a risk, or a set of risks, how often, a priori, is there a risk point where the project will be terminated when any one, or combination of the three, are exceeded? One could ask any large software project currently underway to demonstrate where this point is before they started the project and be fairly confident it could not be shown. One could be confident in this because of (a) the number of projects with runaway costs; and (b) the almost identical comments heard from purchasers of large systems—"If we had known the cost (or substitute "time to deliver" or "performance") before we started, we would never have begun the project."

Cost and schedule estimates are inevitably low because there is not only great pressure for them to be low, but because they mean absolutely nothing at the beginning of a project. If they actually did mean something, then the number of projects that met their cost, schedule, or performance goals would be higher because more programs would not be started. As one software engineering sage has asked, "Why is there never enough money to do it right, but all the money you need to fix it?" Just knowing this is true makes accurate estimation of the cost and schedule suspect.

Figure 5.2, (a) and (b), illustrate the concept of a referent point. The idea is exactly the same as the cross-over point seen in the section on

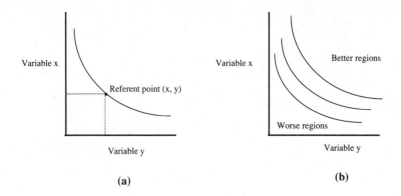

Figure 5.2 Risk Referents: (a) Point, (b) Region

estimation, or the line an expected value can follow at different probabilities. The line shows how the two parameters can be traded off against
one another, whereas the referent point is where either course is
acceptable. Notice in Figure 5.2 (b) that instead of a certain point, we
have a region of acceptability. As shown, above a certain region the risk
and its consequences are acceptable, and below, it is not.

Unfortunately, because of estimation error due to (and because of) the
complexity of multifaceted risk situations, one cannot normally determine a clean line or explicit region, as depicted in these figures. Instead,
one must struggle with the fact that there exists a "gray area," as
depicted in Figure 5.3. Within this gray area, one cannot be certain that
one is in the region of the better-off or the region of the worse-off.

Compounding the search for a referent level are the nonequivalued
risks. Remember from the discussions on expected value and utility, that
one may not necessarily be able to find a single line that can represent
all risks. Even using multiattribute utility theory this proves to be
difficult. Think for a moment about how you would define the success
criteria for a project based on the objectives of maximizing profit,
improving quality, and improving the company's image while meeting
cost, schedule, and performance criteria on a complex project using all
untried and untested new technology. It sounds ridiculous, but that is
what most new software developments entail, along with trying to
achieve a few other objectives. Thus, one may find oneself either

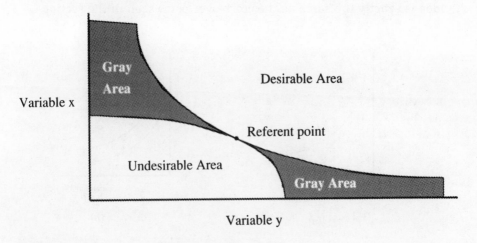

Figure 5.3 Uncertainty in Evaluation Choices

simplifying the referent level by aggregating risks, or prioritizing which referent levels must be met.

One should not feel that finding the correct referent level is an impossible task, and therefore the search should not be bothered with. For example, NASA has, for the Space Shuttle, been able to create a general set of relative system risk thresholds, against which to measure the risks to the Shuttle development and to a particular launch. This is depicted in Figure 5.4. Notice in this conceptual diagram that the initial risk levels are higher than the acceptable level for a launch, but are implicitly within a region to proceed with the project. As the project proceeds, the acceptable level of risk will decrease. Thus, in the beginning of a project, a 40 percent chance of success, or a 60 percent chance of failure, will be acceptable to proceed with the project, given that there is confidence that the probability of success can be increased over time. (Remember, a probability of success of 100 percent, or certainty, only exists *after* the project has been completed.) The graph also shows graphically that risks will change, either in a negative or positive direction, as the project continues, thus demonstrating the necessity of continual risk analysis and management. In employing software engineering risk management, one wishes to be able to duplicate this concept for various stages of the software life-cycle.

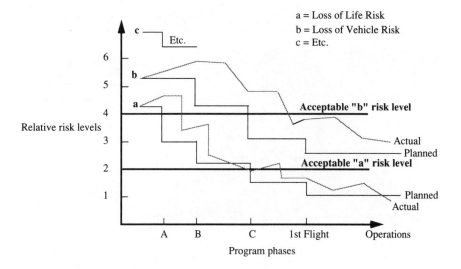

Figure 5.4 NASA Risk Chart

5.2 Determining Level of Risk

The next step in performing risk evaluation is to determine a level of risk that can be used to evaluate the project as a whole. This implies that one needs to understand the various risk interactions, as well as how modifying factors might influence these interactions. To accomplish this, we must understand the concepts of risk exposure and risk coupling.

We have already been introduced to the idea of risk exposure in the section on risk identification. Recall Figure 3.10, which showed a pyramid depicting the general categories of known risks, predictable risks, and unknown risks. One can use the same chart to illustrate not only a risk's frequency and predictability, but also its severity, as shown in Figure 5.5. More generally, one can place the same information into a table and chart the distribution of loss against all three parameters, as shown in Table 5.1 and Figure 5.6.

The distribution of risk consequences should fall into the pattern shown in the figures. Risks possessing high likelihoods should have a low damage impact and a fairly high level of predictability associated with them. On the other hand, severe losses due to a risk should only occasionally appear, and probably can't be predicted with any accuracy.

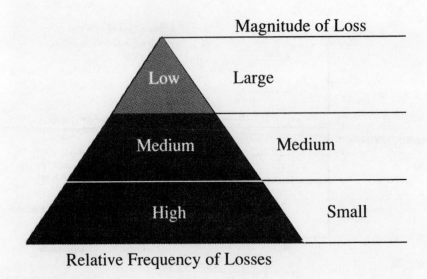

Figure 5.5 Frequency vs. Magnitude of Loss

TABLE 5.1 Risk Characterization

Frequency l_i	Damage x_i	Timing s_i
High	Low	Known
Low	Medium	Predictable
Very Low	High	Unpredictable

This makes sense in light of the Pareto law, which, in this context, states that 80 percent of the negative consequences are caused by 20 percent of the risks. This also says that the most severe risks, the ones that can stop the project if they occur, are limited to a fairly small number. If a project's risk distribution does not follow a normal distribution, then careful consideration of the overall risk to the project must be given.

Ideally, one would like to be able to graph surfaces rather than two-dimensional graphs, although the latter are easier to mathematically

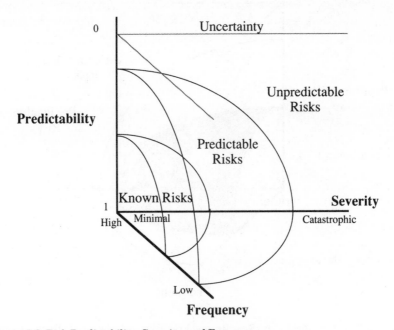

Figure 5.6 Risk Predictability, Severity, and Frequency

manipulate. Graphs of surfaces are useful because one can visualize the various interactions of different risks, and also when some risk stands out. For example, a risk that has a high level of predictability and also has a high damage level will stand out, as shown in Figure 5.7. When this occurs, one must ask whether it is due to risk compounding or coupling.

5.2.1 Risk coupling/risk compounding

Risk coupling or compounding occurs when two risks are linked in some way. Compounding is when, for example, untried technology is used in more than one area of the project concurrently, or when using a new technology in a project may mean that there are fewer trained persons available to work on the effort. Thus, the risk of the new technology is compounded with the risk of not having sufficient numbers of trained personnel. An illustration of this happened in the Department of De-

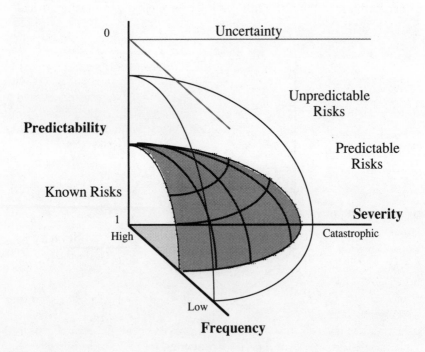

Figure 5.7 Risk Predictability, Severity, and Frequency with Abnormal Distribution

fense with the mandated introduction of the Ada programming language. The language was new, therefore there were few personnel ready to apply it; there were few support tools for the language, other than compilers and debuggers; and it was mandated for use on DoD programs.

An example of risk coupling is when an alternative to a risk causes another risk to increase, or one to appear that was not apparent previously. For instance, motorcyclists in many countries in Europe are now required to wear helmets because of the number of fatalities being caused by head trauma in motorcycle accidents. Although the number of deaths has been reduced, the number of injuries to the neck and spine have been seen to rise. This has been linked to the wearing of the helmet. Thus, reducing the risk in one area may shift it to another. Reducing technical risk in development might later increase evolution costs, for instance.

In many of the evaluation techniques to follow, the compounding and/ or coupling of risks are only implicitly, and not explicitly, accounted for. This is especially true of the network approaches we will examine, where a single risk might appear under many different guises. Wherever possible, when risk compounding is a possibility, a separate risk, called s_{ic}, should be identified as a compounded risk, estimated for, and evaluated. If this is not possible, due to time or budgetary considerations, risks that are involved in a compound situation need to be marked as such and given special attention. It is these compound risks, along with the unidentified or unobservable risks, that pose the greatest hazard to a project. They are as dangerous as walking into a minefield without knowing it. The only time you know you have done it is when you wake up in a hospital with a few limbs torn off, if you have survived. The same result, albeit less physically painful, can be expected in a project.

5.2.2 System risk referent

One is still left with the question of how to determine a system-wide risk referent. An illustration might be most useful. Refer to Figure 5.8, again showing a NASA risk level chart for its major risks.[5] In the case of the Space Shuttle Program, NASA's prioritization of its risks revolved around the one risk that was the ultimate determining factor. For the shuttle, the risk to the lives of the crew was the dominant factor. This one risk, more than any other, is how the success of the Shuttle Program is measured. Losing a vehicle might be terrible, but losing a crew is

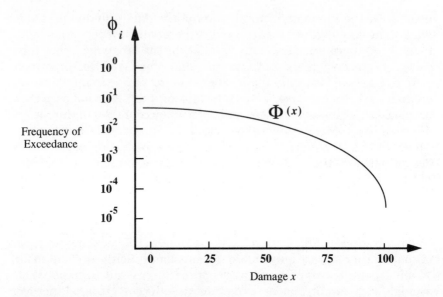

Figure 5.8 Rasmussen Curve

calamitous. The risk reference levels, such as those depicted by NASA, can be developed using a probabilistic technique.[6] We will see how this is done in more detail in a later section, but as a matter of introduction it will be outlined below.

Assume that, given a set of the risk triplets, $\{< s_i, l_i, x_i >\}$, we want to develop specific risk referent levels against which all the possible consequences and damages possible can be compared, i.e., all the x_is against the referent. To do so, let's first map the set of possible x_is against an index scale. This scale will form our measure scale, from which referent lines will be developed. For simplicity, let's set the index scale between zero and a hundred, $[0 \ldots 100]$, where $x_i = 0$ indicates a perfect mission and $x_i = 100$ means loss of the crew. The intermediate values will represent various other levels of loss, such as loss of the vehicle, loss of the mission, partial loss of the mission, etc. One can then enumerate all the possible scenarios, s_is, in order of increasing damage, such that:

$$x_{i+1} \geq x_i \tag{5.1}$$

and let N_s represent the total number of scenarios. Also, let ϕ_i be the fraction of times a particular damage index has occurred, i.e., ϕ_{LOV} equals the fraction of times a vehicle is lost. Given this, one can define the total frequency of all scenarios having damage level x_i or greater:

$$\Phi(x_i) = \sum_{j=i}^{N_s} \phi_i \qquad (5.2)$$

Plotting the $\Phi(x_i)$ on a log scale versus x_i and smoothing the resulting step function, a curve is obtained, as shown in Figure 5.8, depicting $\phi(x)$ versus x. The result has been termed alternately a Rasmussen curve, a frequency of exceedance curve, or a figure of merit curve. This is our referent curve. Its ordinate over any x shows the frequency with which scenarios having damage equal to or greater than x occur.

Since ϕ_i is not known exactly, the risk curve will not be exact either. For example, ϕ_{LOV}, the loss of a vehicle, can only be speculated a priori, and even when it does happen, one is not sure that it will be repeated with the same frequency—there (hopefully) is not a 1 in 25 chance a shuttle will explode. However, from the uncertainty in certain individual ϕ_is (that are better understood), the uncertainty in $\Phi(x)$ can be calculated. The uncertainty can be expressed in a family of risk curves,

$$\{\Phi_p(x): 0 \le P \le 1\} \qquad (5.3)$$

as shown in Figure 5.9. This graph is sometimes called an isorisk contour map.

For a fixed x, the uncertainty about $\Phi(x)$ can be quantified by

$$\text{Probability } (\Phi(x) \le \Phi_p(x)) = P \qquad (5.4)$$

Suppose, for instance, that $\Phi_{.99}(100) = 10^{-6}$. In other words, this means one has a confidence level of 99 percent, that the frequency of the loss of the crew, i.e. $\Phi(100)$, is less than or equal to .000001, or one in a million.

5.3 Compare Risk to the Referent Levels

The final step in performing risk evaluation is the performance of the comparison of the aggregated system risk against the system level referent, and then the individual risks against the referent levels that were determined for each on an individual basis. These are compared, of

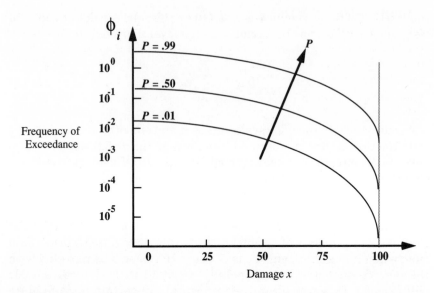

Figure 5.9 Isorisk Curves

course, with cognizance of the limits of error for the risk estimates and the referent levels.

Basically, there are three outcomes of these comparisons: acceptable, impossible, or infeasible. In the first case, the aggregated system risk is less than or equal to the referent, in which case the overall risk is deemed acceptable and the project as planned can proceed. Some cost-benefit trade-offs can be used to decide what alternatives are to be selected for the individual risks that do not pass their referent level. In the other, the aggregate risk estimate is much greater than the system risk referent; in which case, serious thought should be given to abandoning the project. If, however, the referent is only slightly exceeded, then it might only be infeasible, rather than impossible. Risk aversion of individual risks is called for as a minimum course of action, as is the determination of a whole new plan.

There is a point, though, at which the project will not succeed, regardless of what is done. For example, if the risk is "Too short a schedule," there are limits to what can be accomplished. It has been shown that one can compress a software schedule by 25 percent, but not by any more without reducing functionality.[7] Try to reduce it by 30–35 percent, and the probability of failure approaches one.

For the remainder of this chapter, our concern will be on examining the techniques for conducting the comparison between a risk and its risk referent. We have already gained, in the chapter on estimation, a taste of what is necessary. But a survey of techniques will provide a better foundation from which to build the specific ones required for software engineering risk analysis and management.

Before one moves on, two warnings should be heeded, both of which have been heard before. First, even if one meets a risk level, i.e., is at or below the risk referent, there is no guarantee that the next one will be met successfully, too. A success only indicates that there is a higher probability of achieving the next one successfully. The "What have you done for me lately," principle is typically followed.

Second, all evaluation of risk is, at the end of the day, subjective. To reparaphrase an old idea, facts do not make decisions, people do. The issues of risk identification and estimation are in a sense scientific questions, ones concerned with facts. How big, how long, how likely, etc., or what is the effect of risk A causing effect B? However, risk assessment must appraise the information gathered, and a judgement by a person with all his or her biases, beliefs, and judgement comes into play.

Rescher calls the problem above one of fact versus value.[8] He writes that there is no weighing of risks without making certain evaluative commitments that go beyond the strictly factual domain. Even when powerful mathematics are brought to bear, the fact is, one is making hard calculations with what are, for the most part, soft numbers.

In a recent plane crash in England, a pilot mistakenly thought an engine was on fire and shut it down. Unfortunately, he was correct, but it was in the other engine. First speculation was that the fire warning lights were miswired, but an "anonymous industry spokesman" said such a possibility was over 100 million to one against that happening. The spokesman went on to say that the system was designed "with 'Murphy's law' in mind," and dismissed the problem from ever occurring.[9]

As it turned out, the spokesman was right. The plane was wired correctly. However, upon inspection of other similar type airplanes, it turned out that 27 *others* were miswired.[10] One should not get into the habit of believing the numbers. As one pilot said, commenting on an incident in which he took part, where three engines shut down simultaneously (and which was, most aviation experts agreed, an "impossibility"—until it turned out that a wrong oil seal was installed on all three engines during routine maintenance), "My experience shows that aircraft don't listen to the Laws of Probability."

In the following section, we will conduct a survey of the relevant techniques for performing risk evaluation. The survey will not be all inclusive, nor go into great detail on any one technique (the reader is encouraged to consult the references for a more in-depth exploration of any topic). But the survey should allow one to pick out a relevant technique which is the most appropriate for most situations encountered. Before we proceed, one more bit of mathematics needs to be covered.[11]

5.4 Probability—Part II

In the first encounter with probability in Chapter 4, an area that was hinted at but never explored was the concept of probability distributions. Intuitively, we all know what it means—marking "on the curve" is a prime example all of us have encountered one time or another. In risk analysis, one must be concerned with magnitude of a loss, remembering that magnitude includes the aspects of severity, frequency, and timing. Figure 5.6 depicted a three-dimensional graphical representation of a sample probability distribution of a particular risk's frequency, severity, and timing. If we were to instead just graph the frequency versus the timing, we would end up with an illustration much like that shown in

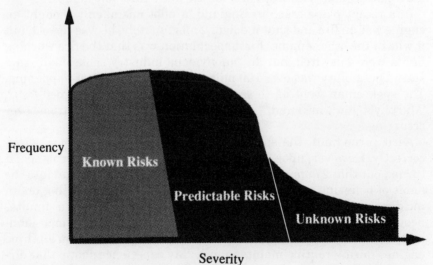

Figure 5.10 Frequency/Severity/Distribution of Loss

Figure 5.10. This distribution shows an array of the likelihood of a risk having a certain severity at a particular time. This particular curve is called a Probability Density Function (PDF) because it is an array of statistics of the instances of a variable arranged by classes according to their value.

More formally, assume that there exists a random variable X, which, in different experiments carried out under the same exact conditions, assumes different values x, each of which represents a random event. The random variable X may be discrete, in which case we assume a finite number, or at most a countably infinite number of values for x (labeled x_i). For example, if one were to keep track of the numeric value of a pair of six-sided dice being thrown over a period of six times, the random events, or realizations of x_i, could appear as follows:

$$x_1 = 5 \qquad x_2 = 4 \qquad x_3 = 5 \qquad x_4 = 12 \qquad x_5 = 2 \qquad x_6 = 8.$$

The random variable may also be continuous, which means that it can take all values in a finite or infinite interval. The heights of all persons over the age of 21 is a continuous random variable, because it can take on every value over some defined interval. Random variables are completely characterized by their probability, density, and distribution functions.

In a discrete random variable, such as the die roll example above, each random event x_i can be considered as a discontinuity, and its probabilities, labeled as before, $P(x_i)$, as the magnitude or size of the discontinuity. The probability function thus relates the magnitudes to the discontinuities. In the die roll example, assuming that there are fair dice $P(X = x_i)$, the probability that the random variable X takes on the value of x_i, is as follows:

$x_i =$	2	3	4	5	6	7	8	9	10	11	12
$P(X = x_i)$	$1/36$	$2/36$	$3/36$	$4/36$	$5/36$	$6/36$	$5/36$	$4/36$	$3/36$	$2/36$	$1/36$

This is also depicted in Figure 5.11. The reason for the distribution is that two dice can fall in one of 36 ways, each with probability ($1/36$). The probability of ($X = 5$) is $4/36$, since the number 5 can occur in any one of five ways.

One can write the definition of the distribution function $f(x)$ (which represents the function of the numerical value of x_i) for the discrete random variable X in the following way:

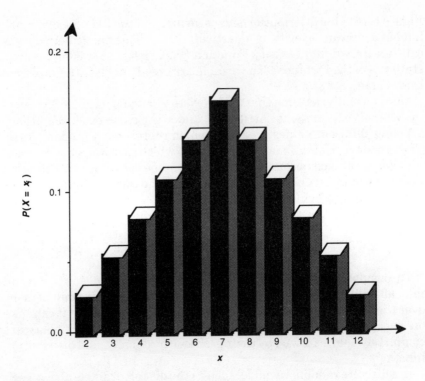

Figure 5.11 PDF of Discrete Random Variable

Definition. The function $f(x)$ is a probability function or a probability distribution of the discrete random variable X if, for each possible outcome x,

1. $f(x) \geq 0$

2. $\sum_x f(x) = 1$

3. $P(X = x) = f(x)$ (5.5)

The first statement just says that the probability of some value of the random variable is equal to zero or greater. The second says that the sum of the functions equals 1 (i.e., the area under the curve shown in Figure

5.12 equals 1). The third states that the probability of the function takes on the probability for that value. The latter just says, $f(3) = P(X = 3)$, or in the above example,

$$P(X = 3) = {}^2/_{36}$$

Sometimes, one wants to know the probability that the random variable takes at or below some specific value. We can compute this by what is known as the Cumulative Density Function (CDF). The CDF $F(x)$ of a discrete random variable X with probabilities $f(x)$ is given by:

$$F(x) = P(X \leq x) = \sum_{t \leq x} f(t) \tag{5.6}$$

For the dice example,

$$F(0) = f(0) = 0$$
$$F(1) = f(0) + f(1) = 0$$
$$F(2) = f(0) + f(1) + f(2) = {}^1/_{36}$$
$$F(3) = f(0) + f(1) + f(2) + f(3) = {}^3/_{36}$$
$$F(4) = f(0) + f(1) + f(2) + f(3) + f(4) = {}^6/_{36}$$
etc.

Thus, the CDF is defined as:

$$F(X) = \begin{cases} 0 & \text{for } x < 2 \\ {}^1/_{36} & \text{for } 2 \leq x < 3 \\ {}^3/_{36} & \text{for } 3 \leq x < 4 \\ {}^6/_{36} & \text{for } 4 \leq x < 5 \\ {}^{10}/_{36} & \text{for } 5 \leq x < 6 \\ {}^{15}/_{36} & \text{for } 6 \leq x < 7 \\ {}^{21}/_{36} & \text{for } 7 \leq x < 8 \\ {}^{26}/_{36} & \text{for } 8 \leq x < 9 \\ {}^{30}/_{36} & \text{for } 9 \leq x < 10 \\ {}^{33}/_{36} & \text{for } 10 \leq x < 11 \\ {}^{35}/_{36} & \text{for } 11 \leq x < 12 \\ 1 & \text{for } x \leq 12 \end{cases}$$

This is shown in Figure 5.12.

One can perform the same type of analysis for continuous random variables. Note, however, one cannot place the values of the variables into some tabular form such as in Figure 5.11 or Figure 5.12. The reason

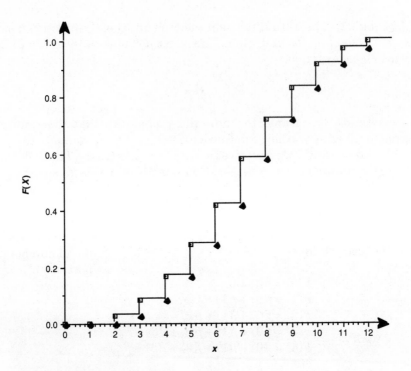

Figure 5.12 CDF of Discrete Random Variable

is, for a continuous random variable X, every value is a random event for which the probability of its occurrence is zero. However, to each value x, there corresponds a value $f(x)$ of the probability density function or cumulative density function.

This may seem a little strange, but recall our example of the height of everyone over the age of 21. Between any two values, say 68.5 inches and 69.5 inches (the average height of American men), or even between 68.99 and 69.01 inches, there are an infinite number of heights, one of which is 69 inches. The probability of selecting an individual at random who is exactly 69 inches tall, and not one of the infinitely large set that is so close to 69 inches that one cannot measure the difference, is so remote that it is assigned a probability of zero. That is,

$$P(a < X \leq b) = P(a < X < b) + P(X = b)$$

$$= P(a < X < b). \tag{5.7}$$

It does not matter whether the end-point of the interval is included or not.

The probability density function is constructed in such a fashion that the area under the curve bounded by the X-axis is equal to 1 when computed over the range of X for which $f(x)$ is defined. If $f(x)$ is depicted as in Figure 5.13, then the probability that X takes on a value between a and b is equal to the shaded area under the density function between the points $x = a$ and $x = b$, and from calculus,

$$P(a < X < b) = \int_b^a f(x)\,dx \qquad (5.8)$$

In the range of X for which $f(x)$ is defined as a finite interval, it is always possible to extend the interval to include the entire set of real numbers defining $f(x)$ to be zero at the points in the extended portions of the interval. One can now write a few more definitions about continuous random variables.

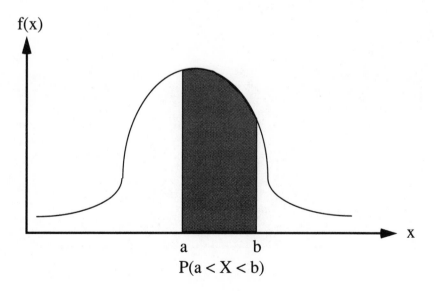

Figure 5.13 PDF of Continuous Random Variable

Definition. The function $f(x)$ is a probability density function for the continuous random variable X, defined over the set of real numbers $\Re$, if:

1. $f(x) \geq 0$ for all x members of $\Re$

2. $$\int_{-\infty}^{\infty} f(x)\, dx = 1$$

3. $$P(a < X < b) = \int_{b}^{a} f(x)\, dx \qquad (5.9)$$

What this means in practice can be shown by an example. If we are given a probability density curve as shown in Figure 5.14, we know that the probability of an event happening is represented by the shaded areas under the curve. Since the areas are equal in size, the probabilities are the same for each interval.

The cumulative density function for $F(x)$ with density function $f(x)$ is given by:

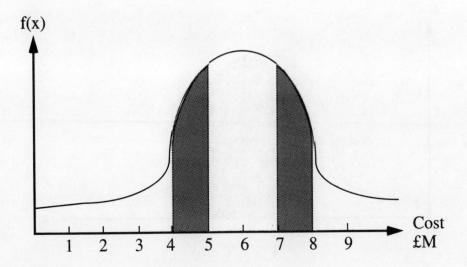

Figure 5.14 PDF of Cost Continuous Random Variable

$$F(x) = P(X \le x) = \int_{-\infty}^{x} f(t)\, dt \qquad (5.10)$$

This means

$$P(a < X < b) = F(b) - F(a) \qquad (5.11)$$

and

$$f(x) = \frac{dF(x)}{dx} \qquad (5.12)$$

if the derivative exists. A representative CDF of the continuous random variable shown in Figure 5.14 is illustrated in Figure 5.15.

PDFs and CDFs are very useful in risk analysis. PDFs graphically show the amount of uncertainty by their spread across the interval. For example, in Figure 5.14 the uncertainty of the cost of this project is the same between the interval £4–5M and £7–8M. In other words, the probability that the project will cost £4–5M is the same as £7–8M. Likewise, the probability of the cost is the same between £5–6M and

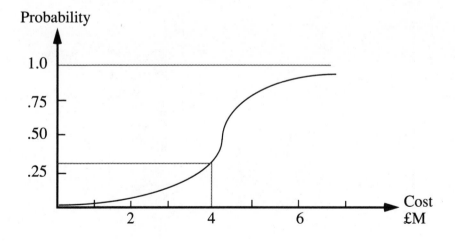

Figure 5.15 CDF of Continuous Random Variable

£6–7M, and these are higher probabilities than the previous probabilities of cost. Looking more closely, one can see how the probabilities "spread" across the intervals in a symmetric fashion (they can be folded along an axis such that the two sides coincide). A PDF that is relatively "flat" (has a low peak) and has a wide spread, indicates a large amount of uncertainty. One with a high peak, and little spread, indicates a high level of certainty concerning the estimate. The "amount of certainty" can be measured computing the standard error and variance.

Not all PDFs will appear symmetric. Most, in fact, will be skewed to one side or the other of its mean, as in Figure 5.16. "Skewness" is measured by the difference between the mean (simply compute the expected value) and its mode (the most likely value). If one divides this difference by the standard deviation, one gets a relative measure of skewness (the measure can be either positive or negative). In this example, the uncertainty of the cost now shows the probability of the project costing £4–5M is less than £7–8M, whereas before they were equal.

The skewness of a PDF can provide some interesting insights. For example, if Figure 5.16 represented a cost estimate (or schedule, or performance, etc.) of a project, a high level of absolute skewness (absolute value > 1) would indicate a great amount of uncertainty. There would be a higher likelihood that the actual cost (i.e., consequence of a

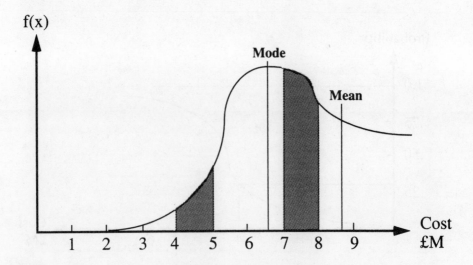

Figure 5.16 Skewed PDF of Cost Continuous Random Variable

situation) would exceed the original estimate rather than falling short. Notice, if the mode and mean are equal, then the PDF is symmetric.

Another use of PDFs is when the same PDF is graphed over time as more information concerning an estimate is obtained. One can graph what are termed, "states of knowledge" PDFs.[12] Let us say one is interested in the estimated cost of a project. One can construct a PDF based upon the set of risks in the risk triplet, $\{< s_i, l_i, x_i >\}$. Enumerate all the possible scenarios, compute the expected value for each consequence, and compute the probability of each consequence (don't be concerned if this isn't obvious—the next sections on evaluation techniques will make it clear how to go about doing this). The resultant PDF will appear as in Figure 5.16. As the evaluation techniques are applied, one will gain (hopefully) more information about the estimate: some alternatives will disappear, new ones might appear, but one should be able to reduce the uncertainty about the estimate. Recomputing the PDF over a period of time will result (again hopefully) in a set of successive curves like those shown in Figure 5.17, each appearing more symmetric, or at least, with less spread, thus indicating more confidence in our estimate.

The CDF is also a useful device in understanding a risk consequence. Examining Figure 5.15 again, one can see that the Y and X axes are labeled probability and cost, respectively. From a CDF, one can measure the "confidence" (in a statistical sense) of something happening at a

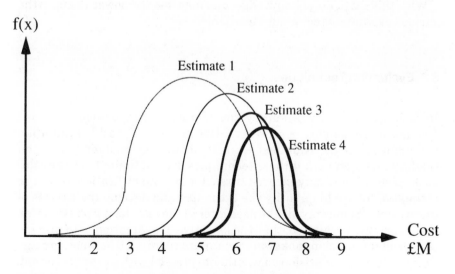

Figure 5.17 Evolutionary Improvements in Cost Estimates

particular point. For instance, one could ask, "What is the probability that the cost of the project will be less than £4M?" Examining the CDF, one could see that it was approximately 30 percent (or, there is a 70 percent chance that it will exceed £4M). Because the CDF gives the cumulative probability over a certain interval, one can also examine the confidence of something occurring over arbitrary intervals.

When more than one parameter of investigation is sought, for example the probability of risk 1 and risk 2 (or more), then one must be concerned with joint PDFs or CDFs. These are a bit more difficult to handle. The basic concepts are the same as described above, but there are some mathematical issues when the random variables are of mixed type. A full treatment of this subject is beyond the scope of this book, and the reader is directed to some other texts for information.[13,14] However, we did see the use of joint probabilities in an earlier section on risk referents, and it will be encountered again in the section on isorisk contour maps.

The PDFs and their resultant CDFs will either be modeled or will be developed from statistical experiments. Some types of discrete random variables commonly used in modeling include Bernoulli, binomial, geometric, Poisson, and uniform. Continuous random variables used in modeling include continuous uniform, (super) exponential, normal, gamma, erlang-k, chi-square, student-t, and Snedcor-F. Results from statistical surveys are usually mapped into one (or are found to be) of the above types, and then used as input into an evaluation technique.

With this extra bit of knowledge, one now has the power to apply the various evaluation techniques available.

5.5 Evaluation Techniques

In this section, we will survey the two general approaches to risk evaluation. In doing so, a representative number of specific evaluation techniques will be examined also. It should be remembered when reading this section that these techniques are not limited to the evaluation phase. Some may be used (first) for risk identification, or in the estimation phase to quantify the estimates and develop their levels of uncertainty. Some may also be used later in the monitoring phase of risk management. Recall, too, that the objective of evaluation is to provide the ultimate decision maker all the inputs required (the final damage index x_i) to make a decision on whether to proceed with the project or not.

The first technique that will be examined is the so-called "soft analysis" approach.

5.5.1 Soft approaches

The simplest evaluation technique is one called "down-side" analysis. This is simply, "Given that everything that can go wrong, does, where does the project stand?" What this means is, given all the risks and their individual consequences, select the one with the most severity and see if it is below our risk referent level for the project. In economic risk terms, this is what is salvageable after an investment goes bad. Obviously, this is the most conservative approach that can be taken and doesn't require much input other than the identified risks s_i, estimates of their likelihood l_i, as well as an informed judgement on the part of the decision maker to figure out the damage index x_i.

This technique is neither elaborate nor sophisticated and is typically the way most decision makers operate. It is not a bad technique to use, either, if one wants to set up a benchmark of what the worst case may be. It also has the added value of removing time as an element—the worst case is considered to be over a project's life. However, there is an implication that the project is only seen in black and white terms, and either it proceeds or it doesn't. And if it does, then risk management is not conducted (there is no need because even the most severe consequence will not have an effect). Again, this is okay if one has confidence in all the estimates of bad things occurring, which seems in opposition to the logic, which says one uses this technique because the positive estimates probably are inaccurate.

Another approach is to refine the above technique a bit more and to prioritize the risks in some manner. This is usually done by using the information developed in risk identification (and estimation) to determine what are called "risk drivers." These are risks that have been recognized over time as the risks that cause the most trouble, and therefore are the ones to watch out for. These are placed in a table, with the ones judged the most important first (either by experience or because of the estimation process), similar to the "10-most-wanted list," and are checked off against the risk referent level. Evaluation then proceeds as above. Table 5.2 provides an example of some candidates for the top-10 software risk drivers.[15]

TABLE 5.2 Unprioritized Candidates for Top-10 Software Risk List

- Overambitious schedule
- Overambitious performance
- Underambitious budget
- Overambitious/unrealistic expectations
- Undefined/misunderstood contract obligations
- Unfamiliar/untried/new technology or processes
- Inadequate software sizing estimate
- Unsuitable/lack of development process model
- Unfamiliar/untried/new hardware
- Inconsistent/underdefined/overdefined requirements
- Inadequately trained/inexperienced personnel
- Continuous requirement changes
- Inadequately trained/inexperienced management
- Inadequate software development plan
- Unsuitable organizational structure
- Over-ambitious reliability requirement
- Unsuitable/lack of software engineering methods/techniques
- Lack of adequate automation support
- Lack of political support/user need for project
- Inadequate risk analysis or management

The development of a list of risk drivers can proceed in an a priori manner, using a generic set of drivers that is checked against the project's risks to see if they are present, or by using the techniques that come later to generate a top-10 list. There are a couple of key points to be careful of, however. One is not to consider other risks as not contributing significantly to the overall system risk. This is a common error in applying this approach. It may be the eleventh on the list that does in the project.

Another issue is risk coupling and compounding, which might cause some problems that will not be noticed. Using an arbitrary cutoff technique tends to mask consideration for a risk that results in the compounding action of many risks interacting. Since no "name" is given to this risk, or its symptoms are only seen via other risks, its consequences are ignored.

Using a top-10 list tends to discount the time element. It is important to recognize that a list of 10 top risks is prioritized for only an instant in time, and that the list order or contents may change. One must either attempt to determine the top 10 for the project's whole life, or continue to do the evaluation throughout the project's life. The latter is a prime argument for performing risk management. A list of the estimated top-10 risks expected be encountered at important intervals in the project's

TABLE 5.3 Risk Table Approach

Life-Cycle Activity	Schd.	Bdgt.	Perf.	Orgn.	Mgt.	Pers.	Proc.	Mthd.	Auto.	Score
Req.'s Anlys.	2	3	3	2	3	3	2	2	1	21
Spec.	2	1	3	2	2	2	1	2	2	17
Prel. Design	1	1	2	2	2	2	1	2	2	15
Design	2	1	2	2	2	3	1	2	2	17
Implem.	1	2	2	3	3	2	1	2	2	18
Test	2	2	2	2	2	3	2	2	2	19
Integration	3	2	3	3	3	3	2	3	3	25
Checkout	1	2	2	3	3	3	2	3	2	21
Operation	2	2	3	3	3	3	3	3	1	23
*Score	16	16	22	22	20	21	15	21	17	176

* Maximum score is 243. Risk level for this example is 176/243, or 72 percent.

life would also be useful for reenforcing the notion of changing risk. It would also help in monitoring the accuracy of the risk analysis process, as in risk identification and estimation.

Another approach that builds on the two previous ones is called the "table-driven" evaluation technique. In this technique, during the estimation phase, risks were given a numeric weighting of some type on a ratio scale. Typically, the weighting is a number between zero and 10, with zero representing no risk, 10 representing the maximum risk, and five some level of medium risk. The perceptive reader will already have questions concerning how these levels are determined, their accuracy and precision, or why not just use a 0, 1, 2, or 3 scale that corresponds to no risk, low risk, medium risk, or high risk. But again, as has been said many times in the previous sections, remember that evaluation and estimation are subjective efforts, and it is up to the analyst to determine what is meant by how much, the measurement scale, its accuracy, precision, etc., and to convey those to the decision maker.

Regardless of how one gets the numbers, the weightings of the risks are added up and compared against some referent level. An example of this is shown in Table 5.3. Across the top are the top-10 risk items, and down the left are various stages of a software life cycle. A score is kept of each risk item across life-cycle activity and for each risk, and a total is taken. The maximum score is computed by multiplying the number of rows by the number of columns by the maximum risk factor. The total risk number is then divided by the maximum number and some comparison is made with a predetermined referent level. The comparison can also be done by life-cycle activity or by risk item.

The table approach is good because it provides in one format a list of risks, where they appear, and the estimate of the risk. Needless to say, the usefulness of this technique depends ultimately upon how accurate are the numbers to be placed into the individual boxes. The previous issues concerning the number of risks to be considered, risk coupling/compounding, determination of the referent level, and discounting of time, also require addressing. But the table technique is easy to develop, does provide a decision maker with most of the inputs required, allows for the asking of more questions and analysis, and provides a standardized technique for making a decision.

The table-driven approach marks the end of the soft approaches. We turn our attention now to the more hard analysis approaches.

5.5.2 Hard approaches

Hard approaches to risk evaluation can be characterized as those using quantitative analysis rather than qualitative. It might be argued that the table-driven approach in the previous section should be considered a quantitative technique, but we consider it only a quasi-hard approach. The reason is, in practice, it is typically used with numbers that are at best, guesses, and the numbers tend to mislead decision makers that the estimates are more accurate than they really are. In all approaches, hard or soft, it should be remembered that "Because mathematics has become so revered a discipline in recent years, it tends to lull the unsuspecting into thinking that he who thinks so elaborately thinks well."[16] An overemphasis on formal mathematics tends to obscure the real risk problems being addressed. Also, because something is quantitative, do not mistake it for being automatically objective. The two do not necessarily equate.

One could, with more work, develop a better quantitative table-driven approach, but this has not been done in practice. More typically, the use of models, either for performing mathematical analysis, the development of simulations, or experimentation such as building prototypes, is

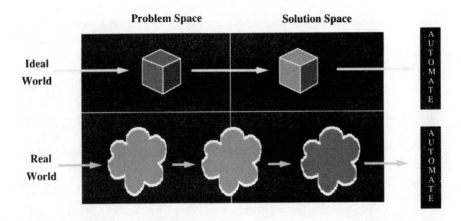

Figure 5.18 Ideal vs. Real World

conducted. In the development of these analyses or simulation models, we need to return again to the risk triplet and the process that brought us to this point.

The risk triplet consists of three items: the risk itself, the likelihood of the risk, and the damage index (the magnitude of the consequence—severity, frequency, and timing). Now, a risk may have many consequences, as was shown in the example concerning the value of developing a test suite. Somehow, one needs to be able to model not only a single risk and its consequences, but all the risks that might be of interest. Remember, the totality of risks make up the set of risk triplets and fully define a project's risk.

5.5.2.1 Models. Models are idealizations of the real world, as shown in Figure 5.18. For models to be useful, one is required to know their limitations. These limitations are centered mainly around modeling uncertainty, or the degree to which an experimental universe differs from the universe it is modeling.[17] This may be caused by omission of events, outcomes, and/or the simplification of models for analytic purposes. A useful piece of information about models is that theories can be right or wrong, but models have a third axis. They can be right, but irrelevant.

A good model needs to be both descriptive, predictive, and manageable. A model is descriptive in the sense that it should convey as much information about the system under study as the evaluation requires.

The more detailed and complex the model is, the more precisely the system can be described, within the limits of uncertainty and manipulability. Whereas descriptive power is a qualitative notion, a model also needs to be predictive, which is a quantitative concept. A model should be able to provide information about what will happen under certain conditions and with certain inputs. Finally, a model must also be manageable within the resources of the project. Money spent on developing a model is money not spent elsewhere; thus, there is need for balance between obtaining the required fidelity and unnecessary realism. The choice of a model or evaluation technique must be made compatible with the realities of the availabilities of project data and resources.

The term model is colloquially used for many different kinds of models: simulation models, mathematical models, queueing models, prototypes, etc. For purposes of this book, we will class models into two general types: *structural models* and *process models*. Both types of models are mathematical abstractions of the real world. A structural model is one that describes the organization or structure of a system. A process model describes the operation of a system.

The models described in this section on evaluation will usually be of the combined type. Sometimes a differentiation is made between a model and a prototype; the former is a mathematical abstraction that is analyzed by a designer or developer, while the latter is an executable model that mimics the real system and its environment and is analyzed by the system user. We feel it is not necessary to make such a distinction in this book.

5.5.2.2 Isorisk contour maps. The first risk evaluation modeling technique is called isorisk contour mapping.[18] This technique is very closely related to the figure-of-merit concept explained earlier, to determine the system referent level, but here we need to concern ourselves with both the probability of failure and its consequences. In other words, a joint probability distribution.

In this technique, one assumes that identified risks fall into one of three categories: low, medium, and high. Low risk is a condition where a risk would have a minor effect or consequence on the project's objectives, but the probability is sufficiently low (less than .3) as to cause only minimal concern. Medium risk is a condition where a risk's probability of occurrence is high enough (.3 to .7) to affect achieving the project's objectives. High risk is a condition where there is a high probability (.7 to .99) of occurrence, and its consequence would have a significant impact on achieving the project's objectives.

One defines a probability of failure, P_f, as the lack of success or the unreliability of the system (subsystem, component, etc.) under development. It is equal to $1 - P_s$, the probability of success. Obviously, from probability theory, $P_s + P_s = 1$.

One also defines the damage index, or consequence (or effect) of failure, C_f, which is the non-utility of the system due to failure or unreliability. C_s is the consequence of success, or the utility of the element. These also sum to one. (Note that these can be true utilities, but in this example value and utility are the same).

One now defines a risk factor $\Re$ which is equal to the likelihood of failure. After a bit of mathematics,

$$\Re = 1 - (1 - P_f)(1 - C_f) \tag{5.13}$$

$$= (P_f + C_f) - (P_f \bullet C_f) \tag{5.14}$$

$$= (P_f \cup C_f) \tag{5.15}$$

If P_f and C_f are mutually exclusive, their joint probability equals zero $(P_f \bullet C_f)$ and thus, $\Re = P_f + C_f$. This only happens when there is no consequence of failure, and thus the risk factor is equal to just the probability of failure.

An isorisk contour map is generated by assigning values to P_f and C_f that will give $\Re$ a constant value when computed in equation 5.13. The values are plotted opposite the assigned values on a rectangular coordinate system, on which the X-axis is C_f and the Y-axis is P_f. This is demonstrated in Figure 5.17. Equal-valued points are joined, providing a contour map for the risk factor.

The computation of P_f and C_f are not particularly difficult, although there are some assumptions to be made. P_f is computed by averaging probability of failure values of a number of attributes that characterize a particular risk, say, for instance, technical risk. The attributes of technical risk in a computer system might include risks due to the degree of hardware maturity, the degree of software maturity, the degree of hardware complexity, etc. Each risk has some probability of failure assigned to it. The values of the probability of failure are determined via the estimation process, and are mapped against an index scale [.1 .... .9].

The various risks are placed into a table, such as is shown in Table 5.4a. Thus, the probability of failure is computed as:

$$P_f = \frac{R_{a1} + R_{a2} + \cdots + R_{ai}}{i} \tag{5.16}$$

where i represents the number of attributes that make up the risk, and R_{ai} represents the specific attribute.

A similar approach is taken with the consequences of failure of a particular risk item. In this case, C_f concerns the impact on the system when a risk item fails to meet a particular requirement, as depicted in Table 5.4b. Thus, C_f is computed as:

$$C_f = \frac{C_{a1} + C_{a2} + \cdots + C_{ai}}{i} \tag{5.17}$$

TABLE 5.4a Attribute Factors Contributing to Probability of Failure (P_f)

ATTRIBUTE

MAGNITUDE	MATURITY FACTOR (P_M)		COMPLEXITY FACTOR (P_C)		DEPENDENCY FACTOR (P_D)
	HARDWARE $P_{M_{hw}}$	SOFTWARE $P_{M_{sw}}$	HARDWARE $P_{C_{hw}}$	SOFTWARE $P_{C_{sw}}$	
0.1	Existing	Existing	Simple Design	Simple Design	Independent of existing system, facility, or associate contractor
0.3	Minor Redesign	Minor Redesign	Minor Increase in Complexity	Minor Increase in Complexity	Schedule dependent on existing system, facility, or associate contractor
0.5	Major Change Feasible	Major Change Feasible	Moderate Increase	Moderate Increase	Performance dependent on existing system performance, facility, or associate contractor
0.7	Technology Available, Complex Design	New Software, Similar to Existing	Significant Increase	Significant Increase/Major Increase in No. of Modules	Schedule dependent on new systems, facility, or associate contractor
0.9	State of Art Some Research Complete	State of Art Never Done Before	Extremely Complex	Highly Complex Very Large Data Bases, Complex Operating Executive	Performance dependent on new system schedule, facility, or associate contractor

where i represents the number of attributes that make up the consequence of failure and C_{ai} represents the specific attribute. Thus, the risk factor, $\Re$, represents a joint probability distribution.

As an example, let's consider the following scenario. Assume that the probability of failure consists of:

R_{a1} – probability of failure due to the degree of hardware maturity

R_{a2} – probability of failure due to the degree of software maturity

R_{a3} – probability of failure due to the degree of hardware complexity

R_{a4} – probability of failure due to the degree of software maturity

R_{a5} – probability of failure due to the degree of dependency on other items

Assume that from our estimation phase, we find:

$$R_{a1} = 0.3 \text{ - minor redesign}$$
$$R_{a2} = 0.5 \text{ - major change feasible}$$

TABLE 5.4b Attribute Factors Contributing to Consequences of Failure (C_t)

MAGNITUDE	TECHNICAL FACTOR (C_t)	COST FACTOR (C_c)	SCHEDULE FACTOR (C_s)
0.1 (low)	Minimal or no consequences, unimportant	Budget estimates not exceeded, some transfer of money	Negligible impact on program, slight development schedule change compensated by available schedule slack
0.3 (minor)	Small reduction in technical performance	Cost estimates exceed budget by 1 to 5 percent	Minor slip in schedule (less than 1 month), some adjustment in milestones required
0.5 (moderate)	Some reduction in technical performance	Cost estimates increased by 5 to 20 percent	Small slip in schedule
0.7 (significant)	Significant degradation in technical performance	Cost estimates increased by 20 to 50 percent	Development schedule slip in excess of 3 months
0.9 (high)	Technical goals cannot be achieved	Cost estimates increased in excess of 50 percent	Large schedule slip that affects segment milestones or has possible effect on system milestones

$$R_{a3} = 0.3 \text{ - minor increase in complexity}$$
$$R_{a4} = 0.1 \text{ - simple design}$$
$$R_{a5} = 0.9 \text{ - performance dependent on new system schedule, facility, etc.}$$

and $P_f = (.3 + .5 + .3 + .1 + .9)/5 = 0.42$

Now, assume that C_f is made up of three attributes:

C_{a1} – consequence of failure due to technical factors

C_{a2} – consequence of failure due to cost factors

C_{a3} – consequence of failure due to schedule factors

Thus, given the risk:

$$C_{a1} = 0.1 \text{ - no technical problems}$$
$$C_{a2} = 0.3 \text{ - cost exceeds estimates by 1–5 percent}$$
$$C_{a3} = 0.3 \text{ - minor slip in schedule}$$

and $C_f = (.1 + .3 + .3)/3 = 0.23$

the risk factor $\Re$ is then computed from (5.14) as

$$\Re = (.42 + .23) - (.42 \bullet .23) = .553$$

This means the risk factor is medium. It is shown on Figure 5.19, which also shows various interpretations of the isorisk contours.

Isorisk contour maps can be used to display all the risks of a project, analyze where they fall, and establish the highest risk referent allowable. They provide an especially useful approach for generating risk referent levels (instead of estimating the risk factor, precompute a risk factor that the project should not fall below). The greatest difficulty is in producing the tables used to define the probability of failure and consequence of failure. The confidence in each should be subject to evaluation, as were the referent levels in the example from NASA earlier. There are some "standard" tables that can be used, as shown in Table 5.4 (a) and (b), as well as some supplemental tables generated by the U.S. Air Force, which can be found in Appendix B. These supplemental tables consider other factors in software project developments such

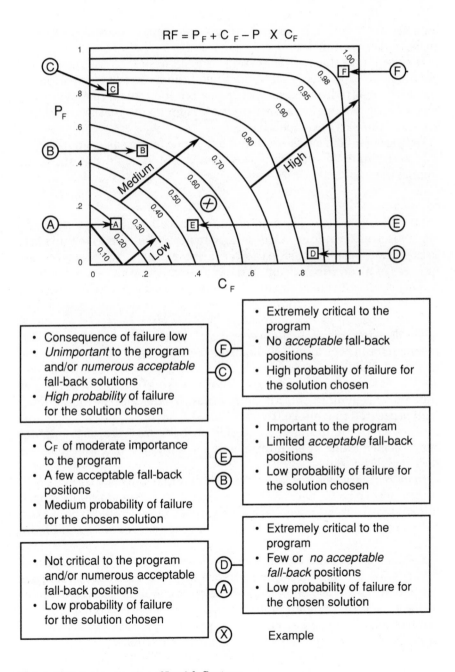

Figure 5.19 Interpretation of Isorisk Contour

as software requirements and design, personnel, reusable software, tools, and environments.

However, note that both these sets of tables are subjectively based, and should be used with an understanding of the uncertainty involved. As has been reported, an increase of 25 percent in problem complexity can lead to a 100 percent increase in program complexity, yet the probability tables are linearly extrapolated.

Development of isorisk contour maps is one of the easiest quantification techniques for evaluation available, but it requires care in its application.

5.5.2.3 Decision trees. The next technique is called decision tree analysis.[19,20] In this technique, a tree is used to portray alternative courses of actions, and the relationship to alternative decisions, to show all consequences of a specific decision. We have already encountered this technique, albeit in disguise, during the exercise on expected values. Instead of creating a payoff matrix, one could have just as easily set up a tree-like structure, as shown in Figure 5.20.

The decision tree explicitly recognizes the future alternatives, possible outcomes, and decisions from an initial decision being taken. The initial decision is modeled as a root node from which a number of alternatives spring. Each branch has a probability of occurring (the sum of the branch probabilities coming out of a node must sum to one), and the consequence (called a leaf) if that alternative is selected. The consequence has a value associated with it. In simple cases, such as in Figure 5.21a, one computes the expected value of each branch in the standard way and makes a decision.

In more complicated cases, a branch can connect to another node with its own set of payoffs. One must then compute the expected values of each alternative from the leaves backwards to each node, through the various alternatives, and then finally back to the root node, as shown in Figure 5.21b.

Decision trees can become very large and complex, and sometimes aggregation (or disaggregation if more detail is desired) of branches takes place. As was said in the section on probability, expected values also allow one to aggregate or disaggregate outcomes without disturbing comparisons among different risk alternatives. Returning to equations 4.12 and 4.13, an expected value is computed as follows:

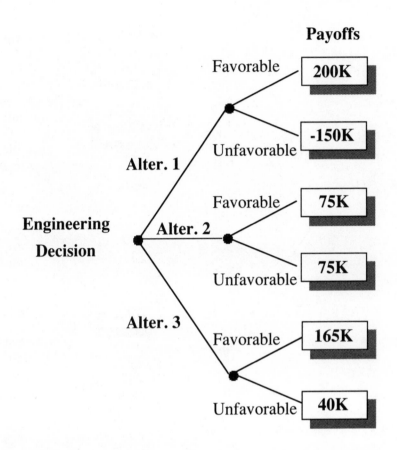

Figure 5.20 Decision Tree of Three Alternatives

$$E_v = v_1P_1 + v_2P_2 + v_3P_3$$

can be rewritten as:

$$E_v = v_1P_1 + v'P' \text{ where } P' = 1 - P_1 = P_2 + P_3,$$

where
$$v' = \left(\frac{P_2}{P_2 + P_3} \bullet v_2 \right) + \left(\frac{P_3}{P_2 + P_3} \bullet v_3 \right)$$

Payoffs

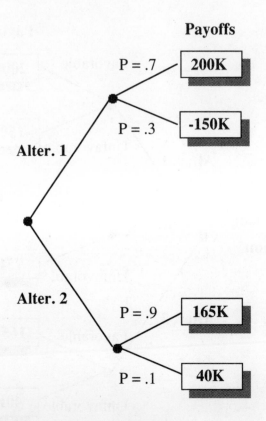

Figure 5.21a Decision Tree Example, Simple Case

However, a note of caution is necessary. One has to be careful not to aggregate risks away that might be of some significance. Given a tree with two branches having equal probabilities of .5, although the expected values are mathematically the same if the consequence values are (+\$1M, –\$1M) or (+\$1, –\$1), there is quite a difference in the result, if the estimates of the probabilities are off. One also needs to be concerned if there are "hidden" costs, such as a cost to picking an alternative that is not explicitly shown. Again, given two branches with equal probabilities, but payoffs of (+3, –1), branch one might be considered the primary choice, but if there was a cost of (–5) to select that branch not shown, then the second branch would be preferred. Always deal in net values (in this case, [–2,–1]), not gross.

Before we leave decision analysis, recall that during the expected value computations concerning decisions under complete uncertainty, there were three rules or strategies we said one could use: *minimax*, *maximin*, and the *Laplace rule*. There are actually a few more, which we include for completeness.[21,22]

The *minimax regret rule* is similar to the minimax and maximin rules, but is intended to counter some of the conservatism of those two rules. Here, the decision maker examines the maximum possible regret (i.e., the loss due to not having chosen the best alternative for each possible

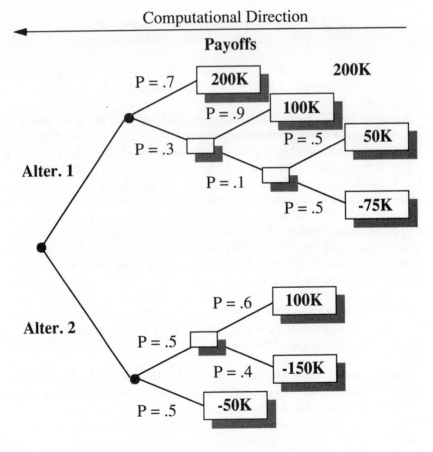

Figure 5.21b Decision Tree Example, More Complicated Case

outcome) associated with each alternative. Then, select the alternative that minimizes the maximum regret.

In other words, in each column, find the maximum payoff and subtract every payoff in that column from it (including itself), substituting the result for the original payoff. Then, find the maximum of each of the rows. The row that has the minimum value of these maximums is the alternative chosen. For Table 4.3, alternative A_2 is the one selected by this technique with value 135, i.e., $(200 - \{75\})$.

The *Hurwicz rule* is intended to reflect a degree of moderation between extreme optimism or pessimism. This states that an index of optimism, §, is selected such that $0 \leq § \leq 1$. For each alternative, compute the weighted outcome:

$$\{§ \bullet (\text{Value of most favorable outcome})\} +$$
$$\{(1 - §) \bullet (\text{Value of least favorable outcome})\} \qquad (5.18)$$

Then choose the alternative that optimizes the weighted outcome. This rule is okay, if one can find the value of §, but as a rule it leaves a bit to be desired.

Another rule is called *satisficing*. Satisficing is a decision rule that satisfies one or more minimum criteria (usually in reference to an individual's needs rather than to an organization's). The alternatives are examined in sequential order, stopping at the first alternative that meets all the minimum criteria. One may not think this is a particularly good rule, since it doesn't seem optimal, but people use it every day. For example, in selecting a house, usually one puts constraints that it cannot be too far away from work, school, grocery store, etc.

The reason for the rule is, if the alternatives are massive in number, it is a quick way to eliminate large numbers quickly. The rule is an expedient for saving time, and when better is not really any better than good enough, it is a useful rule. There is a problem if no alternative meets the rule, as new criteria are required to expand the possible alternatives. There is also a problem if the rule becomes the norm, because satisficing is not optimizing, and thus, the quality of the decision making could suffer.

Another rule is the *Kepner-Tregoe rule*. In this approach, the objectives are divided into two different categories: the "must" objectives and the "want" objectives. An alternative that does not meet one or more of the "must" objectives is eliminated, but unlike satisficing, all the options are searched. After the elimination process, the decision maker sets up a "want" objective index scale, say [1 ... 100], with 100 being the foremost want (musts might also be on this scale). The other wants are mapped against the scale values in order of relative importance. Next, the alternative courses of actions are checked against each of the wants, using another index that measures how well it satisfies each want (again, the higher the value the better). The score of each want is multiplied by the score of the satisfaction measure, and then a total is computed for each alternative. The alternative with the highest score is chosen.

The Kepner-Tregoe rule is good in that it is a systematic procedure that determines the relative importance of each objective. It is also useful as a means for computing utility functions quickly. The difficulties lie in how consistent the rankings are by the assessor(s), how accurate an index scale should be (e.g., what is the real difference between 7 and 8 versus between 79 and 80), and how well described are objectives as either wants or musts.

There is one more technique, called adjusted decision analysis, but this will be left until the next volume. The next area of importance is network models.

5.5.2.4 Network models. Network models in risk evaluation are typically used to simulate the flow of work through a system of project activities, which are related according to their sequencing, in order to evaluate the cost of performing such work. The cost may be measured in either monetary or nonmonetary units, such as time. Many different types of network models exist, such as PERT networks, queueing models, Petri Nets,[23,24] etc. We will look at two of the more popular ones, PERT networks and queueing models.

5.5.2.4.1 Pert. Probably the best known network model is called PERT (Project Evaluation and Review Technique).[25] PERT was developed in the 1950s to aid in the planning for and control of projects. In risk analysis, it can be used to help identify risks, verify or develop estimates, or evaluate risks against known or predicted risk referents. In this technique, a project consists of a collection of activities or tasks, modeled as nodes. Each task has a certain amount of time associated with its duration. An activity can be started and stopped independently of another, even if the resources employed on the activity are not independent of use by another activity. Nodes are connected to other nodes via branches, into a network arrangement in which precedence relationships among nodes exist. These preclude certain tasks from starting until others are completed. Figure 5.22 provides an example of a PERT network.

The arrows on the branches indicate the precedence relationship between two nodes; the number above the branch is the estimate of how long an activity may take. A path is defined as any set of successive tasks that go from the beginning to the end of the project. A critical path is the path that shows the shortest possible time the project will take, if everything goes according to schedule. It is the path whose sum of task times is longer than any other path through the network. Multiple critical paths are possible. In Figure 5.22, the dark line illustrates the critical path.

Another idea associated with the critical path is the slack time of each task. This is the difference between the latest possible completion time of each task that will not delay the completion of the project, and the earliest possible completion time, based upon all its predecessors' tasks.

It should be obvious that one can compute costs, estimate resource allocation, evaluate scheduling problems, etc., using the PERT technique. A technique called link analysis can be used to evaluate the transmission of information on the branches of the PERT chart. The number of variants of PERT charts is too numerous to mention, as are

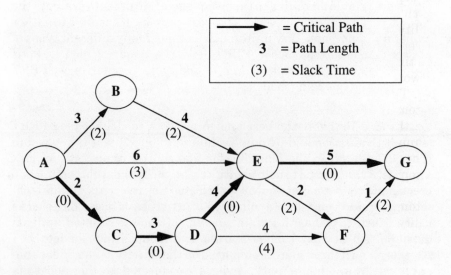

Figure 5.22 PERT Network

all the available commercial software packages that compute critical paths and slack times. The major concern in risk evaluation centers again on how the estimates are made and the uncertainty attached to them. Techniques for providing optimistic, pessimistic, and most likely outcomes have been developed, and have been augmented by the use of Monte Carlo simulation to obtain models of the PDFs and CDFs. PERT is a useful technique to evaluate cost and schedule risks, but is weak on technical risk evaluation.

Although one way to try to improve PERT is to combine the information from the isorisk technique with the critical path analysis. a network model better suited to this role is a queueing model.

5.5.2.4.2 Queueing models. A queueing model is a specialized form of network model. Queues are used to understand the effects of waiting-line phenomena on receiving service. Any system in which arrivals place demands upon a finite-capacity resource may be termed a queueing system.[26] The underlying mathematical principle used to model a queue is called Markov analysis, which is the study of current properties of a system in order to predict its future behavior.

Basically, a queueing model is made up of "customers" (these can be human beings, inquiries from a terminal, orders, incoming or outgoing messages, requests for an I/O device, etc.) from some source population, which enter a network system to demand some service from a service facility (a computer, I/O device, teller, etc.) consisting of one or more servers, which reside in the network. A server can service one customer at a time, but a customer can be served by more than one server in the network. If all the servers are busy, the customer must wait until one is free. The model seems simple enough, but if the arrival times of the customers are unpredictable, or if the size of the demand is unpredictable, then conflicts will arise and lines (queues) of customers will result. A sample queueing network is illustrated in Figure 5.23.

The queueing model is used to discover the expected waiting times for customers, the expected number of customers who are waiting, the expected time it takes a customer to get served, the expected number of customers being serviced, the server utilization, the load on the service facility, etc. Each of these parameters can be described by a (sometimes) nontrivial equation, based upon the conservation of flow principle (the rate at which flow increases in a system is equal to the difference between the flow into and the flow out of that system). As more servers or customers are added, or by varying the network routing, their waiting

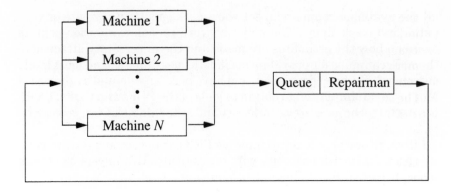

Figure 5.23 Queueing Network: M/M/1/K/K Machine Repair Queueing System With One Repairman

and service times will change. As it turns out, the length of the queue depends upon the average rate at which demands are placed upon the service resources and the statistical fluctuations of this rate. These fluctuations are usually modeled by some continuous random variable, with Uniform, Poisson, and Erlang-k being very popular.

There are many types of standard queueing models, which correspond to different types of networks of different complexities. These are described by a shorthand notation A/B/c/K/m/Z, where A describes the interarrival time distribution, B the service time distribution, c the number of servers, K the system capacity (max number of customers), m the number in the source population, and Z the queue discipline (first-in first-out, first-in last-out, and the like). There are also symbols that map to the distributions (M for exponential, G for general, etc.). For example, an M/G/5/10/50/SIRO system has an exponential interarrival time; five servers with identical, general service time distributions; a system capacity of 10 (five in service and five in a queue); a customer population of 50; and a service in random order queueing discipline.

Many queueing models have standard equations about queue length, waiting time, etc., that can be solved directly, or estimated without too much difficulty. Nonstandard and/or complex network arrangements usually dictate the need for computer simulation of the network.

Queueing models are used in software engineering to understand how well a computer or software system will work under varying assumptions and designs. They can be used to identify potential areas of risk and reduce the uncertainty in risk estimates, as well as evaluate the risks. The difficulty lies in properly modeling a system and selecting the proper average rate of service and service distributions, as well as in the sometimes extremely difficult computations entailed. For a complete treatment of the subject, the reader should turn to references [27–29].

The last set of evaluation techniques we wish to examine concerns cost and schedule evaluation.

5.5.2.5 Cost and schedule models. Predicting a project's costs and schedules, as we have read in the PERT example, has been the target of modeling efforts since the 1950s. For any type of project, predicting costs and schedules accurately is difficult, but for software projects this has been, at least as shown by the results, to be especially difficult. That this supposition is true is borne out by the proliferation of models that has been suggested. Table 5.5, for instance, lists only a few of the ones that have been suggested, and every month or so, there is an article detailing a new model, or a refinement to an existing one. With the use of the programming language, Ada, being mandated as the language of choice for new Department of Defense software systems, researchers and practitioners alike are scrambling to take its impact into account.[30] The same is true with the use of fourth generation languages.[31] We won't attempt to go into any detail on these cost and schedule models, but instead try to explain some of the techniques involved. For the interested reader, the literature is full of information on these models. A small sample can be found in references [32–38].

The problem with all the cost and schedule models that have been suggested is that they depend on past experience for calibration of their estimation accuracies and precision.[39] The issue of scaling is a major

TABLE 5.5 Some Methods of Estimating Software Costs

• Experience method	• Price-to-Win method
• Expert judgement	• Function points
• Constrained method	• Parkinson method
• Top-down estimation	• Number/Cost of instructions
• Ratio estimation	• Quantitative method
• Standards estimation	• COCOMO
• Bottom-up estimation	• Percent of hardware
• Units of Work method	• Putnam

difficulty in all cost and schedule models. For example, if the past data is poor, or if the data was gathered only from small project developments, then the estimation of a schedule for a large project must be viewed with suspicion. Cost and schedule models typically come in three flavors: micro-estimation, macro-estimation, and hybrid.[40] Note: Although they are termed estimation models, they are used to evaluate cost and schedule risks.

Micro-estimation begins with fixing the size, start date, and duration of each phase. Adjustments are then made for a number of parameters, such as personnel experience, product complexity, etc. For example, information such as utility programs are three times as difficult to write as application programs, and system programs are three times harder than utility programs,[41] would be factored in. Dozens of factors are typically used as input.

5.5.2.5.1 Work breakdown structure. Work breakdown structures (WBS) are often used to develop micro-estimation type of information. Although there are many variants of this technique, in general, a project development is broken down into a number tasks, as in the PERT technique. However, instead of defining all the tasks, their precedence relationships, and flows in a networked fashion, the tasks are broken down according to a strict hierarchy that uses the development phase of the project's life as a basis. In other words, the initial or controlling tasks represent the highest level tasks required to be done in each phase of a project development, for a phase to be said to be completed. Then, in hierarchical fashion, each of the controlling tasks is divided into subtasks, in a top-down iterative process, until the lowest level of granularity is reached. Each bottom level subtask then has an associated cost, time, and manpower or other value, which is then used in a bottom-up manner to compute its parents' cost, time, etc., and so on, until the total cost, time, and manpower is computed. Figure 5.24 provides an example of a WBS.

The WBS approach described above is activity driven. The other approach is to describe how products of the development are derived, instead of describing work activities. The same hierarchical decomposition process is followed, however.

Work breakdown analyses can be generated by hand or by use of the computer. They provide a useful way of evaluating cost, schedule, and manpower information, although they tend to force a bias on how a system will actually be designed. Application of other techniques, such as the method of moments and computer simulation, can help define

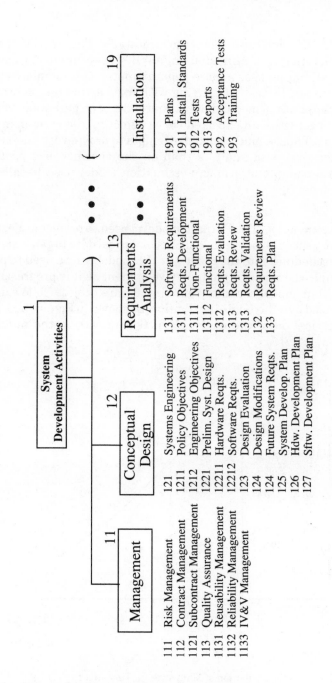

Figure 5.24 Sample Work Breakdown Structure (WBS)

PDFs and CDFs, and the levels of uncertainty.[42,43] The creation of a well-defined referent level is difficult using a WBS type of approach, however.

Macro-estimation uses a more general approach than micro-estimation techniques. Instead of starting with fixed estimates, information such as manpower, time, and effort that have been gathered over time are used to generate an expected curve depicting life-cycle manpower versus time. Thus, a macro-model attempts to provide estimates based more on general case analysis than on the specifics of a particular project. An example of a macro-estimation model used is called the Putnam model.[44,45]

5.5.2.5.2 Putnam model. The Putnam model is used to predict project costs and delivery schedules. The model uses historical data to generate likely costs and schedules into the future, or the model can be used to predict the cost and schedule of a product development as it is progressing.

The Putnam model assumes that all software projects follow a curve characterized by a Rayleigh distribution, as shown in Figure 5.25. Based upon historical data, the model predicts a growth in the number of

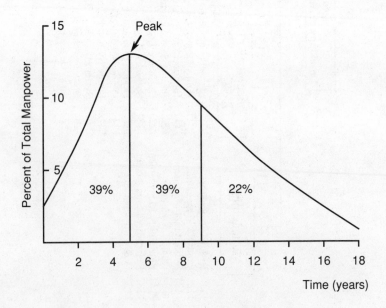

Figure 5.25 Rayleigh Distribution of Manpower vs. Time in a Typical Product Development

personnel until the time when approximately 40 percent of the total budget is expended. At this point, the personnel utilized in a project are predicted to peak. During the consumption of the remaining 60 percent of the project's budget, manpower levels are slowly reduced, following a predictable, downward trend as the project matures and nears completion.

To use the model, the manager plots the number of people in each phase of the development as a function of time,[46] similar to that shown in Figure 5.26. During each phase, the basic 40:60 ratio is used. The result is a composite project curve which is Rayleigh-shaped, having several subcycles corresponding to each life-cycle phase. Each sub-cycle depicts how the manpower will increase and fall off as the project progresses through each phase of the life cycle.

The Putnam model is a good model to use to define risk referent levels, but it has not been found to be tremendously accurate in predicting actual system costs and schedules. It seems to do better on larger projects than smaller ones, however. This seems so in part because original estimations of large projects are so often wildly wrong that gross estimations are good by comparison.

The major weaknesses are that requirements, specifications, and planning work are not included in the model (they are shown as dashed

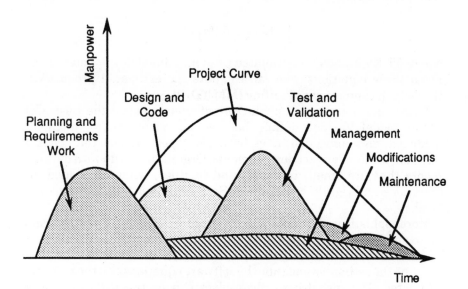

Figure 5.26 Manpower vs. Time—Putnam Model

lines on the figure). The model assumes the project starts at the design phase; and even this is a little inaccurate, as the constitution of the design stage is not made clear (in some people's minds, this phase has aspects of requirements and planning in it, for instance). Another weakness is that project evolution is difficult to model, especially if the system is evolving using a program family or incremental build approach.

5.5.2.5.3 COCOMO model. The Constructive Cost Model (COCOMO) model[47] can be considered a hybrid, using both micro- and macro-estimation techniques. In this approach, equations are used to estimate the cost and schedule. The formulation of these equations is based upon empirical evidence gathered from historical data of 63 development projects and 25 evolution or maintenance projects undertaken by TRW over a period of years.

As a result of these studies, the COCOMO model uses as its basic parameters estimates of delivered source lines of code. To estimate the time a project takes, one uses the basic equations:

$$MM = 2.4 \ (KDSI)^{1.05} \qquad (5.19)$$

where MM stands for man-months, KDSI for delivered source lines of code in thousands, and

$$TDEV = 2.5 \ (MM)^{0.38} \qquad (5.20)$$

where TDEV stands for estimated total scheduled development time. From these equations, one can compute the estimated productivity (KDSI/MM) and average staffing (MM/TDEV).

These equations represent the core of what is called the Basic CO-COMO model. Variants of these basic equations, named organic, semi-detached, and embedded, have been developed to meet the needs of different kinds of project developments. Organic has to do with developments that are small, in-house, and familiar, while embedded are ambitious and tightly constrained. Semi-detached is an intermediate level.

More sophisticated models have also been developed, termed Intermediate and Detailed COCOMO. These use the same basic equations, but include what are termed effort multipliers or cost drivers. These are used to refine the estimates and tune the software equations and the resulting estimates. The cost drivers themselves can be tuned depending on

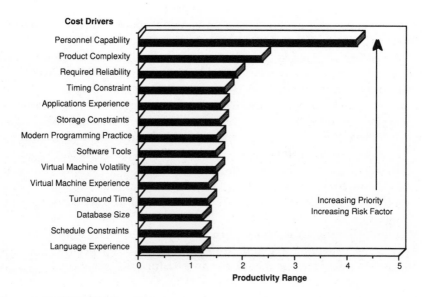

Figure 5.27 COCOMO Cost Drivers

numerous other factors as well. Figure 5.27 lists the cost drivers in their priority of importance. The quality of people working on a software development is the single most important driver. The difference in productivity can be 400–500 percent between the best- and worst-qualified people.

All three types of modeling have their place, but micro-models are more time consuming than macro-models, in that much more information is needed to obtain results than with the macro method. Hybrid models can fluctuate in the amount of effort depending on the sophistication of the modeling effort. Macro-modeling seems to work reasonably well for very large projects, although from a risk perspective the use of it alone for evaluation purposes is not enough. Depending on specific circumstances, all cost estimation models can have wild fluctuations in the magnitude of relative error,[48,49] reportedly 200–600 percent. The magnitude of relative error is the absolute value of the difference between the estimate and the actual effort, divided by the actual effort, as follows:

$$\text{MRE} = \left| \frac{\text{MM}_{est} - \text{MM}_{act}}{\text{MM}_{act}} \right| \tag{5.21}$$

The absolute value allows one to consider both overestimates and underestimates of the effort required.

The outputs of the COCOMO models, especially the Intermediate and Detailed models, are usually reliable if the number of lines of code is reasonably well known and the multipliers can be chosen correctly. However, their projected accuracy is only within 20 percent of actual costs, 70 percent of the time (the model takes into account the random variable created by using the historical data on costs and schedules). This can pose a serious risk to a user of the model if the projected accuracy is ignored. The accuracy achieved in COCOMO currently defines the upper limit of accuracy for software cost and schedule estimation today (and serves as a useful minimum cost and schedule referent point). For this reason, the COCOMO model is becoming a de facto standard. The accuracy falls off in practice when users disregard good estimation practice, or use it to justify a previously predicted result. Neither is a fault of the model, however. Since the basic equations are founded upon historical data, the basic COCOMO equations are periodically updated to reflect changes in technology and software engineering practice.

In using any cost or schedule model, one should not discount other factors, such as that experienced in the OS/360 operating system development. The development took two years because the hardware was to be ready in two years.[50]

5.6 Consequence Appraisal

By applying one or more of the risk evaluation techniques outlined in the previous section, one has (hopefully) developed a good understanding of a project's risks—what they are, what type of losses are associated with them, and how likely they are to happen. One is now at the point to begin consideration of how the risks compare to the individual or system-wide referent point, and whether, due to the risks currently identified, one should proceed with the project as planned, change it, or abandon it. Recall these are not extremely well-defined points, and one sometimes needs to exercise the judgement of Solomon. Also, some other issues which should be taken into consideration before a final decision is reached should be noted.

One such issue that was only lightly touched upon is risk prioritization. It is important that risks be prioritized in some manner, for a number of reasons. First, there is the common sense principle of first things first. Second, if an aggregate risk cannot be easily determined, then, by structuring a priority list of risks, one can quickly tell whether an individual risk or a small group of risks will stop the project as planned. If after evaluation the top priority risks, even after considering compounding effects, do not indicate rework of the plan is required, then early confidence can be gained about the feasibility of continuing on with the risk evaluation process. The opposite also holds, however.

Third, the same principle of first things first holds when one applies risk management, and thus it will be necessary to know, even if the project continues as planned, which risks are seen as the most "dangerous" to the project. One may apply a Delphi-like approach, using the senior engineers and designers as participants, to actually set the priority list and indicate the worst technical risks. However, the priority of risks must take into account the influences from the business and political spheres, or there may be a mismatch of what is considered important. This topic will be explored in more detail in the companion volume.

Fourth, it helps if one understands the opportunities lost, as well as the risks being confronted. Recall from Chapter 2, wherever risk exists, so does an opportunity. The subject of opportunity loss has only appeared in the previous chapters within the context of the expected value of perfect, but to fully understand it, the reader needs to consider this subject further. More on opportunity and risk can be found in *Software Engineering Risk Analysis and Management—Applications*.

There are a few general practical concepts that also should be followed when doing the risk level versus risk referent evaluations. These have to deal with the acceptability of risk. The first concept to remember, as I am sure you all do, is the saying, "De minimis non curat lex"—there is no need to bother with trifles.[51] What this means is, in the context of risk evaluation, risk probabilities that are effectively zero should be treated as zero. Below some threshold, even though a risk mathematically still retains a likelihood of occurring, one need not be worried about it. In safety engineering, probabilities below 10^{-5} are often considered effectively zero, and for NASA's Space Shuttle,[52] this level is in the vicinity of 10^{-7}. The U.S. Food and Drug Administration has a general rule of one in one million over a lifetime, while deaths due to "acts of God" in the United States are also about 1:1,000,000. For risks that are not safety critical, some level above these should be considered as being effectively zero.

However, one must not dogmatically apply the above rule, either. One must also consider the disparity of the risk consequences faced. A disparity of risk exists when the greatest possible loss associated with an alternative is "incomparably" greater than another.[53] When this occurs, the Unacceptable Risk Principle holds, which states that a relatively catastrophic alternative cannot be considered as acceptable (unless its likelihood is effectively zero), the risk being too great to overcome by any aversion approach. Either the risk must be eliminated or changed, so that the catastrophic alternative does not come into consideration. No single point of failure should exist.

The reader can easily conjure up a payoff matrix with the appropriate states of nature that will result in a positive expected value, but where the payoff, if the state of nature is unfavorable, is so catastrophic that a rational person would not even take the risk. In general, where the disparity between risks is three orders of magnitude, the principle of unacceptable risk ought to be considered.[54] Two "lemmas" of the principle should also be applied: View expected value computations with suspicion and, where possible, avoid any real risk of catastrophe at any ordinary cost. We will return to this subject in the next chapter, and discuss the case of risk dilemmas where this may not be possible, such as in projects that are already in trouble, and every way out is unpleasant.

The last practical consideration when performing risk evaluation concerns the issue of time. Risk acceptability changes with time because a risk's likelihood, and its consequences, will change as well. A risk that was once thought monumental may seem inconsequential, and vice versa. As more information is gained about a risk, the estimates become better, new technology might become available which can alleviate some technical strains, or monetary/schedule constraints might be lifted. How time affects a risk, and how it is handled, is called time discounting or futures discounting.[55]

The approach taken is to develop a discount function that is used to "revalue" a risk, or its acceptability. The function is determined using the concept of expected present utility and how it is perceived to change with respect to time. In general, discounting must be understood in the context of the future and the past. For example, an event in the recent past, or one about to happen, is discounted little, while one in the distant past or distant future is discounted heavily. The length of time one is exposed to a risk also affects the rate of discounting. The longer the exposure, the more the discounting function. One learns to "live" with the risk. Other factors that influence time discounting are whether the risks are direct or indirect, voluntarily or involuntarily imposed, reversible or nonreversible, or readily or nonreadily identifiable.

It is beyond the scope of this book to go into the subject of time discounting in any depth, such as how one formulates a time discount function. But one should be aware that the concept does exist. In certain situations, such as determining and/or evaluating the amount of contingency required, the technique might be useful to apply. A full explanation of future discounting can be found in reference [56].

5.7 Summary

The reader may now be bewildered totally by the array of techniques available for risk evaluation. Questions such as, "When should they be

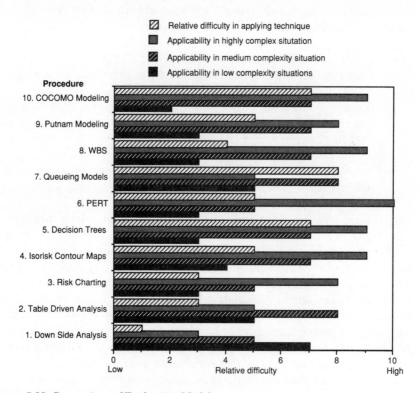

Figure 5.28 Comparison of Evaluation Models

used, what experience is needed, are they good for estimation, etc." are probably rattling around the brain. The remainder of the book should help clear up most of the questions (one needs to walk before one runs), but to help alleviate some of the anxiety, Figure 5.28 provides some *general* applicability guidelines for the techniques mentioned in this book. Note the word *general*. Some of the techniques you will find better to use in certain situations than others, because you will be more comfortable with them, or more familiar, or have/don't have the time to apply them, or the approach and results will be better understood by your clients or management (try explaining the intricacies of PDFs and CDFs, or utility theory, to a harassed corporate president, and see how long you get to speak—they just want an answer they can comprehend). Each of you must select a technique based upon your specific circumstances.

We have come a long way in our examination of risk analysis. The motivation for Chapters 3, 4, and 5 was to be able to perform the following tasks and to address their underlying questions:

- First, comprehensive identification of potential risk items using a structured and consistent method; i.e., what can go wrong?

- Second, estimation of the magnitude of each risk and its consequences, and the creation of options; i.e., what is the likelihood of that happening under the current plan?

- Third, evaluation of the consequences of risk, including their prioritization; i.e., if the risk occurs, what is the damage?

One should now be able to address these questions with a measure of confidence. The next chapter shows what one does with the answers.

The importance of being fully cognizant of the implications, and limitations, of each step above is crucial to successfully performing risk analysis. Getting caught up with the means may easily obscure the ends one is after. Try not to view risk analysis as a new hammer and do not look at a software project as a set of nails. This trap is easy to fall into. All software projects, no matter how well financed, well managed, etc., will have some amount of risk associated with them. A risk analysis will not change that fact. So keep on reminding yourself that risks are just that, risks that sometimes have to be taken, and your job as risk analyst is to try to show which ones are the most dangerous and why.

So where are we, and where are we going from here? In Chapters 1 through 5 we have seen the impact of software on society and the economy. We have also seen that there is a set of techniques called risk analysis and management that can help make the process of building software products a bit more manageable and successful. We now know the mechanics of performing risk analysis and have generated a risk evaluation. The next step is to decide what to do with the risks, now that we know their type, size, and likelihood of visitation.

Questions

1 What is the purpose of evaluation? How can the techniques be used in risk identification or estimation?

2 What is the system risk referent level? When is it computed? How is it different from the individual system referent levels? Is it feasible to use an individual risk referent as the system risk referent?

3 What does risk compounding mean? Why is it different from coupling? Give two examples contrasting the differences.

4 Consider the statement of the local weather man, who says that there is an 80 percent chance of rain today. Now one can either infer that during 8 out of 10 days with the same forecast, it will rain; or it will definitely rain in the forecast area (thus being considered a rainy day in meteorological terms), but at any individual location, it only will get wet 8 out of 10 times on days with the same forecast. Which inference is based in probability theory, and which in statistical theory?

5 How does the system risk referent change with time? Should it be shown as a probability of success or probability of failure?

6 Can the system referent or individual risk referents be determined across the life of the project? Would this be an easier approach than trying to determine a risk referent that is time dependent? How could this be done?

7 If a time independent risk referent were set, explain how the determination of whether to proceed or not could be made. What difficulties arise? (Hint: Discuss the use of differences between the referent and the evaluation.)

8 Turn to Figure 5.14, where the uncertainty of the cost of this particular project is the same between the interval £4–5M and £7–8M. What does this imply?

9 What are the differences between Soft and Hard Approaches to risk evaluation? Which is preferable? Which individual approaches are feasible, and when?

10 Name four limitations to models. How do these limitations relate to estimation and measurement uncertainty?

11 When are techniques like linear programming useful for risk evaluation?

12 What are differences and similarities in the various cost models? What other cost models do you know of? Why are "lines of code" the dominant driver of software cost models?

13 What is meant by the term "time discounting"? Why is it important? When is it used?

References

1. Peter G. Moore, *The Business of Risk*, University Press, Cambridge, England, 1983.

2. William D. Rowe, *An Anatomy of Risk*, Robert E. Krieger Publishing Co., Malabar, FL, 1988.

3. One should be careful to note when the objectives listed are in fact strategies, and not to confuse the two. For example, one may have an objective of maximizing profit by the strategy of minimizing cost.

4. We will see in a moment that the referent point might actually be defined by a line or a region. However, the basic fact is, one must pre-set evaluation points that can

be used to terminate the project, continue with the project, or continue it with prejudice.

5. "Post-Challenger Evaluation of Space Shuttle Risk Assessment and Management," National Academy Press, January 1988.

6. "Post-Challenger Evaluation of Space Shuttle Risk Assessment and Management," National Academy Press, January 1988.

7. Barry Boehm, "Industrial Software Metrics Top 10 List," in *IEEE Software*, September, 1987. Boehm showed that the most effective schedule T_{dev} for a single, industrial-grade software project is

$$T_{dev} = 2.5 \bullet MM^{.33}$$

where T is in months and MM is man-months. Refer to the COCOMO section in this chapter for further details.

8. Nicholas Rescher, *Risk*, University Press of America, Lanham, MD, 1983.

9. "Crash of 737-400 Prompts Stricter CFM56 Engine Checks," in *Aviation Week & Space Technology*, McGraw-Hill, Inc., 16 January 1989.

10. "59 Faults in Wiring, Plumbing Reported on Boeing Jetliners," in T*he Washington Post*, 12 March 1989. This is a prime example of inadvertent exposure as a means of identifying a risk.

11. A general rule in publishing is that for every equation, 10 readers are lost in sales, so please hang in there if you have reached this point. There aren't too many more after this.

12. "Post-Challenger Evaluation of Space Shuttle Risk Assessment and Management," National Academy Press, January 1988.

13. H. Behnke et al., *Fundamentals of Mathematics: Analysis, Vol. 3*, MIT Press, Cambridge, MA, 1974.

14. W. Gellert et al., Eds., *The VNR Concise Encyclopedia of Mathematics*, Van Nostrand Reinhold Company, New York, 1976.

15. Barry Boehm and Philip Papaccio, "Understanding and Controlling Software Costs," in *IEEE Transactions on Software Engineering*, Vol. 14, No. 10, October 1988.

16. C. W. Churchman, "Reliability of Models in the Social Sciences," in *Interfaces*, Vol. 4, No. 1, November 1973.

17. William D. Rowe, *An Anatomy of Risk*, Robert E. Krieger Publishing Co., Malabar, FL, 1988.

18. The information on isorisk contour maps is based upon the work of: Truman W. Howard III, *Methodology for Developing Total Risk Assessing Cost Estimates (TRACE)*, ARMDC, ALM-63-4476-M3, U.S. Army Logistics Management Center, Fort Lee, VA; I. Kabue, "Risk Analysis," in *Management Review*, June 1981; and *Handbook for Decision Analysis*, Cybernetics Technology Office, DARPA, September 1977.

19. William D. Rowe, *An Anatomy of Risk*, Robert E. Krieger Publishing Co., Malabar, FL, 1988.

20. Allen M. Johnson, Jr., and Miroslaw Malek, "Survey of Software Tools for Evaluating Reliability, Availability, and Serviceability," in *ACM Computing Surveys*, Vol. 20, No. 4, December 1988.

21. John Canada, *Intermediate Economic Analysis for Management and Engineering*, Prentice-Hall, Inc., Englewood Cliffs, NJ, 1971.

22. Peter G. Moore, *The Business of Risk*, University Press, Cambridge, England, 1983.

23. See the papers contained in the "Special Section on Petri Net Performance Models," in *IEEE Transactions on Software Engineering*, Vol. 15, No. 4, April 1989.

24. G. Lausen, "Modeling and Analysis of the Behavior of Information Systems," in *IEEE Transactions on Software Engineering*, Vol. 14, No. 11, November 1988.

25. Antony Ralston et al., Eds, *Encyclopedia of Computer Science and Engineering, 2nd Edition*, Van Nostrand Reinhold Company, Inc., New York, 1976.

26. Leonard Kleinrock, *Queueing Systems, Volume 1: Theory*, John Wiley & Sons, New York, 1975.

27. Arnold Allen, *Probability, Statistics, and Queueing Theory*, Academic Press, New York, 1978.

28. Leonard Kleinrock, *Queueing Systems, Volume 2: Computer Applications*, John Wiley & Sons, New York, 1975.

29. Gordon Anderson, "The Coordinated Use of Five Performance Evaluation Methodologies," in *Communications of the ACM*, Vol. 27, No. 2, February 1984.

30. Barry Boehm, presentation given on "The Software Crisis: A Reassessment," *22nd Annual EIA Computer Resources and Data and Configuration Management Workshop*, September 1988.

31. Santosh Misra and Paul J. Jalics, "Third-Generation versus Fourth-Generation Software Development," in *IEEE Software*, July 1988.

32. J. Herd et al., "Software Cost Estimation Study: Study Results (Vol.1)," RADC-TR-220, June 1977.

33. W. Myers, "A Statistical Approach to Scheduling Software Development," in *IEEE Computer*, Vol. 11, No.12, December 1978.

34. Barry Boehm, *Software Engineering Economics*, Prentice-Hall, Inc., Englewood Cliffs, NJ, 1981.

35. R. Goldberg and S. Zelden, *The Economics of Information Processing, Volume 2*, John Wiley and Sons, New York, 1982.

36. C. Behrens, "Measuring the Productivity of Computer System Development Activities with Function Points," in *IEEE Transactions on Software Engineering*, Vol. SE-9, No.6, November 1983.

37. R. Wolverton, "Software Costing," in *Handbook of Software Engineering*, C. Vick and C. Ramamoorthy, Eds., Van Nostrand Reinhold Company, Inc., New York, 1984.

38. V. Gurbaxani and H. Mendelson, "Software and Hardware in Data Processing Budgets," in *IEEE Transactions on Software Engineering*, Vol. SE-13, No. 9, September 1987.

39. T. Abdel-Hamid and S. Madnick, "The Dynamics of Software Project Scheduling," *Communications of the ACM*, Vol. 26, No. 5, May 1983.

40. W. Myers, "A Statistical Approach to Scheduling Software Development," in *IEEE Computer*, Vol. 11, No. 12, December 1978.

41. Fred Brooks, *The Mythical Man-Month*, Addison-Wesley Publishing Company, Reading, MA, 1975.

42. John Canada, *Intermediate Economic Analysis for Management and Engineering*, Prentice-Hall, Inc.,. Englewood Cliffs, NJ, 1971.

43. "Risk Assessment Techniques," Defense Systems Management College, Fort Belvoir, VA, July 1983.

44. L. Putnam, "A General Empirical Solution to the Macro Software Sizing and Estimating Problem," in *IEEE Transactions on Software Engineering*, Vol. SE-4, No. 4, July 1978.

45. W. Myers, "A Statistical Approach to Scheduling Software Development," in *IEEE Computer*, Vol. 11, No.12, December 1978.

46. Roger Warburton, "The Cost of Real-time Software," in *IEEE Transactions on Software Engineering*, Vol. SE-9, No. 5, September 1983.

47. Barry Boehm, *Software Engineering Economics*, Prentice-Hall, Inc., Englewood Cliffs, NJ, 1981.

48. Chris F. Kemerer, "An Empirical Validation of Software Cost Estimation Models," in *Communications of the ACM*, Vol. 30, No. 5, May 1987.

49. Rick Martin, "Evaluation of Current Software Costing Tools," in *ACM Software Engineering Notes*, Vol. 13, No. 3, July 1988.

50. W. Myers, "A Statistical Approach to Scheduling Software Development," in *IEEE Computer*, Vol. 11, No. 12, December 1978.

51. Nicholas Rescher, *Risk*, University Press of America, Lanham, MD, 1983.

52. "Post-Challenger Evaluation of Space Shuttle Risk Assessment and Management," National Academy Press, January 1988.

53. Nicholas Rescher, *Risk*, University Press of America, Lanham, MD, 1983.

54. ———, *Risk*, University Press of America, Lanham, MD, 1983.

55. John Canada, *Intermediate Economic Analysis for Management and Engineering*, Prentice-Hall, Inc., Englewood Cliffs, NJ, 1971.

56. Melvin W. Lifson and Edward F. Shaifer, Jr., *Decision and Risk Management for Construction Management*, John Wiley & Sons, New York, 1982.

Risk Management: Planning, Controlling, and Monitoring

> "No plan survives contact with the enemy."
>
> VON MOLTKE

6.0 Introduction

The oil business is a rather tough business, as anyone who has followed the recent fortunes of Louisiana, Oklahoma, and Texas can attest. Oil is also an extremely competitive business. It was John D. Rockefeller, and his building of Standard Oil, who provided the impetus to competition. He accomplished this by his unending effort to minimize his business' risk, and ensure its profitability, via the systematic destruction of the predictability of his competitors' business conditions, and thus their ability to compete against him. As we all know, Rockefeller was successful at accomplishing his goals.

John D. Rockefeller taught his competitors a powerful and painful lesson in the workings of the free-market system. This lesson has been well learned, as subsequently every oil company has striven to emulate Standard Oil by moving to make each of their own business' markets predictable. Unfortunately, to increase market share or gain a competitive position in respect to a rival may take a decade or more—the time needed to build the necessary infrastructure, such as gasoline stations, pipelines, oil terminals, refineries, etc. This time factor places a premium on good strategic planning.

The oil companies have transformed themselves into probably *the* consummate long-term strategic planners. Market volatility is poison, and they do not like surprises, like the one old John D. gave them. So, they plan and plan, developing scenarios of what might happen to the price of crude if this or that were to occur, all of which goes into their risk analysis plans. The trouble is, they haven't always been successful at it.

The decade of the 1970s, especially the years 1973–74 and 1979, were not what one would call the zenith in the history of long-term petroleum business planning. In fact, the forecasts were dead wrong. Fortunately, results of the errors in the forecasts' accuracy concerning the price of crude in 1973–74 and 1979 were merely intellectual embarrassments, as an *Economist* writer put it.[1] The errors, it seems, were made on the pessimistic side of reality. Instead of remaining stable, which the companies originally wished, oil prices soared, the companies made boatloads of money (almost literally), and the forecasting errors were forgotten among the celebrations of their windfalls. One must be charitable and note that the errors occurred because the free market was manipulated and/or influenced by war, cartels, and revolution. Then along came 1986.

The only thing that oil planners could say about their crude oil price forecasts included in the 1986 strategic plans was "Oops."

Figure 6.1 illustrates the oil companies' views of the future in 1984. Unfortunately, whoever was in charge of 1986 did not read the forecasts. Oil prices plummeted from $30 a barrel to $15. This not only crimped profit, but made many of those decade-long, and very, very expensive, infrastructure projects into ones costing even oil companies serious money. The return-on-investment time-line projections now stretch out over the horizon. Yes, 1986 was not a very good year.[2]

One cannot blame the strategic planners entirely, however. For example, Royal Dutch/Shell planners did provide $15, $30, and $45 a barrel scenarios to demonstrate that there were certain levels of estimation uncertainty associated with the projections. Unfortunately, the senior managers took the most optimistic scenario as a forecast of what was to happen (they also wanted to believe it would be that way), and based their decisions upon that which they wanted to hear.[3] Sound familiar?

The fiasco of 1986 shook the industry, initiating a series of changes in the way strategic planning was, and is, performed. Outsiders have also been brought in to challenge the opinions of senior managers about their previous attitudes, forcing them to recognize their institutionalized biases. Provision of greater risk identification has been undertaken by

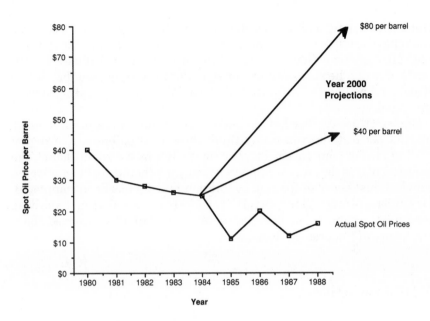

Figure 6.1 Spot Oil Price Projections

conducting more in-depth risk analysis of the elements influencing the industry. Awareness programs have begun, concentrating on what can go wrong when estimating and evaluating risks. As a result, an understanding that risk plans are not forecasts seems to have been realized. Strategic planning in the oil industry sounds to be in great shape, right?

Well, maybe.

The Economist reports that planners now are complaining about their senior managers' complacency. It seems that many managers, after becoming "more aware," are dismissively pushing aside catastrophic scenarios and risk analyses, saying, "any consequences couldn't be worse than 1986." Perhaps, say the frustrated planners, but they will surely be different.[4]

One can almost hear a chuckle from members of other industries, such as ours, that we are not the only ones to mess up in our strategic planning occasionally. One should not gloat too much, nor should one be surprised too much, either. After all, imagine it is 1 January 1990, and *you* have to predict, in a subject that you consider yourself expert in, what will occur over the intervening 10 years to 1 January 2000? How good do you think your predictions will be? Or, instead, how good do you think you could have predicted any of the things that happened last year 10 years back? British Army General Sir Martin Farndale, retired, illustrated the problem when he said of the 85 or so major military crises the United Kingdom has had to face since the end of World War II, only five were predicted.[5]

But isn't this exactly what has been asked of you in Chapters 3 through 5? How accurate do you really think those evaluations are? Are you willing to risk your career or your company's business on them? The objective of this chapter is to show why one's job should not be considered finished, just because the risk evaluation process has been completed. One must still attempt to control the exposure to the risks that have been identified, estimated, and evaluated. We are, after all, concerned about the future of the present decisions we make.

6.1 Risk Management

Thus far in assessing risks, we have followed a number of lines of investigation. Initially, a *risk estimate of the situation* was performed. The RES was done in order to review the project's plans with an eye toward identifying the project's objectives, strategies, tactics, and means. We then went on to *identify* the risks to the plan, categorizing them according to a risk taxonomy. Next, an *estimate* of the likelihood and magnitude of the risks was completed, relating their exposure to their effects. This formed the first draft estimate of overall system risk based upon a completed set of risk triplets, $\{< s_i, l_i, x_i >\}$. Upon completion of the estimate, an *evaluation* of the risk set confronting the project was initiated. Various techniques to evaluate the risks were applied in an attempt to determine the validity of the risk estimates, and to understand how different combinations of the individual risks might make the project as a whole too risky to pursue. The ultimate goal of the investigation process was to obtain sufficient information for a decision maker to make a go/no go decision on whether to proceed with the project as was then planned. In this chapter, we continue the lines of our investigation of the risks a few steps farther.

We find that we can start from either of the two possible positions in which we left ourselves at the end of Chapter 5, as shown in Figure 6.2. In the first one, the project, as it was planned, exceeded its system-wide referent level, and as a result one is confronted with two more possible

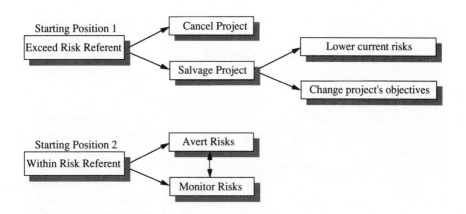

Figure 6.2 Monitoring Starting Positions

courses of action. One can choose to either cancel the project outright or seek a means to salvage it. The latter possibly can be accomplished by (a) lowering the current risks to a sufficient level to allow the project to be reevaluated in a positive manner; or (b) changing the project's objectives, strategies, etc. Once either (or both) of these salvaging operations are completed, portions of the risk identification and estimation phases are redone where required, and a new evaluation is completed. Lowering of the system-wide risk referent level, while tempting, generally should not be used as an expedient to obtain the same result.[6] If on this attempt (or the third, fourth, etc.) the system-level risk is deemed acceptable, then one moves to the other position.

Here, the system-wide risk referent level was not exceeded, in which case the set of risks confronting the project did not warrant changes to the project plan, nor its possible cancellation. The main focus reverts then to monitoring the risks identified, to searching for the (inevitable) new risks that have yet to surface, and to increasing the probability of success of the project above that which it is currently. The individual project risks will be examined with more rigor, the goal being to avert them where it is feasible to do so. Figure 6.3 illustrates the general process.

Four elemental tools exist to effectively apply risk management.[7] They are:

1. Standards against which performance can be measured
2. Information to monitor actual performance

3. Authority to make required adjustments and corrections when they are needed
4. Competence to implement the best solution from available alternatives.

Each of these will be covered in the following sections.

Two primary questions cast a shadow on the efforts listed above, however. These are whether any further risk aversion is worthwhile, and how much is enough? Before we try answering these questions, we need to be aware of one theme, really an assumption, that will recur throughout this chapter. That is, we will be primarily interested in trying to manage risks by emphasizing their control, through risk aversion techniques, rather than trying to eliminate them. Attempts to

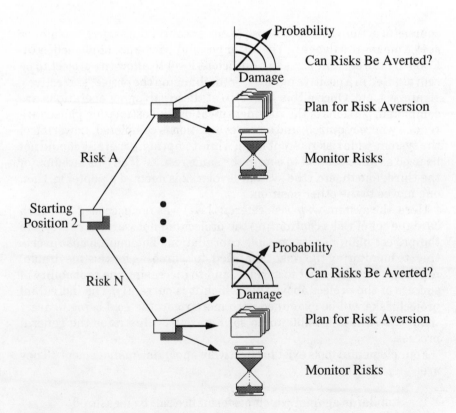

Figure 6.3 Risk Management Process

plan for the elimination of all sources of risk are almost always futile efforts. To succeed in a software project, one must first accept that risks exist, and second, one must balance the contradictory nature of loss and opportunity present in those risks.[8]

If one is lucky, a particular type of loss can be eliminated, but most likely, some new risk will arise to take its place. For example, new risks are created by the very management of risk. If the initial project plan was found to be unacceptable, how much do the expenditures to fix it detract from, or add to, the success of the project? Do the resources spent on risk aversion reduce what are available for the project's implementation?

This does not mean that one should stand by and do nothing, as in general any approach to averting a risk should be vigorously pursued. What it does mean, however, is that the process of risk analysis and management is not only continuous, but also recursive and iterative. The management of risks should be thought of (a) as a renewal process, where new risks are continuously created, mature, and die; and (b) as the actions to control them that take place through a project's life-cycle.

For this chapter, we will assume that the project plan has reached the stage where the system-wide risk referent has not been exceeded. We will say then, that risk management involves the planning, control, and monitoring of a decision about a specific risk, once the system-wide risk has been determined to be acceptable. Each of these three aspects or phases of risk management will be explored in this chapter.

6.2 Planning Phase: Decision Making—Part 1

We said the first phase of risk management is the risk planning phase. During this phase, we are most worried about two issues: first, whether the strategy to be undertaken to carry out risk management itself is feasible and correct; and second, whether the tactics and means available to implement that strategy are in keeping with the overall objectives of the project. The primary objective of risk management strategies is the aversion of individual risks. Let's see if this can be made clearer.

If one has found that the system-wide risk referent level has been achieved, i.e., the overall project risk is of a sufficiently appropriate level to proceed, then one is confronted with two questions. The first is whether one should try to actively increase the probability of success of the project by lowering as many as possible of the known risks. Remember, at this point, it has already been determined that (a) one can proceed with a fair amount of confidence in success of the project as planned; and (b) scarce project resources have been expended to arrive at this conclusion. Now, one asks, what benefits will arise from further expenditures to avert the identified risks? Will these efforts be effective, or will they instead increase the risk to the project because more scarce resources will be spent doing risk management, instead of being poured into accomplishing the project's objectives?

The second question is a related one, but approaches the subject from a different perspective. How much (not whether) effort should be expended to monitor the risks that have been identified, and/or to investigate whether new risks are appearing?[9] One can decide either to avert risks or not, but the question of how much monitoring is enough is a separate issue in its own right. Assuming the project continues on its course, the current system risk will be changing in relation to the original risk referent for the system (i.e., the probability of success line). Without real argument, a periodic check is required to evaluate the project's progress against this referent. Furthermore, the system risk referent sensibly should be made more stringent with the passage of time, i.e., indicating greater levels of success against which the project is to be measured. Consideration is required to determine (a) how often monitoring should be performed; (b) by whom; (c) how extensive it should be; and, (d) at what time, and at what level should the new risk referent be set?

6.2.1 Inputs to risk management decision making

To completely answer the questions posed above, a risk manager requires a number of different types of inputs. One set is needed to understand whether one applies risk aversion procedures, while the other set is required to understand how to do it, if it is so desired. To intelligently make the former decision, one really needs to understand what the latter entails—a classic Alphonse and Gaston situation. Thus, we will begin a little out of sequence and start our examination of risk management with its detailed planning and control aspects. Next, we will explore risk monitoring and then return full circle to examine risk management decision making in the planning context. Think of it as a series of nested subroutine calls. We will, for the time being, assume that we wish to avert our individual risks and want to see how we can go about achieving this.

6.3 Detailed Planning and Controlling

As in all planning exercises, one needs to thoroughly understand the objectives, strategies, tactics, and means available. Although similar to the overall project plan, the planning and implementation phase of risk management is meant to remove obstacles that might get in the way of accomplishing the project objectives. The focus is much more narrow in scope. The information generated in this phase will be contained in planning documents called Risk Management Plan (RMP) and Risk Aversion Plan (RAP), the details of which will be examined shortly.

The planning and implementation phase of risk management is predicated upon the desire to avert the consequences of a risk to some level of acceptability, wherever it is feasible to do so. In the risk management context, feasibility is related to what is realistically possible; whereas acceptability means the consequences are such that one can accept the risk as it currently exists, at a specific level of risk, for some gain or benefit.[10] The difficulty will be in trying to identify what acceptability means for each individual risk. Previously, acceptability meant the comparison of an aggregated ("objective") system risk against the risk referent, while in this case, we are shifting to a new mooring point.

For example, contemplate the concept of the acceptability of a risk as used by Lowrance.[11] He uses it to mean such different things as (a) a conscious decision, perhaps based upon some balancing of good and bad or progress and risk; (b) a decision implying a comparison, possibly subjective, with hazards from other causes, these latter being "acceptable" in relation to one of the senses provided here, or perhaps just historically and possibly unconsciously; or (c) the passive but substantive fact that nothing has to, or can be, done to eliminate or curtail the risk being deemed "acceptable."

Notice throughout each of the uses above, however, there exists a common theme: the idea of balancing the risk against its consequences and against some action to avert it. That is the *core* of the risk management planning problem. In one case, a risk might require a very active approach for averting it, while in another, it may mean acquiescing to it. Therein lies the *complication* of risk aversion. Acceptability cannot be defined identically across different risks, nor is one approach usable in every case. That is why we use the term risk aversion, rather than risk reduction. Reduction is only one available approach to averting risks.

One must be sensitive of the balance that must be struck between what is feasible and what is acceptable. One cannot do everything. Furthermore, aversion of risk is fraught with hazards of its own, because the aversion approach interjects into the project a new management direction or strategy that probably was not originally planned for. For example, aversion might remove the utilization of resources that might be better used on the project itself; or, there may be a possibility that aversion may result in the compounding or coupling of other risks, thus creating even more deadly risks than what was begun with.

Other reasons for requiring sensitivity of the balance between feasibility and acceptability are found in the previous chapters. It was presented there that a risk referent level was determined against which the system-wide risk was measured. The risks, as an aggregated whole, were judged acceptable in relation to this referent. But when considering individual risks, one cannot aggregate, for fear of losing not only opportunities for gain, but of losing or masking the very knowledge necessary to understand the fundamental approaches available to averting them. In other words, the acceptability and aversion strategies of an individual risk may differ greatly from that of a system's risk that has been developed by aggregation. From a practical view, this means one must deal not only with risks on an individual basis, but with cognizance of the system level and environmental intangibles involved.

These different points are not merely semantics, but have wide-spread implications on how one individually views, and takes, a risk. Indirect, non-economic decisions about risk, may need to be substituted for direct economic decisions. Furthermore, these issues are intertwined into the very success of a project. The multiple perspectives must coexist in our planning approach, and for each individual risk, must be made explicit.

One might inquire how one makes the scale balance in the face of the three different forces of a risk, its consequences, and the need for its aversion. One way is shown in Table 6.1. There are listed a number of risk factors and a dichotomous scale, against which each risk can be judged.[12] By rating how an individual risk compares against these factors, one can identify the influence actions have on either accepting the risk as is or trying to avert it. This will become clearer when we later examine how acceptability comes into play when decisions about risk are being made.

Before moving on to examine risk aversion strategies, it would be wise to keep the following old prayer in mind: "Please give me the knowledge to change the things I can, and accept the things I cannot, and the wisdom to tell the difference."

TABLE 6.1 Judgement Criteria for Balancing Risk Acceptability and Feasibility

Risk Factor	Dichotomous Scale		
Volition	Voluntary	:	Involuntary
Severity	Ordinary	:	Catastrophic
Origin	Internal	:	External
Effect Manifestation	Immediate	:	Delayed
Exposure Pattern	Continuous	:	Intermittent
"Dread"/Familiarity	Common/old hazard	:	Dread/new hazard
Benefit	Clear	:	Unclear
Necessity	Necessity	:	Luxury
Controllability	Controlled	:	Uncontrollable

6.3.1 Strategies for risk aversion

After one has positioned oneself to obtain a clearer view as to what level of acceptability is being sought, and assuming passive acceptance of a risk is not called for, three basic classes of strategies can help avert risk. One can either change the consequences of a risk, change its likelihood, or change its magnitude. For all or any one of these classes, a number of specific risk aversion strategies are available. For purposes of this book, we will examine four: *reduction, protection, transference*, and *pecuniary*. Each strategy has a different emphasis: reduction emphasizes direct approaches to lowering of likelihoods or the impacts of the consequences; protection also emphasizes reduction of likelihood and consequences, but at a system level; transference emphasizes the acceptance of risk, but reduces the consequences by sharing the risk with others; and pecuniary emphasizes financial means to avert risk. Which, or how many, aversion strategies are used depends on the unique risk circumstances of the project. All strategies can be used to avert risks in the product, as well as in the process used in building the product.

6.3.1.1 Reduction. Risk reduction, or as it is sometimes also called, risk abatement or mitigation, is the first aversion strategy usually considered. The objectives are either the reduction in the likelihood of a risk occurring, and/or of its magnitude. The direction that is emphasized depends highly on whether the risk is considered a direct risk or an indirect risk.

A direct risk is one over which the project management exerts a large degree of control. In this situation, application of current project resources can be utilized to reduce risks of this type. The risks belonging to this category were described in Chapter 3 as (nonstrategic) "known risks." For example, a particular schedule risk may be reduced by extending the schedule to provide more time.

In apposition to direct risks, an indirect risk is one where there is little or no project control, and the application of work-around procedures will be necessary to achieve their reduction. For example, in government projects, future budget reductions are always a possibility. Since the budget may not be in direct control of the project, politicking may be required to keep the budget from being reduced. This technique, where active indirect approaches are used to reduce the probability of a risk occurring, is sometimes called loss prevention. Direct application of project resources will not do much good in reducing these types of risks. Risks that are categorized as predictable or unpredictable are considered indirect risks. Table 6.2 categorizes the types of risks against the sources of risks.

Ideally, upon application of a reduction strategy, each risk is reduced to a point where it reaches a level of acceptability, and thus is eliminated from further immediate consideration. As each risk is reduced, the probability of failure should be reduced, or the probability of success increased. Remember, these may not be directly related. This is illustrated in Figure 6.4. Thus, the first objective in applying a risk reduction strategy is to try to make as many identified risks as possible, especially the predictable risks, into direct risks. The reason should be obvious. If one can make all the risks direct, they are then within the limits of (feasible) control of the project. Project resources can be applied to reducing them. When it is said that project resources can be applied, it should be clear that one is talking about both tangible items, such as shifting people from one task to another, and intangible items, such as morale.

Time is an important element in risk reduction. Predictable or unpredictable project risks are not usually considered direct risks, because their certainty is "tied to a time in the future." In other words, they are longer-term risks that have not yet occurred, or may never occur, as illustrated in Figure 6.5. To overcome this, one can try to make these longer-term risks more visible, or "shift them to the left" on the time line, a concept of moving "back to the future." As an example, software evolution costs are usually higher than the cost of the original system

TABLE 6.2 Approaches for Risk Aversion

Risk Sources	Known	Predictable	Unpredictable
Lack of Information Cost Schedule Technical Operational Support	Direct Approach	Direct or Indirect Approach	Indirect Approach
Lack of Control Cost Schedule Technical Operational Support	Direct or Indirect Approach	Indirect Approach	Indirect Approach
Lack of Time Cost Schedule Technical Operational Support	Direct Approach	Direct or Indirect Approach	Indirect Approach

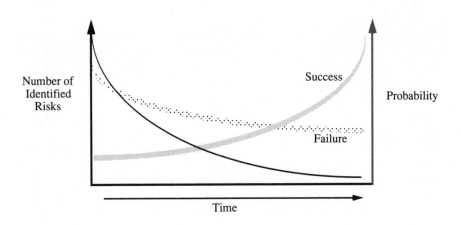

Figure 6.4 Risk Reduction

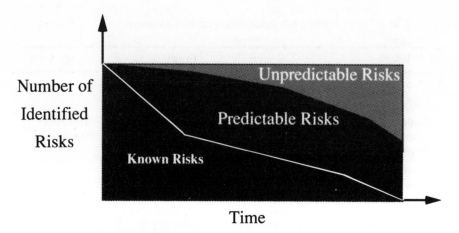

Figure 6.5 Occurrence of Risks in Time

development, with pure bug-fixing costs almost equalling initial development costs. If the future evolution of the system *is placed* at risk due to the possibility of high maintenance costs, then one can shift the responsibility of the reduction of maintenance risks into the requirement phase of the development life cycle. The development of the programming language Ada is a prime example of risk reduction in this manner, as is the application of quality control techniques, including preventive testing.

Another example are risks that have a low frequency of occurrence but high severity (and are usually categorized as unpredictable risks). These are the most difficult to reduce. By arbitrarily "increasing" the frequency of the risk, i.e., assuming the risk is occurring in this instant of time, one can transform it into a known risk; or prototyping, simulation, etc., can be used to buy information (really buying a "time future") about an unknown risk. A variation on this principle is to make parallel risks into sequential ones, shifting the time element into something more understandable.

However, time shifting is not utilized as an approach too often. The only way to make all identified risks, known and unpredictable alike, into direct risks is to set up a contingency plan for each and every risk identified, which is not normally practical nor cost effective. Remember, just because a risk exists does not mean that it will occur. If the risk is of low frequency but of high severity, reduction may not be the best aversion strategy to use. The balance among risk reduction, the risk itself, and its consequences, as mentioned earlier, once again must be considered.

If one knows that it is impractical to convert all the indirect risks into direct risks, or that one must limit the amount of resources available for risk reduction, then one approach is to use the commonly known Pareto 80/20 rule. Some subset of all the risks represents the "peak" risks to the project. These are the ones that represent the greatest danger or threat to its successful completion. Thus, in this approach to risk reduction, instead of attacking all the risks simultaneously, concentration is only focused on the top 10 or so. The reasoning is that 20 percent of the risks contain 80 percent of the real high-risk problems, so it is better to concentrate one's resources on attacking them first. Further, many high risks are caused by risk coupling or compounding, and by reducing one risk, a number of others may also be reduced. This has some justification—the severity and frequency of risks tend to follow this general distribution pattern. Table 6.3 lists a number of risks that follow this 20/80 rule.[13]

The Defense Science Board and others[14,15] have stated that a "top-10 risk watch list" should be developed, not only for candidates for risk reduction, but for monitoring purposes. This makes good sense since too many independent actions place tremendous supervisory and coordination responsibilities on the risk management team. The risks on the watch list are the 10 prioritized as the most severe risks, or the 10 more

TABLE 6.3 Pareto Software Engineering Risks

- 80% of the project's success involves 20% of the software development (i.e., requirements).

- 80% of the cost is contained in 20% of software modules.

- 80% of the errors is contained in 20% of software modules.

- 80% of the cost of error correction is in 20% of software modules.

- 80% of execution time is consumed by 20% of software modules.

- 80% of the automation usage involves 20% of the available automation.

- 80% of the work is contributed by 20% of the personnel.

- 80% of software engineering risk occurs in 20% of the risk.

TABLE 6.4 Prioritized Candidates for Top-10 Software Risk List

	Risk / Priority	Severity	Frequency	Aversion Strategy
1.	Schedule slippage	High	High	Reduction
2.	Requirements changes	High	High	Reduction
3.	Lack of performance	High	Medium	Reduction
4.	Over projected cost	Med/High	Medium	Pecuniary
	•	•	•	•
	•	•	•	•
	•	•	•	•
10.	Personnel inexperience	Medium	Low	Transfer

frequently experienced risks, or some hybrid between the two, as shown in Table 6.4. Note, however, that just because the risks are on a top-10 list does not mean that risk reduction will be applied in every case. Some other approach may be required. We will examine risk charting a bit later in the section on monitoring.

Risk reduction is by far the most popular approach. The next most popular is termed risk protection.

6.3.1.2 Risk protection. The next strategy of risk aversion that should be considered for application is termed protection. The emphasis in this approach is to reduce the likelihood that the occurrence of a risk will affect the total system operation. The philosophy is like preventive medicine, but based upon classic reliability and fault-tolerance techniques.

Protection is achieved usually through some "physical" means, where the likelihood of a risk is reduced by (a) reorganizing the system structure to increase the number of alternatives available; or (b) increasing the reliability of the individual components of the system. In order to maximize the degree of protection offered by the reliability gain, the redundancy must be applied at the lowest level of component complexity in the system being developed.

A prime example of the protection approach is the use of parallel (or triple, quadded, standby, etc.) redundancy in system design. N-version programming and recovery blocks are examples. Here, one attempts to reduce the likelihood that any one failure will put the system at risk. In principle, a system may be made arbitrarily reliable, provided the degree of reliability is made high (i.e., sufficient reliability is available). Many aircraft have multiple engines or multiple subsystems for this reason, and the space shuttle uses four-version redundancy for its operational flight software (five computers—four operational, one backup). However, one should not be overly optimistic about redundancy as a cure-all. Recall the earlier incident with the aircraft that had all three engines flame out at once. Also, adding more software into a system for protection increases the complexity of the software system overall, so there is a definite possibility that protection can be reduced rather than increased.[16]

6.3.1.3 Risk transfer. The third approach to risk aversion is called risk transfer or pooling. Another common name is insurance. In this approach, one arranges for a third party to help share the consequences if a risk occurs. The emphasis is on reducing the magnitude of the loss if the risk comes into play, rather than reducing the risk likelihood or alternatives available. One pays a price to transform a loss that poses a (relatively) unacceptable risk into one that poses no such risk. The price one has to pay depends on expected value (or utility) calculations.

Risk transfer usually is applied when there are limited resources available for risk reduction or protection, or where risks are of high severity and low frequency. Flood insurance is an example of the latter. Another way of transferring risks is to reallocate risks to other parts of the system, if it is a product risk, or project, if it is a process risk. Sometimes, risk transfer may not be available until after reduction has occurred, because the third party's acceptability level of a risk has to be reached. The use of a third party's view of a risk means that there is less direct control of the project as well.

There is a whole body of literature on the subject of risk transferring or insurance, and most of the literature on risk is derived from these beginnings. The reader should consult any library for further information on the subject.

6.3.1.4 Pecuniary. The final approach to risk aversion is the financing of the risks. This is similar to risk transfer, but it means that for each risk, for a selected set of risks, or for an aggregation of all the risks, a contingency "fund" of project resources is set aside in case any or all of the risks occur. The reason for a contingency is obvious if one considers Figure 6.6, which shows the accuracy of an estimation of the cost of the project versus life-cycle phase.[17] Notice that the accuracy of cost estimation improves with time, or to say it another way, the accuracy of the

Relative Cost Range

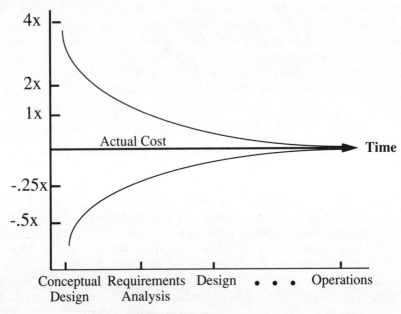

Figure 6.6 Improvement in Estimation Over Time

estimation is likely to have its largest error at the beginning of a project. Since no one knows the true estimation error, but one can be sure that some error is present (remembering from Chapter 3 and the subject of continuous random variables, that the probability of the estimate being correct is zero), a contingency fund is set up to finance the difference between the actual cost and an acceptable level of inaccuracy contained within the estimated cost. As such, more contingency is required in the beginning, rather than toward the end of the project.

Contingency planning makes eminent sense, and many project managers talk about it, but in practice, this approach to risk aversion is almost never used. Only in military operations has it been institutionalized. Most software projects have little fat explicitly left in them, although some might be deliberately left under the commonly applied "fudge factor" approach. The lack of explicit contingency is one of the major drivers for the continuation of the machismo management style exhibited today in software projects. Project managers are forced to manage close to the edge of what is feasible, especially on government-type contracts, where low cost is the essential risk driver. The main difficulty is that creating and maintaining a contingency is difficult to cost-justify using straight economic analysis.

6.3.2 Tactics for risk aversion

It can be said that the four strategies for risk aversion outlined above are fairly well defined. The same cannot be said, however, for specific aversion tactics available that should be used within a software engineering project. Aversion tactics are primarily based upon the process of software engineering, i.e., the process models, methods/techniques, and their automation. The reality is, there does not exist a large body of knowledge to draw upon that systematically classifies, for example, software engineering methods or techniques according to an aversion strategy, nor describes which technique to use, when to use it, and how effective it will be. Again the lack of forensic software engineering and the unique nature of most software projects leaves everyone guessing as to what to do. As a result, one is usually left to one's own judgement.

This isn't totally correct, because if one looks for help in selecting a risk aversion tactic, there are a multitude of people with very vocal opinions willing to give advice. For some reason, certain tactics tend to be "in style" over a period in time, developing cultists in their wake. These are touted as the "best" approach to avert risk in a software development by these advocates. Common examples of the fad today are the incessant push for prototyping and reuse. Before those it was "build it twice," "apply software complexity measures," "apply theorem proving," "simulation," or "automatic programming." The latter started in 1958 and is still promised as a way to proceed.[18]

One should not be too cynical, as each new technique does add to the knowledge base about how to reduce risk. One of the fads might actually work as advertised. Fads also demonstrate the ever increasing maturity of software engineering and the vitality of the field. Further, as new technology becomes available to increase risks, the same technology expansion makes new methods for their aversion feasible. The trouble is, though, as more techniques are developed, the less they seem to be applied. One begins to wonder if, after hearing so often that there is this "wonder cure" just around the corner and being disappointed by its actual effectiveness, managers just do not bother to listen anymore. The same, we fear, with risk analysis and management.

Any technique, be it redundancy, structured programming, prototyping, etc., helps in risk aversion, but none alone will avert all the software engineering risks being confronted. A mixture of techniques is required, some of which are good only in certain circumstances. Therefore, you still need to determine what the objectives of the risk aversion strategy are, and then find the appropriate tactics and means that suit the specific situation. In the companion volume, guidelines to the selection of the proper tactics are provided.

A complementary attempt at categorizing the different techniques of risk aversion across a system's life cycle can be found in a Department of Defense manual DoD 4245.7-M entitled, "Transition From Development To Production."[19] This manual focuses on the process of system engineering and the methods used to control it. The manual creates what are called Critical Path Templates (CPT), which describe the most

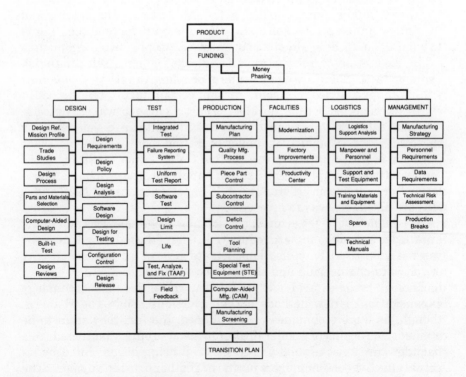

Figure 6.7 Critical Path Templates

critical (path) events in the design, test, and production elements of the industrial process. Figure 6.7 depicts the total network of CPTs as defined in the manual.

Each template was derived from the opinions and recommendations from panels of experts in their specific areas, concentrating on how *technical* risk could be minimized, using *reduction techniques*, during the transition of a DoD program from development to production. Each template describes an area of risk and then prescribes technical methods for reducing that risk. Where in the life-cycle time-line these risks can be expected, and where they should be reduced, are also provided as input. The templates are typically a two- or three- page description of a technical problem or scenario that, if left unchecked, can create a high-risk program. The templates then describe a readily available "solution" based upon lessons learned on other programs. Figure 6.8 provides one specific example, out of over 50.

Interestingly, the manual states that the causes of acquisition risk are not managerial but technical. This shows up very clearly in the CPTs' descriptions. The view expressed by the manual's authors is that by providing and following a rigorous engineering discipline that focuses on low-risk approaches, an affordable and reliable DoD system can be delivered. It still is too early to determine the success rate of this approach, but it definitely is a step in the right direction.

6.3.3 Risk management plans

The final step in the planning process is to document what was discovered, which means to develop risk management plans. Recall from Chapter 3 that the very first action undertaken was to reformat the overall project plans into what was called a Risk Estimate of the Situation (RES). The RES explicitly stated the plans' objectives, strategies, tactics, and means. It was said at that time that it was important to understand how each element interacted and contributed to the other, in order to see how they contributed to the overall project's success criteria.

Recall also that one of the key benefits of performing an RES was that one learned to consider only the capabilities inherent in the project, not the intentions of senior management. Wishful thinking, as presented in Augustine's Law of Surrealistic Planning, "If today were half as good as tomorrow is supposed to be, it would be twice as good as yesterday was,"

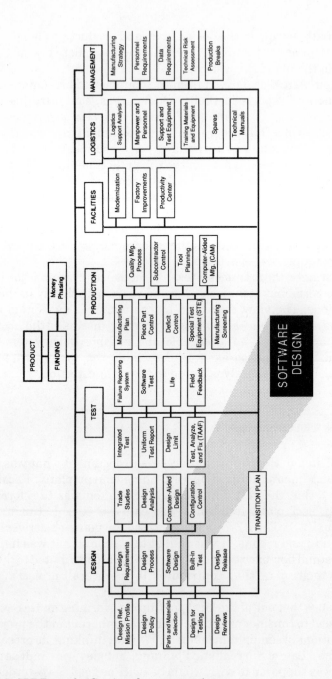

Figure 6.8 CPT Example (*Continued on next page*)

AREA OF RISK

Many weapon systems now depend upon software for their operation and maintenance. Whether the software is embedded ("tactical" or "firmware") or loaded into main memory from peripheral storage devices, the problems are the same—the weapon systems cannot be qualification tested and they can't function, in most cases, without proper software. A software error can cause a weapon system failure. Nevertheless, software frequently fails to receive the same degree of discipline as hardware early in FSD. Failure to allocate system requirements clearly between hardware and software greatly increases the difficulty of isolating and correcting design problems. Industry experience shows that 64 percent of all software errors are traceable to functional or logical design, with the remaining 36 percent due to coding.

OUTLINE FOR REDUCING RISK

• The applicability to software in the outline for reducing risk of every design template is considered. Most templates are as applicable to software as to hardware, especially design process and design analysis.

• Functional requirements are allocated either to hardware or to software, as appropriate, at design start. These allocations usually are trade study topics, since it often is not clear initially which functions should be implemented in hardware, and which in software. Hardware and software responsibilities reside with one individual.

• Proven design policies, processes, and analyses governing software design are employed, including, but not limited to the following: rigorous configuration control, chief programmer/design teams and modular construction, structured programming and top-down design, structured walkthroughs, good documentaiton, traceability of all design and programming steps back to top level requirements, independent review of requirements analyses and design process, thorough test plan developed and utilized from design start, compliance with standards, structured flowcharting.

• Computer software developers are accountable for their work quality, and are subject to both incentives and penalties during all phases of the system life cycle.

• A uniform computer software error data collection and analysis capability is established to provide insights into reliability problems, leading to clear definitions and measures of computer software reliability.

• A software simulator is developed and maintained to test and maintain software before, during, and after field testing.

• Security requirements are considered during the software design process.

• It is essential that software design practices follow a disciplined process similar to proven hardware design practices. Design schedules for software coincide with the hardware schedule.

Figure 6.8 (*Continued*) CPT Example

must be avoided as much in risk aversion as in project planning.[20] Recall again the story at the beginning of this chapter. One of the key, if not *the* key, reason oil companies' senior managers did not, and may still not, understand where things went wrong with their forecasts is that their plans were based upon their "intentions" of the elements influencing the oil market and not on their inherent capability to change under alternate circumstances.

Thus, as part of whatever subsequent formal risk aversion planning documents are created, an updated RES should be completed. The RES should evaluate the project's capacity to conduct the risk aversion strategy or strategies selected, focusing on what is to be gained from each step. The RES will nail down what the risk aversion objectives are, identify the strategies, tactics, and means necessary, and evaluate any contingency required. It will also determine the cost effectiveness of performing the risk aversion (how, will be discussed later). The general format is the same as in Chapter 3, Figure 3.6.

Along with the RES, there are two other planning documents that should be considered.[21] The first is the controlling document called the Risk Management Plan (RMP). The RMP states how the total risk analysis and management procedures are applied to a project. It describes all aspects of the process of risk identification, estimation, evaluation, and control. The RMP states what the system risk referent levels will be and the preferred method for evaluating project risks against these referents. A general format for the RMP is shown in Table 6.5.

The second planning document is called the Risk Aversion Plan (RAP). The RAP is the detailed plan for risk aversion, after the general risk analysis process has been conducted. As a minimum, a RAP should include:

1. The identification of all the risk areas of the project, and the constituent risk factors in each area

2. The identification of the priority risk items, including a description of the risk item's importance, in relation to project objectives

3. An assessment of the risk factors identified, including the probability of occurrence and potential damage, as extracted from the risk evaluation

4. The identified alternatives considered, and their costs

TABLE 6.5 Risk Management Plan

I. INTRODUCTION
  1. Scope and Purpose of Document
  2. Overview
    a. Objectives
    b. Risk Aversion Priorities
  3. Organization
    a. Management
    b. Responsibilities
    c. Job Descriptions
  4. Aversion Program Description
    a. Schedule
    b. Major Milestones and Reviews
    c. Budget

II. RISK ANALYSIS
  1. Identification
    a. Survey of Risks
      i. Sources of Risk
    b. Risk Taxonomy
  2. Risk Estimation
    a. Estimate Probability of Risk
    b. Estimate Consequence of Risk
    c. Estimation Criteria
    d. Possible Sources of Estimation Error
  3. Evaluation
    a. Evaluation Methods to be Used
    b. Evaluation Method Assumptions and Limitations
    c. Evaluation Risk Referents
    d. Evaluation Results

III. RISK MANAGEMENT
  1. Recommendations on Risk Evaluation Results
  2. Risk Aversion Options
  3. Risk Aversion Recommendations
  4. Risk Monitoring Procedures

IV. APPENDICES
  1. Risk Estimate of the Situation
  2. Risk Abatement Plan

---

5. The recommended risk aversion strategy, including an implementation plan for resolving each risk item; risks that require no aversion strategy should be so noted

6. An integration strategy of individual risk aversion plans, with other risk aversion plans with exploration of the possibility of compounding or coupling among risks

7. An integration strategy of the RES, RMP, and RAP

8. The assignment of appropriate resources required to implement the risk aversion strategy including a description of cost, schedule, and technical considerations

9. The risk organization, its responsibilities, how it fits into the project, and the person(s) responsible for implementing risk aversion

10. Implementation start-date, schedule, and key milestones

11. The criteria for success, i.e., when will a risk be considered averted, and the monitoring approach to be used

12. Tracking, decision, and feedback points, including the development of an updated list of priority risk items, plans, and monthly results

13. Contingency requirements for each prioritized risk

14. Corporate sign-off of the RAP.

Once the planning process is complete, the next step is to implement the project plans in cognizance with the guidance provided in the risk management and aversion plans.

6.3.4 Plan implementation and control

We will not dwell much on implementation, or the control aspects, other than to say they involve making the projected risk decisions happen in reality. This is accomplished in normal management fashion, by providing the actual required resources to do the job and meet the various aversion plans' objectives. Conflicts between competing organizations for aversion resources need to be sorted out, and any decisions that are different from the plans developed must be documented. The key element is that definitive action is taken to ensure that the risk management and aversion plans are being followed. Replanning is initiated whenever risk levels either go up or don't come down as expected. This will be discussed more in risk monitoring.

6.3.5 Summary

In summary, during the detailed planning and control phases of risk management, the risk manager makes the final selection as to what actions will be taken about the risks likely to be encountered during the project. Once the decisions are made, a plan for carrying them out is formulated. Often, this means a second analysis phase is conducted to ensure the plan's feasibility, especially checking that it does not interfere with other decisions made, or about to be made. This may seem a bit redundant, or somewhat late, but the principle of late binding applies (wait until the last possible moment before making a decision to ensure maximum flexibility). Once a decision has been made, it becomes a "certainty," and so brings with it more information about future potential risks, as well as the elimination of others. Because of dependency relationships, a decision that was previously acceptable may no longer be feasible.

The next phase is the monitoring phase, which in essence serves as an early warning system. Here one asks, "Given that I have implemented the plan for averting risks, how well am I doing, and do I need to adjust my plans in any way?"

6.4 Monitoring

The issues involved in monitoring can be illustrated by the following conversation from the book, *Yes, Prime Minister*:[22]

"I foresee all sorts of problems, Prime Minister, with that proposal."

"If they are unforeseen, how can you foresee them?"

Monitoring occurs after the decisions concerning aversion strategy and tactics have been implemented in order to (a) check if the consequences of the decision were the same as envisioned; (b) identify opportunities for refinement of the risk aversion plan; and (c) help provide feedback for future decisions about how to control new or current risks that are not responding to risk aversion, or whose nature has changed with time. The value of continual reassessment cannot be underestimated as the development progresses.

Risk monitoring is a vital activity, required to be performed, independent of whether risk aversion occurs. There are, after all, no assurances that good outcomes necessarily follow from good judgements. If a wrong decision has been made, it must be recognized early enough so that corrective action can be immediately taken. But it is just as important to recognize when a decision is correct, and not to panic or change it prematurely. Constant changing of direction will not only reduce any contingency available, but increase tremendously the likelihood and magnitude of the consequences of any subsequent risks occurring.

Monitoring becomes a necessity because of the one attribute of risk whose influence is difficult to predict—time. The generalizations about risk that were made early in the project can be said to decay with time. "At one time a conclusion describes the existing situation well, at a later time it accounts for rather little variance, and ultimately it is only valid as history."[23] The long-term rewards of such vigilance will lead to increasing numbers of successfully completed projects.

As a project proceeds, more information is obtained about the true nature of the risks involved. The basic causes of risk, either due to the lack of information, lack of control, or the lack of time, become readily apparent. Older risks are better quantified or are removed from concern, new ones are identified and controlled, and the better managed the program becomes (hopefully)—that is, if the initial identification, estimation, and evaluation of the risks were correct. Recognition of the current state of project growth, and risk decay, is of more than passing interest.[24]

6.4.1 Monitoring techniques

As was the case with risk aversion techniques, there is not yet an agreed, well-defined set of monitoring methods available to use off-the-shelf. Some of the techniques used in the estimation, evaluation, or aversion of risk can be thought of, and used as, monitoring techniques. Of course, one of the main reasons for performing monitoring is to keep a predictable, unpredictable, or an unknown risk from becoming a known risk. A prime example of this happening is when a new development alters the risk priority list, new technology is used to overcome some other risk, or some other corrective action is performed. The risk organization should be sensitive to these changes.

Of course, to be sensitive to these changes means being able to recognize them first. It would be useful not to have to rely only on experienced personnel to "sniff out" where the trouble spots lay ahead. As was the case in the section on risk estimation, the first issue to be resolved, then, is how to measure what is being monitored.

Much effort is currently being spent on trying to develop risk monitoring measurement scales and the standards to be used. One such effort is the IEEE Project P982, whose purpose is to identify measures that can be used to optimize the development of reliable software and to standardize the implementation of the metrics defined.[25] The culmination of the work, which is currently in draft form, will sometimes in mid/late 1989 become an IEEE standard on software reliability measures. When complete, it will form one of the best standard sources of information covering an aspect of software risk monitoring.

Recall from the chapters on risk analysis that we were concerned with risks that affected the process and products of software engineering. The interesting aspect of the document is the division of the measures into two functional categories, product measures and process measures, which is exactly what we required. In the draft standard are descriptions of some 39 measures. The utility of these measures is then cross-referenced against the two functional categories, and then further subcategorized into specific dimensions of reliability. Some measures can be utilized in more than one category or subcategory. Furthermore, the measures are cross-referenced to software life-cycle phases to show where each is most applicable. Also included are the levels of experience that currently exist in the community in actually applying them. These range from "0," indicating a measure has been formalized, but not sufficiently validated to have operational experience (five measures are rated this way), to "3," where there has been extensive experience in applying and validating the measure (seven possess this rating). Table 6.6 illustrates the measures and major cross-referencing.

It would be useful to examine one or two of the measures defined by the IEEE P982 Group, but of course there are other monitoring techniques available for use as well. Thus, to simplify things a little, and in keeping with our focus on product risks and process risks, and in keeping with P982 as well, the remainder of this section will be divided into product-oriented monitoring techniques and process-oriented monitoring techniques.

6.4.1.1 Product-oriented techniques. In the application of product-oriented monitoring techniques, one starts with the assumption that the kinds of risks being averted and monitored are related to the software

TABLE 6.6 IEEE P982 Reliability Measures

Measures	Maturity	Process	Product
Mean Time to Remove Next K Faults	3		•
Man-hours Per Major Defect Detected	2		•
Rely	1		•
Error Distribution(s)	1		•
Software Release Readiness	0		•
Software Science Difficulty	3	•	
Cyclomatic Complexity	3	•	
Failure Counting	3	•	
Mean Time to Failure	3	•	
Failure Occurrence Rate	3	•	
Minimal Test Cases Determination	2	•	
Run Reliability-Nelson Method	2	•	
Estimated Number of Faults Remaining (seeding)	2	•	
Reliability Growth Function	2	•	
Software Source Listings and Documentation	2	•	
Completeness	2	•	
Fault Density	1	•	
Defect Density	1	•	
Cumulative Failure Profile	1	•	
Number of Exits/Entries per Module	1	•	
Graph-Theoretic Complexity	1	•	
Design Structure	1	•	
Software Purity Level	1	•	
System Performance Reliability	1	•	
Predicted Number of Remaining Faults	1	•	
Data or Information Flow Complexity	0	•	
Independent Process Reliability	0	•	
Combined HD/SW Operational Availability	0	•	
Requirements Traceability	3	•	•
Cause and Effect Graphing	2	•	•
Test Coverage	2	•	•
Number of Conflicting Requirements	2	•	•
Software Maturity Index	1	•	•
Fault-days Number	1	•	•
Functional Test Coverage	1	•	•
Defect Indexes	1	•	•
Test Accuracy	1	•	•
Requirements Compliance	1	•	•
Testing Sufficiency	0	•	•

product itself. These may be related to a specific risk, such as the complexity of the software in the system being developed. In the risk analysis phase, this risk may have been identified and evaluated as being a high risk (generally, the higher the complexity of a system, the more difficult it is to implement). Thus, a decision to proceed with risk aversion via the strategy of risk reduction might have been taken to lower the complexity of the software. This may have been done by decomposing the system in a different way than was originally envisioned. Further, levels of complexity may have been specified that cannot be exceeded. By monitoring the complexity using product-oriented techniques, such as a software complexity measure, a check can be made against this possibility.

Since the monitoring process itself is concerned with any condition that deviates from the expected (i.e., deviations from the acceptable levels of risk, as defined in the risk aversion plan), anything that meets those criteria will be termed "anomalies."[26] An anomaly is not necessarily a problem, as the original expected condition may be incorrectly specified, or the perception or interpretation by an individual of the expected condition may not match the intent of the original specifier of the condition. To aid in determining what is its true nature, classes of anomalies, in the terms of *errors*, *failures*, or *faults*, have been defined.[27,28]

An *error* is a discrepancy between a computed, observed, or measured value or condition and the true, specified, or theoretically correct value or condition. A *failure* is the inability of a system to perform a required function within specified limits. A *fault* is a manifestation of an error, which, when encountered, may cause a failure. Faults may also contain a subclass of product deficiencies or weaknesses, such as being overly complex, difficult to use, etc. The latter are related to the "ilities" shown in Figure 3.3.

6.4.1.1.1 IEEE P982 product-oriented measures. As an illustration of the type of IEEE P982 product-oriented measures available that can be used for monitoring purposes, we will look at what is called the Software Maturity Index (SMI) measure.[29] The SMI is used to provide a measure of the relative impact that software changes and additions are making to the total software configuration. It also can be used to demonstrate the stability of the software throughout the period of user test and evaluation. Thus, the measure can be applied during the concepts and requirements phases of the system life cycle, as well as the installation and checkout phase. The maturity level is listed as "one," meaning there has been some limited use of the measure in real programs. The risks that relate to this measure are those that require risk aversion techniques that involve making changes to a system (i.e., those risks that fall into the P829 category of reliability growth and projection). An example might be requirements changes.

There are two implementations of the index—the appropriate selection depends on the availability of data. The basic data required are:

M_T = Number of software functions (modules) in the current software delivery

F_c = Number of software functions (modules) in the current delivery that include internal changes from a previous delivery

F_a = Number of software functions (modules) in the current delivery that are additions to the previous delivery

F_{del} = Number of software functions (modules) in the previous delivery that are deleted in the current module.

Thus, the Software Maturity Index is calculated as:

$$SMI = \frac{M_T - (F_a + F_c + F_{del})}{M_T} \tag{6.1}$$

Note that the total number of current release functions (modules) equals the previous release functions (modules) plus the number of current release functions (modules) that were added to the previous release, minus the number of functions (modules) that were deleted from the previous release. The deletion of a function (module) is treated the same as an addition of a function (module).

The second implementation of the SMI represents the ratio of the number of functions (modules) that remain unchanged from the previous release to the total number of functions (modules) delivered in the present release. Thus, the SMI is calculated as follows:

$$SMI = \frac{M_T - F_c}{M_T} \tag{6.2}$$

The changes and addition of functions (modules) are tracked and the index is calculated for each release. Estimates of changes would be included for any problem reports currently held, but not yet resolved.

By computing the SMI, each software release can be monitored to determine what impacts changes are having on the software configuration. If the impacts are small, then the product is maturing, and the risks due to change are being reduced.

As has been stated earlier, 38 other measures are included in the IEEE P982 draft standard. Each is useful to some degree for risk monitoring. Another will be examined in the process-oriented measures.

6.4.1.1.2 Software quality indicators. Another group that has also been developing product-oriented measures is the U.S. Air Force Systems Command. It has developed a number of Software Quality Indicators (SQI), contained in AFSCP 800-14, which provide insight into the quality of mission-critical computer resources.[30] The SQI are meant to reflect the quality of the software products developed in defense-related acquisitions. The measures are based upon the experience gained on previous acquisition programs and are meant only to indicate the results of, and not replace, existing quality practices.

The measures are basically a subset of those contained in IEEE P982 but are tailored for the defense environment using DoD STD-2167A type development standards. AFSCP 800-14 covers only the following seven areas: completeness, design structure, defect density, fault density, test coverage, test sufficiency, and documentation.

Where AFSCP 800-14 differs from IEEE P982 is in its application. In the pamphlet are rules of thumb on what to look for when applying a particular SQI. One measure relates to the design structure. This measure is supposed to indicate the simplicity or clarity of the design, independent of the overall complexity of the implemented functions. Values associated with the measure can also be used to identify problem areas within the design that could affect future maintainability of the product, as well as identifying potential hidden or missing linkages between internal design structures. The inputs for the indicator are:

S_1 = Total number of units (modules) in the program

S_2 = Number of units (modules) dependent on the source of input data (a result of prior processing or calling sequence) or destination of output data (post-processing or display)

S_3 = Number of units (modules) dependent on prior processing

S_4 = Number of database items

S_5 = Total number of unique database items

S_6 = Number of database segments

S_7 = Number of units (modules) with a single entrance/single exit; branch on error detection is not considered as a multiple condition.

A number of other inputs are also required. These are weighted factors related to the design structure.

D_1 = Structure: Design is organized top-down, bottom-up, or object-oriented as applicable: D_1 = "1" if yes, "0" if no

D_2 = Unit (module) independence: $D_2 = 1 - (S_2/S_1)$

D_3 = Units not dependent on prior processing: $D_3 = 1 - (S_3/S_1)$

D_4 = Database size: $D_4 = 1 - (S_5/S_4)$

D_5 = Database compartmentalization: $D_5 = 1 - (S_6/S_4)$

D_6 = Unit single entrance/single exist: $D_6 = (S_7/S_1)$.

The Design Structure Quality Indicator (DSQI) is computed as a weighted sum, where $\Sigma\, \omega_i = 1$ and indicates a component's relative priority. For example, the weight ω_1 might be higher if object-oriented design is being used in an object-managed situation, versus a strict top-down approach. A figure of .167 is suggested for use when and if it is not feasible for a priority weighting to be assigned. Thus, DSQI is computed as follows:

$$\text{DSQI} = \sum_{i=1}^{6} \omega_i D_i \qquad (6.3)$$

The value of DSQI will be scaled to be between 0 and 1, with 1 representing the simplest and most maintainable design. If monitoring

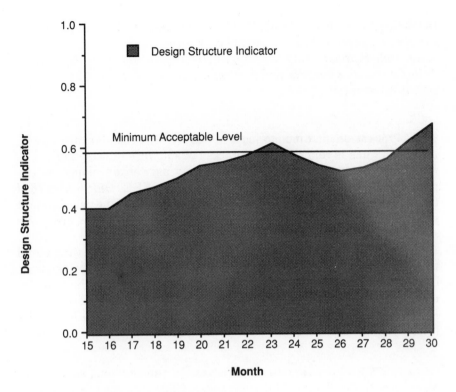

Figure 6.9 Design Structure Quality Indicator

indicates low values, these should be investigated to determine where a risk aversion strategy should be incorporated to change the specific design approach, or if one is already being used, whether it should itself be changed. Comparison between units can show where additional monitoring and/or risk aversion techniques emphasis might be required. A level of complexity, say between .5 and .75, should be set to indicate the minimum level of acceptability for the design structure. Figure 6.9 provides an example of its use.

There is a raft of other measures that can be used for product-oriented monitoring, many aimed specifically at determining software complexity.[31] The main difficulty is in matching the correct measure to the risk that is to be averted. Remember that a measure may be used to monitor the risk aversion strategy directly, as in the design structure metric, or indirectly, as in the software maturity index. The reader should consult the details contained in IEEE P982 and AFCS 800-14 for more specific examples, as well as the computing literature such as the *IEEE Transactions on Software Engineering, IEEE Transactions on Reliability, ACM Computing Surveys,* and the *Communications of the ACM,* for more recent information.[32–37]

6.4.1.2 Process-oriented monitoring techniques. The second set of monitoring techniques is related to the process of software development. The measures involved in this area are nearly as well developed as the product-oriented ones. This is demonstrated in IEEE P982, where 16 of the 39 measures can be used to monitor some aspect of the development process. However, this is caveated with the fact that only three measures are solely process-oriented.

There are also a number of more informal measures about, which tend to be based less on experimentation and more on experience gained from best industry practice. We will begin by examining IEEE P982 again, move to a companion of AFSCP 800-14, called the Software Management Indicators, AFSCP 800-43, and then take a quick look at a few of the informal measures that may be of general interest.

6.4.1.2.1 IEEE P982 process-oriented measures. In the previous section, we examined the Software Maturity Index (SMI), as an example of a product-oriented measure. In truth, the SMI is also an example of a process-oriented metric. Take again the example of the possible necessity of requirement changes. An assessment is therefore necessary of the resultant trade-offs among cost, schedule, and performance if the changes are made. By estimating the change and applying the SQI, some indication of the impact on the software stability can be acquired. The risks that relate to the measure used in this manner require risk aversion techniques that emphasize the control of changes to a system (i.e., those risks that fall into the P982 category of risk/benefit/cost evaluation).

A measure that is only process-oriented in its emphasis is the mean time to remove the next K faults.[38] This measure also fits into the risk/benefit/cost evaluation category of IEEE P982. Basically, the measure is used to project the average length of time until the next K faults are discovered. This measure is most useful in monitoring risk aversion strategies associated with test, installation and checkout, and operational and maintenance phases of a project's life-cycle. The experience level is rated a "3" (i.e., there has been extensive experience in applying and validating the measure). The inputs required to apply the measure are:

i = Number of failures found from the beginning of the testing to the present time

Q' = Estimate of the proportionality constant

N' = Estimate of the total number of faults in the program.

The estimate of the mean time to failure (MTF) between the ith and $(i + 1)^{st}$ failure can be calculated using any number of models—for instance, the Jelinski and Moranda "De-Eutrophication" model.[39] Using this model, the estimate of the MTF between the ith and $(i + 1)^{st}$ error is:

$$E'\{\text{Time between } i^{th}, (i + 1)^{st}\} = 1/(Q'(N' - i)) \qquad (6.4)$$

and the estimate of the mean time to remove the next K faults is:

$$E'' = \sum_{i=1}^{n-k+1} \frac{1}{Q'(N' - i)} \qquad (6.5)$$

The estimate of the mean time to remove the next K faults can be plotted against K (where $K = 1, \ldots, \ldots$, remaining number of faults) to judge the integrity of the system at any point in time. Other measures that can be used to estimate the number of residual errors can be found in references [40, 41].

Similar to the IEEE P982 process-oriented measures are those that have been developed by the Air Force. These are called Software Management Indicators.

6.4.1.2.2 Software management indicators. The U.S. Air Force and MITRE Corporation have taken the lead in trying to develop techniques to monitor the process of software development along the lines of the military view of risk. Recall from Chapter 2 that these centered on cost, schedule, technical, operational, and support risks. In a document called AFSCP 800-43, *Software Management Indicators,* some general indicators or rules of thumb based upon experiences gathered over a long period of time on Air Force programs have been captured. These rules of thumb have been codified and, where possible, quantified. By plotting the metrics associated with the indicators, an Air Force manager can get insight into when a risk aversion strategy is or is not working, or when it is becoming necessary to employ one.

Some of the areas that are considered ripe for monitoring in AFSCP 800-43 are computer resource utilization, software development manpower, requirements definition and stability, software progress, cost/schedule deviations, and software development tools. Below are overviews of two of the indicators found in the document.

The Computer Resource Utilization (CRU) management indicator provides a tracking and assessment mechanism that shows the degree of memory, CPU, and I/O utilization; magnitude of changes on these; and resource availability limits. If a risk reduction program is underway to lower utilization, these measures can be used to monitor the acceptability of the efforts.

The metrics used to support the CRU indicator are:

1. The maximum possible deliverable resource is the total computer resources (memory, CPU, I/O) that can be physically accommodated by the design
2. The minimum deliverable resource is the resource (proposed to be delivered) that the contractor maintains is necessary to implement the specified system requirements
3. Actual utilization is the amount of the deliverable resource being utilized.

The anomalies or indications of acceptability that should be monitored (in new projects) are:

*   CPU utilization with less than a minimum of 50 percent spare

*   Planned memory utilization with less than a minimum of 50 percent spare

*   Deterioration of performance expected when CPU utilization exceeds 70 percent for real-time applications

*   Dramatic increase in schedule and cost when the spare rates drop below 10 percent.

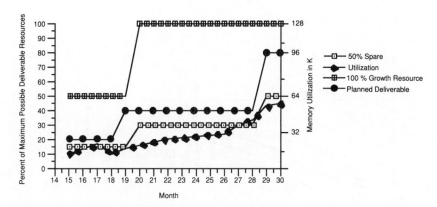

Figure 6.10 Computer Resource Utilization

Figure 6.10 provides an example of the type of graph likely to be seen when using the computer resource utilization indicator.

The cost/schedule deviation (C/SD) management indicators provide a tracking and assessment mechanism that shows deviations from the cost, schedule, and technical performance baselines of a software project.

The metrics used to support the C/SD indicators are: (a) the budgeted cost of the work schedule (BCWS); (b) the budgeted cost of the work performance (BCWP); (c) the actual cost of work performance (ACWP); and (d) the budget at completion (BAC). Given these, the following are then computed to produce the C/SD management indicators:

$$\text{Cost variance} = \text{BCWP} - \text{ACWP} \tag{6.6}$$

$$\text{Schedule Variance} = \text{BCWP} - \text{BCWS} \tag{6.7}$$

$$\text{Cost Performance Index (CPI)} = \text{BCWP/ACWP} \tag{6.8}$$

$$\text{Schedule Performance Index (SPI)} = \text{BCWP/BCWS} \tag{6.9}$$

$$\text{Estimated at completion} \\ \text{(EAC)} = \text{ACWP} + \{(\text{BAC} - \text{BCWP}) / (.2(\text{SPI}) + .8(\text{CPI}))\} \tag{6.10}$$

$$\text{Variance at completion (VAC)} = \text{EAC} - \text{BAC} \tag{6.11}$$

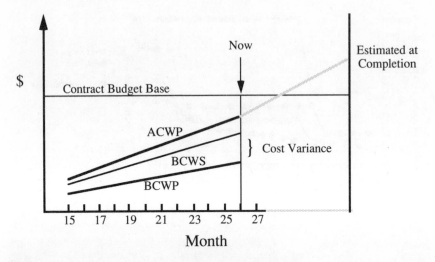

Figure 6.11 Cost/Schedule Deviation Management Indicator

Because of project uniqueness, each project is required to develop its own unique rules of thumb for this indicator. Figure 6.11 provides an illustration of an application, called the C/SD indicator.

A main weakness, which is recognized by the Air Force, in applying the management indicators described in AFSCP 800-43, is that data for individual metrics need to be gathered to effectively utilize the indicators. It is assumed that the required data can be obtained. However, neither standard procedures nor standard metrics are available that can be used by government and contractor personnel in gathering this data. Furthermore, specific indicators must be interpreted and tailored to each individual program to make them truly effective. Finally, the guidelines for using the indicators are based upon linear extrapolations of data, which is dangerous to do unthinkingly, even if the state of software development shows this is what really happens. There is a fear that the indicators, when applied and interpreted by inexperienced risk managers, may cause more harm than good.

Less formal than the monitoring measures and techniques described in either IEEE P982 or AFSCP 800-43 are those found in reviews, walkthroughs, and inspections.

6.4.1.2.3 Reviews, walkthroughs, and inspections. Reviews,[42,43] walkthroughs,[44,45] and inspections[46,47] provide other ways that the project can be monitored for the acceptability of the risk aversion strategies and tactics. These techniques are used across the project life-cycle phase, from requirements analysis through to the evolution phase. Reviews, walkthroughs, and inspection techniques have been in existence for a long time, and are normally part of the quality assurance arsenal of techniques that can be brought to bear in risk management.[48]

Reviews are concerned with determining the internal completeness and consistency of the product's requirements, specification, design, implementation, and test information. They are meant to find inaccuracies, omissions, and extraneous information. Reviews also assess the current information produced with respect to consistency with its predecessor information.

Reviews are conducted by a broad range of personnel, including developers, managers, users, and outside experts. They are not a permanent body in the organization, but are set up as necessary and conducted as meetings. Typically, a review is conducted at the end of a life-cycle phase, when a product of that phase can be reviewed. Each review group has specific objectives and questions to be addressed, depending on what type of review is initiated. Review groups do not review their own generated information. When completed, the findings are returned to the proper development group for any required actions. Once these actions are finished and signed off, the product produced and reviewed at the end of that life-cycle phase is baselined.

Structured walkthroughs are different from reviews in that they are conducted "in-process" (i.e., in-between life-cycle phases), rather than "ex-process," at the end of a phase. Here, the intent is to provide immediate feedback to the developers on the quality of the product. As the name implies, the software product is "walked through" (i.e., a lecture is given on it) by the person or persons responsible for it, conveying as much information as possible to the audience. This includes their perceptions of what must be done, how they plan to accomplish it, and when. The audience is usually made up of knowledgeable experts, other developers, and includes the chief project designers and the system engineer. General improvements to the product are suggested in a more informal fashion than in a review. It is up to the participants to use the information provided.

As it happens, walkthroughs also are one of the most effective techniques for eliminating errors. Sixty percent of software errors are claimed to be caught in walkthroughs.[49] They also have the added benefit of reducing a predictable risk of personnel leaving by ensuring backup knowledge is spread throughout the project.

Inspections are used to detect errors at their source. They evaluate the correctness of the component-level specification, design, implementation, test plans, and test results. They are much more formal and more rigorous than either reviews or walkthroughs, and are normally conducted during the design and implementation phases. Here, a very focused set of questions is asked, such as going over a checklist of faults that might appear in the product. The questions are formulated such that a Boolean answer can be obtained (i.e., either a pass or a fail). The makeup of this group is very specific, usually all members having the same level of expertise. At the end of the inspection, errors that are detected are fixed and reviewed for sign-off.

Inspections have been found to be as effective as walkthroughs for defect removal. It is claimed that 60–90 percent of software defects can be detected with inspections, and that significant reduction in cost can be accrued.[50] Whether or not the claims are totally correct, all three techniques should be seriously considered.

6.4.1.2.4 Risk charting.

One final monitoring technique we wish to examine is what we call risk charting. As was mentioned in the previous sections on risk aversion and planning, it is common that one try to reduce the number of risks actively monitored to some set, say approximately 10 in number. These 10 are checked every month, with progress reported via the RAP on the success of the risk aversion strategies. Each risk in the top 10 is charted as to its priority, its last previous priority, and how many weeks it has appeared on the chart. It's much like *The New York Times* best-seller book list. If new entries are made, or if little progress is being made against an identified risk, then a risk reanalysis might be called for. Again, it is important to recognize trouble as early as possible in order that a small problem does not get out of control. Equally important is the recognition of the progress being made in risk aversion. So risks successfully controlled should also be charted.

Another useful technique is to keep track of the category of risks that appears in the top ten. If the risks that are starting to appear have been listed previously as unpredictable, or unknown, then there is a very large possibility that the project is beginning to get out of control. It may also indicate the original risk analysis was not accurate, and the project is at a risk higher than was first suspected. This is a constant nightmare to a risk analyst. Hopefully, by combining this view in the chart below, illustrated in Table 6.7, one can easily and effectively keep track of the risk, and surface any major problems very early.

TABLE 6.7 Risk Chart

Risk	Current Priority	Previous Priority	Risk Type	Aversion Strategy
Schedule Slippage	1	3	Predictable	Reduction
Reqs. Changes	2	4	Predictable	Reduction
Lack of Performance	3	2	Known	Reduction
Over Projected Cost	4	1	Known	Pecuniary
.	.	.	.	.
.	.	.	.	.
.	.	.	.	.
Pers. Inexperience	10	10	Known	Transfer

6.4.2 Summary

It is obvious by now that to do proper monitoring, one needs many sources of information. Applying metrics is one approach. Another good source of evidence that builds up over time is the milestone charts. The risk-monitoring organization should be actively searching for new sources of evidence of risk that may be uncovered in the course of the everyday project work. Information from other support agencies, including contracts, personnel, finance, and marketing, all can help in this endeavor.

TABLE 6.8 Other Sources of Evidence to Be Consulted During Risk Monitoring

- Panel Meetings
- Conference Reports
- Software Engineering Literature
- Company Financial Reports
- Personnel Reports
- Milestone Reviews
- Lessons Learned Reports
- Engineering Change Proposals
- Waivers and Deviation Requests
- Safety Studies
- Insurance Reports
- Marketing Reports
- Hot-Line Reports
- Consultancy Reports
- Government Risk Reports

Table 6.8 illustrates just some of the sources of evidence that can be considered.

In summary, monitoring techniques belong to one of the two general classes of software project support activities: those that monitor the risks related to the process involved, and those that monitor the risk related to the product. As with the evaluation techniques, most can be used in either case. Included in these are techniques from project management, quality assurance, software reliability, verification and validation, and configuration management. Those found in project management and quality assurance loosely deal with the risks involved with the process, while the remainder generally involve monitoring the product.

In the next section, we once again return to the issue of making a decision about whether to perform risk aversion, and how much monitoring is necessary.

6.5 Planning Phase: Decision Making—Part 2

In the discussion presented in Part 1 concerning the planning phase of risk management, we were in a quandary about how to proceed. We couldn't, at that time, make an intelligent decision about whether to perform risk aversion or not, nor decide how much monitoring was sufficient. We didn't have enough information to make a competent planning decision. Well, now we have.

Before we begin, however, recall that the basic questions were (a) whether the risks identified and evaluated posed an unacceptable hazard to the project, and (b) whether there were any feasible methods to avert them if they did. There are basically two approaches to answering these questions.[51] In the first approach, one "simply" compares the direct gains to direct losses that are involved in accepting a risk or not. The analysis in this case is basically economic. If the balance is negative, there is no motivation for proceeding unless the balance is redressed. On the other hand, a favorable balance will provide incentives for taking a risky alternative. The decision is basically Boolean—either yes or no, with no marginal areas to consider. The evaluation techniques in previous chapters were based upon this approach.

The second approach is a noneconomic approach to making a decision. It involves the comparison of indirect gains to indirect losses. With this method, the "unquantifiable" aspects associated with a risk must be

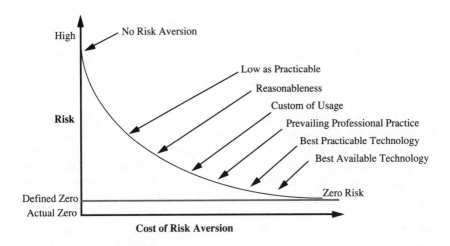

Figure 6.12 Risk vs. Technology

taken into account. Environmental impact studies are an example of this approach. Factors other than purely economic are involved, and must be considered in the balancing of the risk against its consequence. Some factors that might be considered are the difficulty and cost in performing risk aversion to achieve a certain benefit,[52] as illustrated by the curve in Figure 6.12. Shown are the relative costs of achieving different levels of risk aversion effectiveness that one might want to consider as input. The leftmost point is where *no risk aversion* is done at all. This in essence means there is no money spent on risk aversion, and the project fails or not, due to the course of nature or the vagaries of fate.

The second level is termed as *low as practicable*. This is a subjective area, but has to do with the generally accepted belief of what can and cannot be done to reduce a risk. Drinking alcohol was considered a health risk (after all, it is literally a poison) and was banned in the United States, but this turned out to be impracticable. Now its sales are regulated, as is its advertisement, and the health risk is assumed by the general public in both a personal and public manner (through tax dollars to pay for alcoholic rehabilitation).

The next five categories of increasing effectiveness, but also cost, are *reasonableness, custom of usage, prevailing professional practice, best practicable technology,* and *best available technology.* Reasonableness, custom of usage, and prevailing professional practice are the middle levels of risk aversion effectiveness. They are best understood in comparison to the last two categories of risk aversion effectiveness listed. Best practicable technology is where a risk can be reduced given "best industry practice," whereas "best available technology" is the point where a technology for risk aversion has been demonstrated, but has not yet been applied on a wide scale.

The last level is where there exists "zero risk" in the sense that a risk has been averted to the greatest possible extent. It is not, however, the actual zero risk point where the risk becomes a certainty. The risk is, however, no longer considered a risk. The zero risk point is based upon subjective judgement, but it can be considered the point where all parties would agree that no risk exists. It is also the point of prohibitive costs.

One can use the concepts above with the idea of risk leveraging.[53] Risk leveraging reflects the cost-benefit considerations in prioritizing risk aversion tasks. Risk leveraging is computed as:

$$\frac{\text{Risk Exposure}_{[\text{Before}]} - \text{Risk Exposure}_{[\text{After}]}}{\text{Risk Aversion Cost}} \qquad (6.12)$$

where Risk Exposure = (Risk Probability) (Loss of Utility). The loss of utility includes the "unquantifiables" to be given consideration.

In indirect approaches, there exists a number of different balancing points to evaluate. Where the consequences overwhelmingly favor the benefits over the cost, one says there is a favorable balance, and a decision can be made with assurance. However, if the balance is only slightly in a positive direction, then one has a marginal balance. Now the decision may be in doubt. Likewise, if the costs generally outweigh benefits, then an unfavorable balance exists. Where the costs far outweigh benefits, there is an unacceptable balance.

When one considers the acceptability of a risk, one must not only balance the decision with consequence, but with the cost effectiveness of risk reduction and any reconciliation of inequities as a result of the decision. Cost effectiveness is an economic issue with social overtones. If the decision under consideration is purely economic, then one should use the first decision approach. In this situation, if the expected gain after risk aversion, minus the cost involved, exceeds the expected gain without risk aversion, then proceed with risk aversion. How much monitoring is required can be evaluated in the same way, using the same techniques as found in Chapter 4 for finding the value of perfect information.

On the other hand, if the decision is based upon indirect gains and losses, then the decision maker must reconcile the possible inequities that will result. There are elements to be considered that can shift the balancing point. For example, a risk, and whether aversion is necessary, might be viewed differently from the perspectives of the sponsor, developer, and user, respectively. Not to reduce a particular risk, the manifestation of which might be acceptable to the developer, might not be anywhere near acceptable to the user. This is especially true in the area of operational risks. As the report on the Challenger disaster said, "Safety criteria are designed to permit launch. They should not be allowed to force a launch."[54] Even when positive decisions are made, some group might suffer, or the benefits might not be evenly distributed.

Finally, once the risk acceptability levels are known, one can then strive to attain the level of "optimal" risk. That is, the point where the sum of the cost of risk aversion and the expected losses that result from the risks after aversion, are at a minimum. This point is considered where the marginal cost of risk aversion equals the marginal reduction in societal cost, as shown in Figure 6.13.

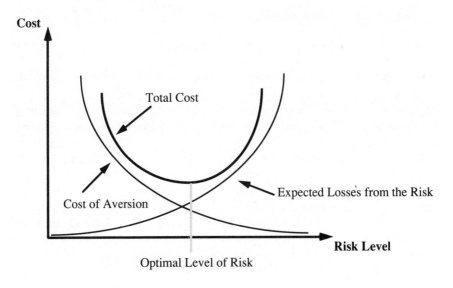

Figure 6.13 Optimal Risk

6.5.1 The cardinal rules of risk management

Given the issues above, the first cardinal rule in risk management decision making is the following:

First, do no harm.

The physicians' credo is one to live by in risk management. If, by doing risk aversion, more risks are created than averted, either by risk coupling or compounding, then do not do it. In the evaluation stage of the previous chapter, one could simply choose not to accept the risk of undertaking the project. One still has that option in deciding whether to employ risk aversion, but as time moves on, more certainty about the risk estimates and their evaluation will occur. One must not be afraid to say, "Wait," to applying risk aversion, but make sure you *watch*. If the risks are equal to or less than the estimates, then the only sources of concern will be from the unpredictable or (then) unknown risks. The last category includes not only new risks, but risks caused by risk compounding or coupling. A watch for these sources of concern should be considered a high priority.

The second cardinal rule is, as Ovid said,

"Adde parvum parvo magnus acerus erit."

Add little to little, and there will be a big pile. A risk analysis can assess the overall chance that some unwanted event will occur, but it is powerless to predict any specific event. Since the presence of risks does not indicate that they may necessarily occur, it doesn't necessarily mean they will not, either. The goal of risk management is to constantly, in measured steps, improve the probability of success, or the opportunity for success, wherever it is feasible. All project support activities are, in fact, outgrowths of that fundamental purpose. Whether it be through program management, quality assurance, or any other one that is chosen, each is meant to improve the probability of an individual or the group to succeed. Risk management is meant to have this objective as well. It is not meant to be there for its own sake. Any means to increase the probability of success should be considered.

The third cardinal rule is:

Never intentions, always capability.

One must keep repeating this over and over. It is easy to fool oneself into thinking that, because there are intentions to do this, or do that, things will work out that way. The road to project failure is paved with good intentions. Risk management is based upon what feasibly can be accomplished, not what is hoped to be accomplished. The COCOMO and Putnam cost estimation models, for example, examined in Chapter 5, both define areas where , no matter how many people are applied to a project, there exists a minimum time required. Demanding or hoping for a system to be developed earlier than this lower limit is not risk, it is nonsensical, as there is a certainty of failure occurring.

The final cardinal rule is:

No management commitment, no risk management.

Henry Petroski wrote, "We have learned how to calculate the failure due to risk, but did not learn how to calculate how to obviate the failure of the mind."[55] If management, both corporate and line, does not actively support nor foresee the need for risk management, then there is little point in pretending to do it. Risk management is a proactive way of doing business, and requires a patient and enlightened management to look at problems straight in the eye without flinching or running for cover. No one likes problems, but they exist, and must be accepted professionally as part of the field we operate in. If this is too difficult to accept, than an acceptance of mediocrity is the only result.

6.5.2 Summary

To answer the questions about whether to perform risk aversion, or about how much monitoring is enough, requires quiet thinking about the trade-offs involved. Very few, if any, projects have resources that are adequate to perform unlimited risk management. Only if the cost of reducing a risk is not more than the benefits derived, or if the consequence of a known risk or an unknown risk cannot seriously jeopardize the project's probability of success, should risk aversion not be considered a serious option. Monitoring must *always* be conducted, however.

6.6 What Happens If Things Already Are Bad?

The reader might be tempted to say at this point, this is all very interesting. But what am I supposed to do when I have been monitoring a project and things start to turn sour, or if I have been asked to come in to do a risk review of a project suspected to already be in trouble? How does one "wriggle off the hook"?[56]

Well, the first thing one can do is declare victory and leave. If this isn't practical, the second thing one must try is to figure out why things are going badly, by separating the symptoms from the causes, from the effects. As an example, on one particular project that was in trouble already, the author was called in to lead a risk analysis team to try to figure out why, and to recommend a way out. Upon completing a risk review, it turned out that all the currently faced high-risk elements were either predictable or unknown risks only six months before. The program office had not realized that a shift had occurred because they had not done any in-depth risk monitoring to see how future decisions were affecting past plans. The program office had moved from a position of dealing with risks that they were in control of (direct risks), to ones that they had little control over (indirect risks). Management then exacerbated the problem by making arbitrary decisions without understanding that they had already lost control of the project. This is what had gotten themselves into trouble in the first place. Of course, these actions naturally increased the likelihood of the predictable risks occurring.

Since they did not know the true causes of their problem, they came face to face with what are called *risk dilemmas*.[57] These are risks where all the alternatives have undesirable consequences. Each alternative can be considered a catastrophe in itself. This situation quickly spooked management into a crisis mode. When this happened, the amount of decision making increased even more dramatically. The full impacts of previous decisions made were never allowed to mature before some new, equally uninformed, decision was made because every alternative was such a poor choice. They hoped that by making a decision, some new, positive alternative course of action would appear. Replanning cycles were occurring so rapidly that there was never a plan against which to monitor progress. The project was in a permanent state of flux, with management acting like a circuit with only increasingly negative feedback as input. The harder it tried to salvage the situation, the worse it became.

The first step that the risk team did was to follow the first cardinal rule of risk management: Do no harm. Therefore, we insisted on a reduction of the number of decisions being made. We reasoned that doing nothing for a while could not make things worse. Damping the circuit was also important to reducing the crisis-mode attitude.

The second step was to perform a rapid risk estimate of the situation to find out what the original project objectives were, and the deviation of the current project plans from those objectives. If the decision flow hadn't been curtailed, this could never have been accomplished, as one could never get a triangulation for computing the project bearing.

The third step was to try to identify and estimate the risks, and place them in some kind of priority order. Typically, there is not enough time to do a formal risk evaluation, so one must use all the sources of information available, especially from the developers on the ground, to get a feel of the actual situation. From this information, and after some thrashing around with management about what were the nonnegotiable priority project objectives (i.e., the lowest risk referents), the team developed decision trees illustrating what could feasibly be accomplished, given the resources and capability of the project at that current time. Expected value calculations were done to ascertain the most practical path to follow, and any probability less than a certain threshold was dismissed as currently unimportant.

Corporate commitment to support the outcome, whatever it was (within a negotiated reasonableness), was gained before the final decision analysis was underway. This ensured the advice wasn't going to be changed later. The time-lines used for planning when the consequences of the risk management decisions were to be checked occurred at intervals of 6 weeks, 12 weeks, and 18 weeks. Anything further was not considered because it was deemed irrelevant. Success (or failure) had to be achieved in small increments.

When the recommendations were formulated, any that were based upon some future intention of something occurring, like more experienced personnel, more time, etc., were dismissed. Only resident capability within the project at that time was considered relevant. *Everyone* in the project had assigned tasks to perform, and each person on the project knew what the criteria were for the task to be considered a success.

By a rather painful process, the project was slowly, day by day, brought under control, as small successes in meeting deadlines six weeks out, were met with successes at the 12-week period, and then at the 18-week period. The risk management team stayed active during the first 18 weeks, performing intensive risk monitoring on every aspect of the project. Especially critical during the first few weeks was determining how accurate the risk analysis team's risk estimation and forecasts were. If these were off, then the recommendations would also be off. Luckily, only a relatively minor amount of adjustment was required. Gradually the team was reduced in size, as things returned to a more normal lifestyle. Planning continued on 18-week cycles for awhile, until a more formal RAP and RMP were completed with six months and one year objectives. As a result, longer term trade-offs and objectives were planned with more confidence of achieving them.

The primary reason for things getting into trouble on the project was the lack of a risk management plan. Without it, there was no monitoring of risks performed, no recognition of compounded or coupled risks, no recognition that the original plan was fragile and could be placed into trouble without it being noticed, etc. It was, at the end of the day, a failure on management's part. They did not exercise proper control of the project. Things started to go bad one day at a time, which is a phenomenon that has been plaguing software developments for a long time.[58] In this case, most of management was so traumatized by the experience that when the risk team returned for its 6-month progress visits, risk management plans were automatically and proudly shown first.

If one examines situations as above in greater detail, along with the four cardinal rules, three other principles were being applied by the team.[59] They are, in order of precedence:

1. Dismissal of extremely remote possibilities

2. Avoidance of catastrophes, insofar as possible

3. Maximization of the expected values.

The first principle is meant to focus the risk management activities on the most important, i.e., most likely, risks. The second principle is meant to help prioritize the risks. And the third principle says that expected value calculations should be used whenever possible, because they provide the most objective, understandable, and standard way of making decisions about risks and which courses of action to follow. There will be circumstances where these rules must be modified (as when one is faced with only catastrophes), but, in general, these are the three guiding principles for getting oneself out of trouble. Together with the cardinal rules, they form the basis for all risk decision making in whatever situation one is faced with.

6.7 Summary

The error in the 1986 oil price forecasts provided us with a classic example of the need for risk management. The nature, likelihood, and magnitude of the risks facing the petroleum industry turned out to be inaccurate. The inaccuracy was not seen nor questioned because of the biases of the people reading the risk and planning reports. The costs to the industry, and to the workers in the industry and states that depended on it, were, and still are, high.

This chapter tried to provide a sense of what is required to do risk management, and the need for controlling and monitoring the risks in a project. Whether to employ risk aversion techniques, how much aversion is enough, and/or how much monitoring is enough will need to be decided in the context of either economic or social decision making and the particular circumstances of the project. There is no pat answer, which sometimes leaves one with an uncomfortable feeling. Remember, though, that at the beginning of the book we stated that one was faced with dilemmas to manage, not problems to be solved. Living and feeling comfortable with chaos is part and parcel of a risk analyst's job.

From what has been described so far in the book, you should be able to stop here and begin to apply the general principles of risk analysis and management to your own software projects. Apply the four cardinal rules, especially the one about corporate commitment, as well as the three principles of decision making, and the probability of project success should begin to improve.

Software Engineering Risk Analysis and Management—Applications examines the process of software engineering and the risks contained therein.With that book our universe of discourse will be expanded beyond the mechanics we have learned in this book. We will be shown why some of the risks commonly considered within software engineering really originate outside the software engineering project domain. Only by comprehending these domains can software engineering risk analysis and management become truly effective. This will, in turn, force us to reconsider the scope of what is included in software engineering risk analysis and management. That book also examines the risks inherent in the different application areas one might encounter when performing risk analysis. Certain application types provide different sources of risk, and by studying them, one can (hopefully) find better ways to avert the risks when they are encountered.

Questions

1 In your opinion, is the elimination of software risks possible? Feasible? Futile? Explain why or why not.

2 What are the differences between acceptability and feasibility in the context of risk management? How about in the context of attaining software systems that are safe and/or secure?

3 What are the essential differences among the four risk aversion strategies? Set up a hypothetical software development situation requiring a risk transfer aversion strategy, and describe two different tactics (and the means necessary) that can be used to implement the strategy. Do not forget to describe the objectives of the project.

4 For the situation described in Question 3 above, write out an accompanying Risk Aversion Plan.

5 How are software reliability and software quality related?

6 The division of risk monitoring measures into the categories of product and process measures provides a number of interesting implications. As has been suggested by Sherer and Clemons in a paper entitled "Software Risk Assessment," National Computer Conference, 1987, pp. 703–707, does it make more sense to say software risk should be redefined in terms of software quality, rather than as presented in this book? Or should software quality be redefined in terms of software risk?

7 It should be obvious that the DSQI metric, and others like it, is useful in the risk analysis. Where might it, and similar metrics that you are aware of, be used?

8 In a March 1989 *IEEE Computer* article, entitled "Faults, Failures and a Metric Evolution," John Musa has noted a "revolutionary change" in the way software quality is being viewed. Instead of viewing program quality from a developer-oriented viewpoint, it is shifting to a user-oriented perspective.

Software quality is now being measured as that which the user experiences in the operation of the software. How does this shift in perspective affect the risk monitoring techniques presented? Give some examples if you believe it does.

9 What are risk dilemmas? Why is it important to recognize when they occur? What are the steps necessary to avert them?

10 The third cardinal rule of risk management is "Never intentions, always capability." What impacts or implications are there concerning how software engineering risks should be viewed?

11 How can the optimal level of risk shown in Figure 6.13 be used to determine system risk reference levels?

12 One possible use of risk monitoring is to verify the accuracy and effectiveness of the original risk analysis, especially the identification and estimation of risk. Explain how one could improve risk identification and estimation via risk monitoring. Include a discussion of possible "lessons learned," and how forensic software engineering might be created using risk monitoring techniques.

13 If risk monitoring indicates that the original risk process was not accurate or effective, what possible implications and ramifications does it have on the state of the project? Should project management be notified that the risk to the project may be higher than suspected? What else is required?

References

1. "Crystal balls-up," in *The Economist*, 4 February 1989.

2. War again, the final breakdown of cartel, and softening demand due to conservation originally caused by cartels, actions, were in part to blame.

3. I am fairly confident that the planners did not aggressively challenge their managers' beliefs, either, with their probabilities of uncertainty about their analyses. After all, the conditions in 1986 were not unique, but the outcomes were.

4. Rather reminiscent of King Lear's line, "The worst is not, so long as we can say, 'this is the worst.' "

5.   Private conversation with General Sir Martin Farndale, KCB (retired). General Farndale spent over 35 years with the British Army, was head of British forces on the Rhine, and was an advisor to Her Majesty, the Queen.

6.   There are times when this approach seems to be the only way to get things done. A very real but somewhat bizarre case in point is in government: It is often easier to get funding to fix something than to get money to do it right the first time. When the author was working for the Department of Defense, he came across the following example. A military service, which will remain nameless, needed a new computer to replace the currently existing one, which could no longer perform the required tasks. Unfortunately, there was a lack of funding in the budget for new computer architecture developments. However, it was possible to bring an existing machine up to scratch, using the money available for maintenance and repair, which was plentiful. So, the enterprising program sponsor specified and developed a new machine that could never be built with the existing funding available, and went ahead and delivered it. Needless to say, it did not work, but with all the money available to fix it, the machine turned out to be one of the mainstays of militarized 16-bit computing.

     The classical risk approach would be to reduce the technical risk of the program; i.e., the specification of the computer would be reduced to match the available budget. However, the risk to the users would have been severely increased. This was because a "properly" developed computer with reduced capability would not have been able to meet the required processing needs, and the money necessary to improve it wouldn't have been available (can't get money for something that isn't broken, right?). While I will let others argue the ethics and morals of the story, and figure out which program it was, it does point out the importance of keeping the objective in mind, understanding the strategies at hand, and picking the proper tactics.

7.   F. T. Haner and James C. Ford, *Contemporary Management*, Charles E. Merrill Publishing Company, Columbus, OH, 1973.

8.   Fritjof Capra, *The Tao of Physics*, Bantam Books, New York, 1984.

9.   One might be moved to argue that the question is whether to monitor risks or not, rather than how much monitoring is required. This is only true if the original system-wide risk referent reflects a "life-time" referent; i.e., it will never change during the life of the project. To meet such a criterion, it would have to be set so high that one is doubtful that it would be of much use in practice.

10. William D. Rowe, *An Anatomy of Risk*, Robert E. Krieger Publishing Co., Malabar, FL, 1988.

11. William W. Lowrance, *Of Acceptable Risk: Science and the Determination of Safety*, William Kaufman, Inc., Los Altos, CA, 1976.

12. N. C. Lynd, Ed., *Technological Risk: Proceedings of the Symposium on Risks in New Technology*, in First University Symposium, University of Waterloo, 15 December 1981.

13. Barry Boehm, "Industrial Software Metrics Top 10 List," in *IEEE Software*, September 1987.

14. "Report of the Defense Science Board Task Force on Military Software," Office of the Under Secretary of Defense for Acquisition, Washington, DC, September 1987.

15. Barry Boehm and Philip Papaccio, "Understanding and Controlling Software Costs," in *IEEE Transactions on Software Engineering*, Vol. SE-14, No. 10, October 1988.

16. Ken S. Lew et al., "Software Complexity and Its Impact on Software Reliability," in *IEEE Transactions on Software Engineering*, Vol. 14, No. 11, November 1988.

17. Barry Boehm, *Software Engineering Economics*, Prentice-Hall, Inc., Englewood Cliffs, NJ, 1981.

18. Charles Rich and Richard Waters, "Automatic Programming: Myths and Prospects," in *IEEE Computer*, Vol. 21, No. 8, August 1988.

19. "Transition from Development to Production," DoD 4245.7, 1982.

20. Norman R. Augustine, *Augustine's Laws,* American Institute of Aeronautics and Astronautics, New York, 1983.

21. Truman W. Howard III, *Methodology for Developinmg Total Risk Assessing Cost Estimates (TRACE),* ARMDC, ALM-63-M3, U.S. Army Logistics Management Center, Ft. Lee, VA; and *Handbook for Decision Analysis*, Cybernetics Technology Office, DARPA, September 1977.

22. Jonathan Lynn and Antony Jay, *Yes, Prime Minister*, BBC Books, London, England, 1987.

23. R. M. Hogarth, "Generalization in Decision Research," in *IEEE Transactions on Systems, Man, and Cybernetics*, Vol. SMC-16, No. 3, May/June 1986.

24. As a related note, the phenomenon of decay also explains why getting a project into trouble is easier than getting out, and why there is a continuous requirement to perform analysis during each project life-cycle phase. As an example, imagine you are involved in a long cross-country trek across mountainous terrain. If one starts at point "X" and tries to reach point "Y" that lies in direction "Z," as one marches away, one doesn't follow a strict path. One zigzags around, always in the general direction of "Z." However, it is likely, that without checking the compass and map to see where one is and where one is heading, the magnitude error will increase. Now, if one goes too long, then small errors will increase into larger ones. One is likely to get lost, and the effort required to get "unlost" is liable to be much more than the effort to get lost in the first place. One reason is that one doesn't know when one is getting lost, so one cannot backtrack optimally. The other is, the conditions that occurred during the original trek are impossible to repeat exactly. If something untoward occurs, such as bad weather, the magnitude of effort increases manyfold. The moral of the story, and it is common sense really, is that one needs to continuously check one's position against the risk referents. Although it is common sense, people do get lost hiking anyway.

25. "IEEE Draft Standard Software Reliability Measurement," IEEE Project P982, IEEE Computer Society, 1 June 1985.

26. This section is in keeping with the intent of IEEE draft standard, "A Standard Classification for Software Errors, Faults, and Failures," IEEE P1044/D3, IEEE Computer Society, December 1987.

27. "IEEE Standard Glossary of Software Engineering Terminology," ANSI/IEEE Std. 729-1983, IEEE 1983.

28. C. S. Ramamoorthy and Farokh Bl. Bastani, "Software Reliability—Status and Perspective," in *IEEE Transactions on Softwae Engineering*, Vol. SE-8, No.4, July 1982.

29. This section is taken from "A Standard Classification for Software Errors, Faults, and Failures," IEEE P1044/D3, IEEE Computer Society, December 1987, pp. B-42–B-44.

30. "Management Quality Insight," AFCSP 800-14, 20 January 1987.

31. Leslie Waguespack and Sunil Badlani, "Software Complexity Assessment: An Introduction and Annotated Bibliography," in *ACM Software Engineering Notes*, Vol. 12, No. 4, October 1987. This provides an excellent source of information on software complexity.

32. John D. Musa et al., *Software Reliability: Measurement, Prediction, Application*, McGraw-Hill, Inc., New York, 1987.

33. "IEEE Transactions on Software Engineering, Special Issues on Software Reliability," Vols. SE-12 and SE-11, December 1985 and January 1986.

34. T. J. Yu et al., "An Analysis of Several Software Defect Models," in *IEEE Transactions on Software Engineering*, Vol. 14, No. 9, September 1988.

35. E. J. Weyuker, "Evaluating Software Complexity Measures," in *IEEE Transactions on Software Engineering*, Vol. 14, No. 9, September 1988.

36. Virginia R. Gibson and James A. Senn, "System Structure and Software Maintenance Performance," in *Communications of the ACM*, Vol. 32, No. 3, March 1989.

37. Capers Jones, *Programming Productivity*, McGraw-Hill, Inc., New York, 1986.

38. "A Standard Classification for Software Errors, Faults, and Failures," IEEE P1044/D3, IEEE Computer Society, December 1987, pp. B-42 – B-44.

39. Paul L. Moranda and Z. Jelinski, "Final Report on Software Reliability Study," McDonnel Douglas Astronautics Company, MDC Report No. 63921, 1972.

40. S. Yamada and S. Osaki, "Software Reliability Growth Modeling: Models and Application," in *IEEE Transactions on Software Engineering*, Vol. SE-11, No. 12, December 1985.

41. Tohma et al., "Structural Approach to the Estimation of the Number of Residual Software Faults Based upon the Hypergeometric Distribution," in *Proceedings of Compsac 1987*, Computer Science Press, Los Alamitos, CA, October 1987.

42. D. Freedman and C. Weinberg, *Handbook of Walkthroughs, Inspections and Technical Reviews*, Little & Brown Company, Boston, 1982.

43. "Tactical Embedded Computer Software Audit Manual," U.S. Naval Material Command, 2 May 1980.

44. K. Kishida et al., "Quality-Assurance Technology in Japan," in *IEEE Software*, September 1987.

45. Michael S. Deutsch and Ronald R. Willis, *Software Quality Engineering*, Prentice Hall, Inc., Englewood Cliffs, NJ, 1988.

46. Michael E. Fagan, "Design and Code Inspections to Reduce Errors in Program Development," in *IBM Systems Journal*, Vol. 15, No. 3, 1976.

47. Michael E. Fagan, "Advances in Software Inspections," in *IEEE Transactions on Software Engineering*, Vol. SE-12, No. 7, July 1986.

48. In the companion volume the subject of quality assurance and its relationship to risk analysis and management will be explored in more depth.

49. Barry Boehm and Philip Papaccio, "Understanding and Controlling Software Costs," in *IEEE Transactions on Software Engineering*, Vol. SE-14, No. 10, October 1988.

50. Michael E. Fagan, "Advances in Software Inspections," in *IEEE Transactions on Software Engineering*, Vol. SE-12, No. 7, July 1986.

51. William D. Rowe, *An Anatomy of Risk*, Robert E. Krieger Publishing Co., Malabar, FL, 1988.

52. ———, *An Anatomy of Risk*, Robert E. Krieger Publishing Co., Malabar, FL, 1988.

53. Barry Boehm, "Software Risk Management Tutorial," TRW-ACM Seminar, April 1988.

54. "Post-Challenger Evaluation of Space Shuttle Risk Assessment and Management," National Academy Press, January 1988.

55. Henry Petroski, *To Engineer Is Human: The Role of Failure in Successful Design*, St. Martin's Press, New York, 1982.

56. Edward deBono, *Tactics: The Art and Science of Success*, Fontana/Collins, London, 1985.

57. Nicholas Rescher, *Risk*, University Press of America, Lanham, MD, 1983.

58. Fred Brooks, *The Mythical Man-Month*, Addison-Wesley Publishing Company, Reading, MA, 1975.

59. William D. Rowe, *An Anatomy of Risk*, Robert E. Krieger Publishing Co., Malabar, FL, 1988.

A Review Guide to the Mechanics of Risk Analysis and Management

> *"Every art or applied science and every*
> *systematic investigation, and similarly,*
> *every action and choice, seem to aim*
> *at some good . . . But it is clear there is a*
> *difference in the ends at which they aim:*
> *in some cases the activity is the end, in*
> *others the end is some product beyond*
> *the activity."*
>
> ARISTOTLE, ca. 345 B.C.
> *Nicomachean Ethics*

7.0 Introduction

Pigeon racing is still a popular sport in the British Isles. One reason, I suppose, is all one has to do during the race itself is to go home, watch the football match on the telly, and wait. Most times, a pigeon will return home within a day of being released, as was expected when one such bird was sent on its merry way one fine June morning in Pembrokeshire. Well, the bird didn't return home that evening, nor the next day. Nor any day after, until eleven years later, when it was received by post from Brazil in a cardboard box, dead. The owner, in typical British manner, commented, "We had given it up for lost."[1]

Like that pigeon, we have covered much territory in this book about the mechanics of risk analysis and management, and it is now time to take stock. What we intend to do in this chapter is provide a quick-look review guide of the mechanics of the risk analysis and management, crib notes as it were. Like crib notes, we propose a specific question concerning an aspect of risk analysis and management, and then give a general answer. These notes highlight some of the important aspects of risk analysis and management, and are cross-referenced to the primary section or sections where more detailed information can be found. They can be used either to review the material or as checklists to ensure proper risk analysis and management procedures are being followed.

We have also provided a bit of space to write down personal observations. Within that space a software project manager may wish to write down pertinent questions to ask his project team leader about the risks to the project, or a senior manager may want to do the same but to the software project manager. I would suggest that for each review section questions exploring the why, where, when, who, how, and what-fors of the particular topic be listed for later consultation. For example, questions such as the following may be helpful to ask during the risk planning process, or during reviews of the project:

- What are the top 10 risks?

- How accurate are the risk estimates?

- What accounting for estimation biases have been made?

- Have all the risks been identified?

- How were the risk referents set?

- Why were the risk referents set at that level?

- How are the evaluations going to be compared against the risk referents?

- How much will that aversion strategy cost in time and effort?

In earlier chapters, we noted that risk analysis and management are iterative in nature, and one should bear this in mind when applying the material provided within this book. Some of it may not be applicable to the specific situation under study, and, as shown in *Software Engineering Risk Analysis and Management—Applications*, there are many other issues that must be addressed when applying risk analysis and management to a real software engineering project.

Recall that the goals of software engineering risk analysis and management are meant to find the best available answers to the following questions:

- What are the risks?

- What is the probability of loss from them?

- How much are the losses likely to cost?

- What might the losses be if the worst happened?

- What alternatives are there?

- How can the losses be reduced or eliminated?

- Will the alternatives produce other risks?

How well one can get objective answers to these questions, and make rational decisions about the risks confronting the software project will determine the ultimate success of the risk analysis and management processes.

7.1 Risk Analysis and Management Overview

> What is a risk?
> [Refer to Sections 2.1.4 and 3.1]

Definition. For an event, action, thing, etc., to be considered a risk, there must be:

1. A loss associated with it

2. Uncertainty or chance involved

3. Some choice involved.

The triplet, $< s_i, l_i, x_i >$, constitutes a particular risk, where s_i represents the scenarios of what can go wrong, l_i represents the generic likelihood of the scenarios happening, and x_i represents a measure of the consequences of the "ith" scenario. The set of all such triplets forms the totality of risk to the software development being performed. Thus, the definition:

$$\text{Risk} = \{< s_i, l_i, x_i >\}$$

becomes our formal definition of software engineering risk.

> What is risk analysis?
> [Refer to Section 2.2.1 and Chapters 3, 4, and 5]

The process of identification, estimation, and evaluation of risk, is called risk analysis. Risk analysis is used to identify potential problem areas, quantify risks associated with these problems, and generate alternative choices of actions that can be taken to reduce risk.

> What is risk management?
> [Refer to Section 2.2.2 and Chapter 6]

The planned control of risk and monitoring the success of the control mechanisms is termed risk management. Risk management is involved with making a decision about the risk(s) after it has been analyzed. Four elemental tools are needed to effectively apply risk management. They are (a) standards against which performance can be measured; (b) information to monitor actual performance; (c) authority to make required adjustments and corrections when they are needed; and (d) competence to implement the best solution from available alternatives.

> What are the benefits of risk analysis and management?
> [Refer to Section 2.2.4]

- Better and more defined perceptions of risks, clarification of options, trade-offs, their effects on a project, and their interactions

- Systemization of thought, thereby providing a consistent view of the problem situation

- Confidence that all available information has been accounted for and that explicit identification of project assumptions has been made

- Improved credibility of plans produced and communication of rationale for actions made, inside and outside the organization

- Better contingency planning and a better selection of reactions to those risks that do occur

- More flexible assessment of the appropriate mix of ways of dealing with risk impacts, allowing for less reactive management and more pro-active management

- Better means to identify opportunities, and ways to take advantage of them

- Feedback into the design and planning process in terms of ways of preventing or avoiding risks

- Feed-forward into the construction and operation of projects in ways of mitigating the impacts of risks that do arise, in the form of responsible selection and contingency planning

- Compatibility of decisions with project policies, goals, and objectives

- Insight, knowledge, and confidence for better decision making, and overall reduction in project exposure to risk.

What are risk analysis and management not?
[Refer to Section 2.3]

- Are not philosophers' stones

- Do not solve problems in an engineering sense

- Will not make the operating environment friendlier

- Will not turn bad things into good ones

- Will not provide hard, concrete data where there is none

- Will not assure perceived risks are real ones

- Will not assure a successful outcome every time

- Are not blame analysis and management.

Risk analysis overview

> When should a risk analysis be performed?
> [Refer to Section 3.2]

- Are significant amounts of software being developed for the system?

- Do software costs dominate the total system development cost?

- Will software contribute greatly to the operational and/or support costs of the system?

- Is software essential for the successful performance of the system's function?

- Does the software integrate or interface with a number of systems that must inter-operate?

If any of the answers are yes, then risk analysis and management are recommended.

> What are the tasks required in the performance of a risk analysis?

Task 1: Risk identification

Task 2: Risk estimation

Task 3: Risk evaluation

Risk identification

> ## What is risk identification?
> ### [Refer to Chapter 3]

Risk identification is the comprehensive identification of potential risk items using a structured and consistent method; i.e., it tries to answer the question, "What can go wrong?" Risk identification, therefore, is the reduction in descriptive uncertainty of the situation under study.

> ### What are the steps to performing risk identification?

> ### Step 1: Perform a risk estimate of the situation.
> ### [Refer to Section 3.2.1]

- The basic goal of the software risk estimate of the citation is to clearly identify four elements of a project: its objectives, strategies, tactics, and means or assets to be used in accomplishing the objectives identified.

- Assure that objectives are measurable, and what constitutes their achievement, i.e., the project success criteria. Additionally assure that there exist at least two alternative strategies and/or tactics for achieving the objectives, and identify the constraints that the resources place upon the objectives. Also identify any implicit project assumptions.

- Consider some of the following as possible project success criteria:

  - Maximize profit

  - Minimize cost

  - Minimize risk of loss

  - Maximize sales

  - Minimize cyclic fluctuations

  - Create a favorable image

- Maximize quality of service

- Maximize growth rate

- Maximize employee satisfaction

- Maximize firm's prestige.

Step 2: Gather information to try to identify relevant risks.
[Refer to Section 3.3.1]

Check the following sources of information:

- Traditional or folk knowledge

- Analogies to well-known cases

- Common-sense assessments

- Results of experiments or tests

- Reviews of inadvertent exposure

- Epidemiological surveys.

Step 3: Categorize each risk.
[Refer to Section 3.3.2]

- Categorize risks by whether they are:

  - Known
  - Predictable
  - Unpredictable, unidentifiable, unknown, or unobservable

or

  - Direct or operational
  - Indirect or strategic

or

  - Technical
  - Schedule
  - Cost

    - Operational
    - Support.

- Categorize risks by whether they are caused by:

    - A lack of information
    - A lack of control
    - A lack of time.

- After categorizing the risks in an appropriate manner, go on to the next step of risk analysis, risk estimation.

Risk estimation

What is risk estimation?
[Refer to Chapter 4]

A risk estimate measures the chance of potential loss (i.e., the values of the risk variables identified during risk identification) and the exposure to potential loss (i.e., the consequences, or magnitude, of the risks identified). Overall, risk estimation is the reduction of measurement uncertainty.

What are the steps involved in risk estimation?

Step 1: Select a measurement scale.
[Refer to Section 4.1]

- The values of the variables describing the system are determined. This requires determination of a measurement scale against which these values will be evaluated.

- Choose a measurement scale which best matches the accuracy and precision required for the estimate and later evaluation. The scale types available are:

    - Nominal (identity-taxonomy) scale
    - Ordinal (order-risk) scale
    - Cardinal (interval) scale
    - Ratio (zero reference) scale.

> Step 2: Match the source of estimation information to the selected
> measurement scale.
> [Refer to Section 4.1.1]

Risk estimation information will either be narrative, qualitative, or quantitative in nature. Narrative information requires a nominal or ordinal scale. Qualitative information requires an ordinal scale. Quantitative information requires a cardinal or ratio scale.

> Step 3: Evaluate the biases of the persons or techniques involved in
> making a risk estimation.
> [Refer to Section 4.1.3]

- The lack of availability of information from which to make judgements limits the accuracy of the risk estimates. As information is disseminated, individuals often misinterpret or misunderstand its meaning. This is termed "information availability bias."

- A number of other possible estimation biases bear watching:

  - Selective perception
  - Anchoring
  - Expert bias
  - Sample size insensitivity
  - Sample matching
  - Revision bias.

- Be especially aware of biases and their impacts on conjunctive and disjunctive events.

> Step 4: Reduce the uncertainty of the risk estimates.
> [Refer to Section 4.1.4]

- The uncertainty in a risk estimate can be reduced by a number of techniques. However, these techniques are limited by the process to which the risk belongs: behavioral, natural, or random.

- Select the proper uncertainty reduction technique. The techniques available include:

- Delphi
- Probability encoding
- Buying information using prototypes, simulations, etc.

Step 4a: Determine the value of the reducing uncertainty.
[Refer to Section 4.3]

In conjunction with Step 4, one should determine how worthwhile is the reduction risk uncertainty. The use of expected value calculations can be made to determine:

- The expected value of possessing perfect knowledge
- The expected value of buying sample information
- The expected value of possessing imperfect information
- The expected net value of buying sample information.

Step 4b: Determine the value and utility of the information.
[Refer to Section 4.3.3]

- In conjunction with Steps 4 and 4a, one should determine the value and/or utility of the information being sought for a risk estimate. Depending on the utility of the information being sought, a risk and its estimate may be accepted more easily than another, thus reducing the need for buying information.

- When the estimation of risk is completed, move on to risk evaluation.

Risk evaluation

What is risk evaluation?
[Refer to Chapter 5]

Risk evaluation is the process whereby the response to the risks is anticipated. Insight is sought into the consequences of the various possible decisions confronting the decision maker, with the general acceptability of individually projected consequences to a decision postulated.

What are the steps involved in risk evaluation?

Step 1: Determine the risk evaluation criteria.
[Refer to Section 5.1]

Determine the criteria against which a risk consequence will be judged to be acceptable for different points in a project's life. The criteria should be related to the success criteria that were determined during the risk estimate of the situation phase.

Step 2: Determine the level of risk.
[Refer to Sections 5.2 and 5.5]

- Risk referents against which risks can be evaluated are required. These referents are stated as a probability of failure, or conversely, probability of success level for each individual risk, as well as for the system as a whole. A value should be agreed upon where by a project should not continue, may continue, or may continue but with prejudice.

- The system risk referent may be an aggregation of the individual risks, or may be instead one or more risks that are prioritized as causing the most harm to the project.

- Care should be taken to identify any risk coupling or compounding that may occur.

- Apply evaluation techniques to determine the level of risk. These techniques include soft and hard approaches.

- Soft approaches to risk evaluation include:

  - Down-side analysis
  - Risk prioritization
  - Top-10 risk evaluation
  - Table-driven evaluation.

- Hard approaches to risk evaluation include:

  - Expected value calculation
  - Isorisk contour maps

- Decision trees
- PERT evaluation
- Queueing models
- Work breakdown evaluation
- Putnam cost evaluation
- COCOMO evaluation.

Step 3: Compare risk to the risk referents.
[Refer to Sections 5.3 and 5.6]

- Compare the evaluated risk against its risk referent that was determined earlier. There are three possible outcomes:

  - Acceptable (the evaluated risk is less than the referent)
  - Impossible (the evaluated risk is much greater the referent)
  - Infeasible (the evaluated risk is greater than, but almost equal to the referent).

- If the system risk is evaluated as acceptable, then proceed to evaluate individual risks.

- If the system risk is evaluated as impossible, then determine whether the project should continue. If a determination is made that it should, then a project replanning effort to avert the identified risks must be made. Whatever course of action is selected, the risk analysis process should be repeated, because both replanning and risk aversion change the likely risks encountered.

- If the system risk is judged as infeasible, then determine whether the project should continue. If a determination is made that it should, then either replan the project to avert the risks, or continue with the plan as is, but with risk aversion strategies applied. Replanning is generally the recommended course of action. However, further evaluation of selected risks may prove valuable, and only minor replanning may be necessary. Risk aversion strategies are also highly recommended, and may prove more feasible in some cases than replanning.

- After the system-wide evaluation, the evaluation of individual risks should be completed and judged against the same evaluation criteria. The evaluation results should be used to determine risk aversion strategies.

Risk management overview

When should risk management be performed?
[Refer to Section 3.2 and Chapter 6]

- Have significant software risks been identified?

- Do these risks potentially impact the objectives of the project?

- Will these risks contribute greatly to the operational and/or support costs of the system?

- Can these risks be averted?

If any of these questions can be answered yes, then risk management is recommended.

What are the tasks required to perform risk management?
[Refer to Section 6.0]

Task 1: Risk planning

Task 2: Risk control

Task 3: Risk monitoring

Risk planning

What is risk planning?
[Refer to Sections 6.1, 6.2, and 6.5]

Risk planning is concerned with two issues: first, whether the strategy to be undertaken to carry out risk management itself is feasible and correct; and second, whether the tactics and means available to implement that strategy are in keeping with the overall objectives of the project.

What are the steps involved in planning?

Step 1: Determine the feasibility of risk control and/or monitoring. [Refer to Section 6.2]

If the system risk referent was not exceeded during evaluation, then risk control may not be required at this immediate time. If the project was only just infeasible, or barely feasible/acceptable, then risk control is required. However, risk monitoring is required in either instance.

Step 2: Determine new risk referents for the project's risks. [Refer to Section 6.2]

The level of acceptable risk, both on a system level and at an individual risk level, will change in time, as the project proceeds along its way. Some effort should be applied to make the original system and individual risk referents more stringent with the passage of time to judge future aversion progress against them.

Step 3: Determine the appropriate management approach. [Refer to Section 6.5]

- The level of acceptability of a risk and the cost to achieve that level of acceptability must be considered. In economic approaches, one compares the direct gains to direct losses that are involved in accepting a risk or not. In non-economic approaches, one requires the comparison of indirect gains to indirect losses.

- Consideration of the difficulty and cost in performing risk aversion to achieve a certain benefit might also be warranted. Aversion of risk to levels of reasonableness, low as practicable, etc., should be investigated.

Step 4: Apply the cardinal rules of risk management. [Refer to Section 6.5.1]

- Four cardinal rules of risk management must be applied when making decisions:

First, do no harm.

"Adde parvum parvo magnus acerus erit."

Never intentions, always capability.

No management commitment, no risk management.

- Three rules should be applied in order, and in conjunction with the three principles of risk decision making. They are, in order of precedence:

  1. Dismissal of extremely remote possibilities

  2. Avoidance of catastrophes, insofar as possible

  3. Maximization of the expected values.

Risk control

What is risk control?
[Refer to Section 6.3]

Risk control involves the development and evaluation of the feasibility of the implementation of the plan's control mechanisms for the aversion strategies. It establishes control over any contingency that was placed into reserve.

What are the steps involved in risk control?

Step 1: Determine strategies for risk aversion.
[Refer to Section 6.3.1]

Three basic classes of strategies can be used to avert risk. One can either change the consequences of a risk, change its likelihood, or change its magnitude. For all or any one of these classes, there are a number of specific risk aversion strategies available. These include:

- Reduction strategies
- Protection strategies
- Transference strategies
- Pecuniary strategies.

Step 2: Determine tactics for risk aversion.
[Refer to Section 6.3.2]

Specific tactics for risk aversion are based primarily upon the process of software engineering, i.e., process models, methods, and automation. Selection of the proper tactic is dependent upon the specific aversion strategy required.

Step 3: Create a plan for risk management.
[Refer to Section 6.3.3]

Develop a Risk Management Plan (RMP), a Risk Aversion Plan (RAP), and an updated RES. The RMP, RAP, and RES serve to detail the risk aversion strategies, tactics, and means to be used during risk control and monitoring. These plans are used as input to the risk management decision process.

Risk monitoring

What is risk monitoring?
[Refer to Section 6.4]

Risk monitoring occurs after the decisions concerning aversion strategy and tactics have been implemented in order to (a) check if the consequences of the decision were the same as envisioned; (b) identify opportunities for refinement of the risk aversion plan; and (c) help provide feedback for future decisions about how to control new risks or current risks that are not responding to risk aversion, or whose nature has changed with time.

What are the steps involved in risk monitoring?

Step 1: Select the proper monitoring technique. [Refer to Section 6.4.1]

Risk monitoring techniques are basically of two types: those that monitor the process of software engineering and those that monitor the products of software engineering. Various techniques are available for each, some of which can be found in:

- IEEE Project P982 Software Reliability Measures
- AFSCP 800-14 Software Quality Indicators
- AFSCP 800-43 Software Management Indicators
- Reviews
- Walkthroughs
- Inspections
- Risk charting.

Step 2: Apply the monitoring technique. [Refer to Section 6.4.1]

Periodic application of risk monitoring is required to judge progress in averting the currently known risks, and to surface any unobservable risks. Results of the monitoring effort should be used to determine the effectiveness of the risk aversion strategies, and the original accuracy and effectiveness of the risk analysis process. If the accuracy or effectiveness is found to be suspect, then senior management needs to be informed immediately, and a determination must be made as to whether a new risk analysis is called for.

7.2 What Comes Next?

Risk analysis and management are just some of the tools that are available for the software engineer to use in his or her quest to develop systems that are cost effective, on-time, and of a quality one can be proud of. Their value lies not in risk evaluation numbers that can be thrown around in meetings, but in helping the process of discovery of finding out where things might go wrong. They still might go wrong, but it is always better to fight an enemy whose strength and disposition are known, than to fight one who is invisible.

The companion to this book, *Software Engineering Risk Analysis and Management—Applications*, takes a broader perspective than the mechanics of risk analysis and management. This book has provided us the tools, but tools alone do not make a competent software engineering risk analyst. We need to understand the greater context in which software engineering resides, and the risks and limitations within software engineering itself. Thus, the companion volume examines the total software engineering enterprise, its associated risks, and constructive ways to avert them.

Software Engineering Risk Analysis and Management—Applications is divided into two subgroupings. The first logical grouping contains Chapters 1, 2, 3, and 4. Chapter 1 reviews quickly the fundamentals of risk encountered in this book. Chapter 2 provides a systemic view of risk analysis and management as it applies to the systems engineering and business environments. This helps us identify the sources of risk that originate outside of, and are carried into, the software engineering enterprise. Chapter 3 then examines the software engineering risks that may exist in the software engineering process, i.e., the process models, methods, and automation applied throughout the software enterprise. Chapter 4 investigates the software engineering risks associated with the development of computer applications.

The second logical grouping includes Chapters 5, 6, and 7, and focuses on specialized aspects of risk analysis and management. Chapter 5 investigates the risks associated with software safety, security, and operation. Chapter 6 looks at risk-taking as it applies to individuals' risk reduction programs. Chapter 7 provides a look at future risk issues and provides another step-by-step review. These chapters provide other perspectives on software engineering risk analysis and management that are required to obtain a complete understanding of what is involved when they are actually employed on a project.

References

1.   Stephen Pile, *The Book of Heroic Failures*, Routledge & Kegan Paul Ltd., England, 1979.

Defense System Software
Development DoD-STD-2167A

This appendix provides a brief description of the system life-cycle model and associated system development cycle. More detailed information is available in DoD-STD-2167A, Defense System Software Development, 29 February 1989.

The life cycle model and associated system development cycle are illustrated in Figure A.1. The software development cycle and related products are illustrated in Figure A.2.

System Life Cycle

The system life cycle consists of four phases: Concept Exploration, Demonstration and Validation, Full-Scale Development, and Production and Deployment. The software development cycle consists of six phases: Software Requirements Analysis, Preliminary Design, Detailed Design, Coding and Computer Software Unit (CSU) Testing, Computer Software Component (CSC) Integration and Testing, and Computer Software Configuration Item (CSCI) Testing. The total software development cycle or a subset may be performed within each of the system life-cycle phases. Successive iterations of software development usually build upon the products of previous iterations (see Figure A.2).

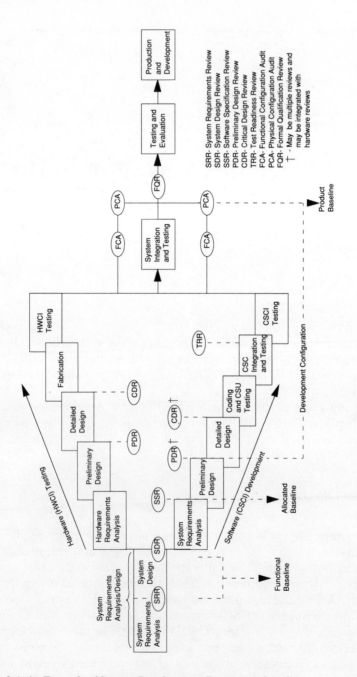

Figure A.1 An Example of System Development Reviews and Audits

1. *Concept Exploration.* The Concept Exploration Phase is the initial planning period when the technical, strategic, and economic bases are established through comprehensive studies, experimental development, and concept evaluation. This initial planning may be directed toward refining proposed solutions or developing alternative concepts to satisfy a required operational capability.

2. *Demonstration and Validation.* The Demonstration and Validation Phase is the period when major system characteristics are refined through studies, system engineering, development of preliminary equipment and prototype computer software, and test and evaluation. The objectives are to validate the choice of alternatives and to provide the basis for determining whether or not to proceed into the next phase.

3. *Full-Scale Development.* The Full-Scale Development Phase is the period when the system, equipment, computer software, facilities, personnel subsystems, training, and the principal equipment and software items necessary for support are designed, fabricated, tested, and evaluated. It includes one or more major iterations of the software development cycle. The intended outputs are a system that closely approximates the production item, the documentation necessary to enter the system's Production and Deployment Phase, and the test results that demonstrate that the system to be produced will meet the stated requirements. During this phase, the requirements for additional software items embedded in or associated with the equipment items may be identified. These requirements may encompass firmware, test equipment, environment simulation, mission support, development support, and many other kinds of software.

4. *Production and Deployment.* The Production and Deployment Phase is the combination of two overlapping periods. The production period is from production approval until the last system item is delivered and accepted. The objective is to efficiently produce and deliver effective and supported systems to the user(s). The deployment period commences with delivery of the first operational system item and terminates when the last system items are removed from the operational inventory.

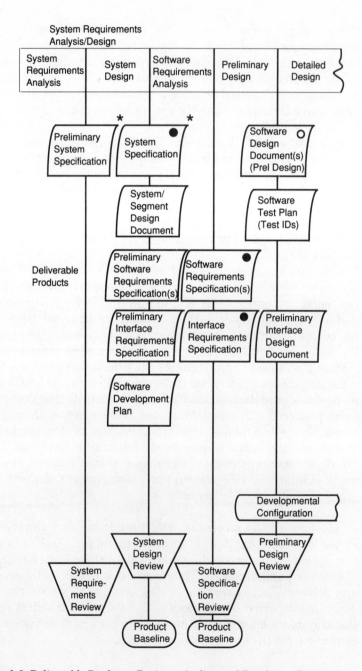

Figure A.2 Deliverable Products, Reviews, Audits, and Baselines (*Part 1*)

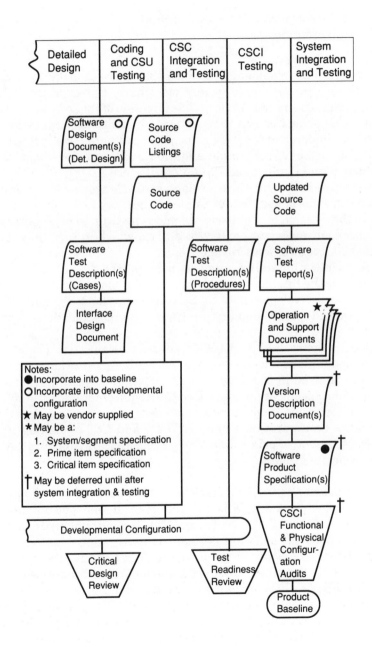

Figure A.2 Deliverable Products, Reviews, Audits, and Baselines (*Part 2*)

Software Development Cycle Application and Documentation

The Software Development Cycle may span more than one system life-cycle phase, or may occur in any one phase. For example, mission simulation software may undergo one iteration of the software development cycle during Concept Exploration, while mission application software may undergo many iterations of the software development cycle during the Demonstration and Validation, Full-Scale Development, and Production and Deployment Phases (see Figure A.1).

The phases in the software development cycle may involve iterations back to previous phases. For example, design may reveal problems that lead to the revision of requirements and reinstitution of certain analyses; checkout may reveal errors in design, which in turn may lead to redesign or requirements revision, etc.

Prior to initiating software development during the Full-Scale Development and the Production and Deployment Phases, documented plans for software development (e.g., Software Development Plan—SDP), authenticated system, segment, and prime item specifications, typically exist.

In earlier life-cycle phases, such plans may not yet exist. The software development plans include descriptions of all organizations and procedures to be used in the development effort. The system, segment, or prime item specification identifies the requirements of the system, segment, or prime item. In addition, these specifications identify the Hardware Configuration Items (HWCIs) and CSCIs making up the system, segment, or prime item. The six phases of the software development cycle are discussed below.

1. *Software Requirements Analysis.* The purpose of Software Requirements Analysis is to completely define and analyze the requirements for the software. These requirements include the functions the software is required to accomplish as part of the system, segment, or prime item. Additionally, the functional interfaces and the necessary design constraints are defined. During Full-Scale Development and Production and Deployment, this phase typically begins with the release of the System/Segment Specification (SSS), Prime Item Development Specification(s) (PIDS), Critical Item Specifications (CIDS), or preliminary Soft-

ware Requirements Specifications (SRS), Software Development Plan (SDP), and Interface Requirement Specifications (IRS). It terminates with the successful accomplishment of the Software Specification Review (SSR). During this phase, analyses and trade-off studies are performed, and requirements are made definitive. The results of this phase are documented and approved requirements for the software. Also, at the initiation of Software Requirements Analysis, plans for developing the software are prepared or reviewed (as applicable).

2. *Preliminary Design.* The purpose of Preliminary Design is to develop a design approach that includes mathematical models, functional flows, and data flows. During this phase various design approaches are considered, analysis and trade-off studies are performed, and design approaches selected. Preliminary Design allocates software requirements from the Software Requirements Specifications (SRS) and associated Interface Requirements Specifications (IRS) to the CSCs of each CSCI, describing the processing that takes place within each design of critical lower-level elements of each Computer Software Configuration Item (CSCI) and external interface. The result of this phase is a documented and approved Software Design Document (SDD) for each CSCI, and an Interface Design Document (IDD) for each interface design. The top-level design is reviewed against the requirements prior to initiating the detailed design phase.

3. *Detailed Design.* The purpose of Detailed Design is to refine the design approach so that each CSCI is decomposed into a complete structure of CSCs and CSUs. The detailed design approach is provided in detailed design documents and reviewed against the requirements and top-level design prior to initialing the coding phase.

4. *Coding and CSU Testing.* The purpose of Coding and CSU Testing is to code and test each unit of code described in the detailed design code and test each unit of code described in the detailed deign documentation. Each unit of code is reviewed for compliance with corresponding detailed design description and applicable coding standards prior to establishing internal control of the unit and releasing it for integration.

5. *CSC Integration and Testing.* The purpose of CSC Integration and Testing is to integrate and test aggregates of coded units. Integration tests should be performed based on documented integration test plans, test descriptions, and test procedures. CSC Integration test results and CSCI test plans, descriptions, and procedures for testing the fully implemented software are reviewed prior to the next phase of testing.

6. *CSCI Testing.* Testing during this phase concentrates on showing that the software satisfies its specified requirements. Test results should be reviewed to determine whether the software satisfies its specified requirements.

Software Engineering
Risk Tables

The following five supplemental risk evaluation probability tables are from the Air Force Systems Command Pamplet AFSCP 800-45. AFSCP 800-45 describes software risk identification, assessment, reduction, and management techniques that are aimed at significantly contributing to the improvement of the acquisition of mission-critical computer resources. The supplemental tables consider factors in software project developments such as software requirements and design, personnel, reusable software, tools, and environments. They can be used in conjunction with other probability risk tables, but one must be aware of the underlying assumptions and limitations in their creation.

TABLE B.1 Quantification of Probability and Impact of Technical Failure

TECHNICAL DRIVERS	MAGNITUDE		
	LOW (0.0–0.3)	MEDIUM (0.4–0.5)	HIGH (0.6–1.0)
REQUIREMENTS			
Complexity	Simple or easily allocated	Moderate, can be allocated	Significant or difficult to allocate
Size	Small or easily broken down into work units	Medium, or can be broken down into work units	Large or cannot be broken down into work units
Stability	Little or no change to established baseline	Some change in baseline expected	Rapidly changing or no baseline
PDSS*	Agreed to support concept	Roles and missions issues unresolved	No support concept or major unresolved issues
R & M	Allocated to hardware and software components	Requirements can be defined	Can only be addressed at the total system level
CONSTRAINTS			
Computer Resources	Mature, growth capacity within design, flexible	Available, some growth capacity	New development, no growth capacity, inflexible
Personnel	Available in place experienced, stable	Available but not in place, some experienced	High turnover, little or no experience, not available
Standards	Appropriately tailored for application	Some tailoring, all not reviewed for applicability	No tailoring, none append to the contract
GFE/GFP	Meets requirements, available	May meet requirements, uncertain availability	Not compatible with system requirements, unavailable
Environment	Little or no impact on design	Some impact on design	Major impact on design
TECHNOLOGY			
Language	Mature, approved HOL** used	Approved or non-approved HOL	Significant use of assembly language
Hardware	Mature, available	Some development or available	Total new development
Tools	Documented, validated, in place	Available validated, some development	Unvalidated, propriatory, major development
Data Rights	Fully compatible with support and follow-on	Minor incompatibilities with support and follow-on	Incompatible with support and follow-on
Experience	Greater than 3 to 5 years	Less than 3 to 5 years	Little or none
DEVELOPMENTAL APPROACH			
Prototypes & Reuse	Used, documented sufficiently for use	Some use and documentation	No use and/or no documentation
Documentation	Correct and available	Some deficiencies, available	Nonexistent
Environment	In place, validated, experience with use	Minor modifications, tools available	Major development effort
Management Approach	Existing product and process controls	Product & process controls need enhancement	Weak or nonexistent
Integration	Internal and external controls in place	Internal or external controls not in place	Weak or nonexistent
IMPACT	Minimal to small reduction in technical performance	Some reduction in technical performance	Significant degradation to nonachievement of technical performance

* Post-deployment support software
** Higher order language

TABLE B.2 Quantification of Probability and Impact of Schedule Failure

	MAGNITUDE		
SCHEDULE DRIVERS	LOW (0.0–0.3)	MEDIUM (0.4–0.5)	HIGH (0.6–1.0)
RESOURCES			
Personnel	Good discipline mix in place	Some disciplines not available	Questionable mix and/or availability
Facilities	Existent, little or no modification	Existent, some modification	Nonexistent, extensive changes
Financial	Sufficient budget allocated	Some questionable allocations	Budget allocation in doubt
NEED DATES			
Threat	Verified projections	Some unstable aspects	Rapidly changing
Economic	Stable commitments	Some uncertain commitments	Unstable, fluctuating commitments
Political	Little projected sensitivity	Some limited sensitivity	Extreme sensitivity
GFE/GFP	Available, certified	Certification or delivery questions	Unavailable and/or uncertified
Tools	In place, available	Some deliveries in question	Uncertain delivery dates
TECHNOLOGY			
Availability	In place	Some aspects still in development	Totally still in development
Maturity	Application verified	Some applications verified	No application evidence
Experience	Extensive application	Some application	Little or none
REQUIREMENTS			
Definition	Known, baseline	Baseline, some unknowns	Unknown, no baseline
Stability	Little or no change projected	Controlled change projected	Rapid or uncontrolled change
Complexity	Compatible with existing technology	Some dependency on new technology	Incompatible with existing technology
IMPACT	Realistic, achievable schedule	Possible slippage in IOC*	Unachievable IOC

* Initial operational capacity

TABLE B.3 Quantification of Probability and Impact of Cost Failure

COST DRIVERS	MAGNITUDE		
	LOW (0.0–0.3)	MEDIUM (0.4–0.5)	HIGH (0.6–1.0)
REQUIREMENTS			
Size	Small, non-complex, or easily decomposed	Medium, moderate complexity, decomposable	Large, highly complex, or not decomposable
Resource Constraints	Little or no hardware imposed constraints	Some hardware imposed constraints	Significant hardware imposed constraints
Application	Non real-time, little system interdependency	Embedded, some system interdependency	Real-time, embedded strong interdependency
Technology	Mature, existent, inhouse experience	Existent, some inhouse experience	New or new application. little experience
Requirements Stability	Little or no change to established baseline	Some change in baseline expected	Rapidly changing or no baseline
PERSONNEL			
Availability	In place, little turnover expected	Available, some turnover expected	High turnover, not available
Mix	Good mix of software disciplines	Some disciplines inappropriately represented	Some disciplines not represented
Experience	High experience ratio	Average experience ratio	Low experience ratio
Management Environment	Strong management approach	Good personnel management approach	Weak personnel management approach
REUSABLE SOFTWARE			
Availability	Compatible with need dates	Delivery dates in question	Incompatible with need dates
Modifications	Little or no change	Some change	Extensive changes
Language	Compatible with system & PDSS* requirements	Partial compatibility with requirements	Incompatible with system or PDSS requirements
Rights	Compatible with PDSS & competition requirements	Partial compatibility with PDSS, some competition	Incompatible with PDSS concept, noncompetitive
Certification	Verified performance application compatible	Some application compatible test data available	Unverified, little test data available
TOOLS & ENVIRONMENT			
Facilities	Little or no modifications	Some modifications, existent	Major modifications, non existent
Availability	In place, meets need dates	Some compatibility with need dates	Nonexistent, does not meet need dates
Rights	Compatible with PDSS & development plans	Partial compatibility with PDSS & development plans	Incompatible with PDSS & development plans
Configuration Management	Fully controlled	Some controls	No controls
IMPACT	Sufficient financial resources	Some shortage of financial resources, possible overrun	Significant financial shortages, budget overrun likely

* Post-deployment support software

TABLE B.4 Quantification of Probability and Impact of Operational Failure

	MAGNITUDE		
OPERATIONAL DRIVERS	LOW (0.0–0.3)	MEDIUM (0.4–0.5)	HIGH (0.6–1.0)
USER PERSPECTIVE Requirements	Compatible with the user environment	Some incompatibilities	Major incompatibilities with 'ops' concepts
Stability	Little or no change	Some controlled change	Uncontrolled change
Test Environment	Representative of the user environment	Some aspects are not representative	Major disconnects with user environment
OT&E Results	Test errors/failures are correctable	Some errors/failures are not correctable before IOC*	Major corrections necessary
Quantification	Primarily objective	Some subjectivity	Primarily subjective
TECHNICAL PERFORMANCE Usability	User friendly	Mildly unfriendly	User unfriendly
Reliability	Predictable performance	Some aspects unpredictable	Unpredictable
Flexibility	Adaptable with threat	Some aspects are not adaptable	Critical functions not adaptable
Supportability	Responsive to updates	Response times inconsistent with need	Unresponsive
Integrity	Secure	Hidden linkages, controlled access	Insecure
PERFORMANCE ENVELOPE Adequacy	Full compatibility	Some limitations	Inadequate
Expandability	Easily expanded	Can be expanded	No expansion
Enhancements	Timely incorporation	Some lag	Major delays
Threat	Responsive to change	Cannot respond to some changes	Unresponsive
IMPACT	Full mission capability	Some limitations on mission performance	Severe performance limitations

* Initial operational capacity

TABLE B.5 Quantification of Probability and Impact of Support Failure

SUPPORT DRIVERS	MAGNITUDE		
	LOW (0.0–0.3)	MEDIUM (0.4–0.5)	HIGH (0.6–1.0)
DESIGN			
Complexity	Structure maintainable	Certain aspects difficult	Extremely difficult to maintain
Documentation	Adequate	Some deficiencies	Inadequate
Completeness	Little additional for PDSS incorporation	Some PDSS* incorporation	Extensive PDSS incorporation
Configuration Management	Sufficient, in place	Some shortfalls	Insufficient
Stability	Little or no change	Moderate, controlled change	Rapid or uncontrolled change
RESPONSIBILITIES			
Management	Defined, assigned responsibilities	Some roles and mission issues	Undefined or unassigned
Configuration Management	Single point control	Defined control points	Multiple control points
Technical Management	Consistent with operational needs	Some inconsistencies	Major inconsistencies
Change Implementation	Responsive to user needs	Acceptable delays	Nonresponsive to user needs
TOOLS & ENVIRONMENT			
Facilities	In place, little change	In place, some modification	Nonexistent or extensive change
Software Tools	Delivered, certified, sufficient	Some resolvable concerns	Not delivered, certified, or sufficient
Computer Hardware	Compatible with "ops" system	Minor incompatibilities	Major incompatibilities
Production	Sufficient for fielded units	Some capacity questions	Insufficient
Distribution	Controlled, responsive	Minor response concerns	Uncontrolled or nonresponsive
SUPPORTABILITY			
Changes	Within projections	Slight deviations	Major deviations
Operational Interfaces	Defined, controlled	Some "hidden" linkages	Extensive linkages
Personnel	In place, sufficient, experienced	Minor discipline mix concerns	Significant concerns
Release Cycle	Responsive to user requirements	Minor incompatibilities	Nonresponsive to user needs
Procedures	In place, adequate	Some concerns	Nonexistent or inadequate
IMPACT	Responsive software support	Minor delays in software modifications	Nonresponsive or unsupportable software

* Post-deployment support software

Index